NUTRITION AND DIET RESEARCH PROGRESS

LOW AND HIGH-FAT DIETS

MYTHS VS. REALITY

NUTRITION AND DIET RESEARCH PROGRESS

Additional books in this series can be found on Nova's website
under the Series tab.

Additional E-books in this series can be found on Nova's website
under the E-book tab.

PUBLIC HEALTH IN THE 21ST CENTURY

Additional books in this series can be found on Nova's website
under the Series tab.

Additional E-books in this series can be found on Nova's website
under the E-book tab.

NUTRITION AND DIET RESEARCH PROGRESS

LOW AND HIGH-FAT DIETS

MYTHS VS. REALITY

JOÃO EDUARDO FERREIRA
AND
NATALIA MUNIZ
EDITORS

New York

For permission to use material from this book please contact us:
Telephone 631-231-7269; Fax 631-231-8175
Web Site: http://www.novapublishers.com

Library of Congress Cataloging-in-Publication Data

Library of Congress Control Number: 2012945370

ISBN: 978-1-62257-797-2

Published by Nova Science Publishers, Inc. † New York

Contents

Preface

In this book, the authors gather and present current research on the myths and reality of low and high-fat diets. Topics include new insights into high-fat diets and metabolic disorders; cactus stems (opuntia spp.) as an anti-hyperlipidemic and cholesterol lowering aid; dietary fat and its impact on health; the efficacy and safety of low-fat diets in children; and lipid profiling in the mouse brain and liver after starvation and a high-fat diet.

Chapter I – It has been recognized that one major risk factor present in current lifestyle that contributes to the development of metabolic dysfunctions like obesity, type II diabetes mellitus and other associated diseases is the long-term ingestion of high-fat diets. However, the relationship between high-fat diet and the mechanisms involved in the pathogenesis of these metabolic disorders has been subject of extensive studies and seems to involve a broad range of physiological changes that affects several tissues. Initial investigations to comprehend these changes showed that the central feature of insulin-resistant state installation in obese animals is the chronic low-grade inflammation promoted by a pro-inflammatory cytokine tumor necrosis factor-alpha (TNF-α), synthesized and released by white adipose tissue. After that, new areas of research have been arising in the understanding of several other alterations that explain the relationship between the high-fat diet ingestion and various pathologies. In this way, lipid accumulation and mitochondrial dysfunction in skeletal muscle, changes in the gut microbiota and impairment in hypothalamic and hippocampus neuronal remodeling have been pointed as new candidates to the development of metabolic disturbances as a consequence of high-fat diet ingestion. In this chapter will be described the most recent scientific evidence about the mechanisms of the changes promoted by a high-fat diet in the development of metabolic disorders.

Chapter II – Recently, nutritional studies are focused on examining foods for their protective and disease preventing potential. Furthermore, consumers are increasingly becoming aware of diet related health problems, therefore demanding natural ingredients which are expected to be safe and health-promoting. The importance of functional foods, nutraceuticals and other natural health products has been well recognized in relation to health promotion, disease risk reduction and reduction in health care costs. In this line, recent studies on *Opuntia spp.* have demonstrated cactus pear fruit and vegetative cladodes to be excellent candidates for the development of healthy food. Experimental evidence suggests that cactus cladodes reduce cholesterol levels in human blood and modify low density lipoprotein (LDL) composition. Italian researchers have found that the cholesterol, LDL and triglyceride plasma levels of rats were strongly reduced after 30 days of a daily administration (1 g/kg) of lyophilized cladodes of *Opuntia ficus-indica* L. Mill. While another stuff of researchers reported a reduction of total cholesterol, LDL, apolipoprotein levels, triglycerides, fibrinogen, blood glucose, insulin and urate, while body weight, high-density lipoprotein (HDL)-cholesterol, apolipoprotein A-1 and lipoproteinA levels were found to remain unchanged. The anti-hyperlipidemic effect after cladode ingestion was investigated in many studies. Other positive health effects were confirmed by various researchers. The purpose of this chapter is to highlight current knowledge on the beneficial health effects of cactus stems with particular emphasis on its use as food and medicine.

Chapter III – Dietary fat intake (more specifically the type of fat consumed) together with a sedentary lifestyle, have been considered responsible for the increase in the prevalence of obesity and co-morbidities of obesity. While high-fat diets (>30% of energy from fat) have been shown to contribute to obesity and to a number of diseases including type 2 diabetes, hypertension and cardiovascular disease, low-fat diets (≤20% from fat), especially those low in saturated fat and cholesterol, have been promoted as healthier and recommended for weight loss and to reduce cardiovascular risk. However, doubts have been raised with regard to the effectiveness of this type of diet. Low-fat diets have been associated with an increase in carbohydrate intake from plant-based foods. Furthermore, there is the possibility of deficiencies in the amount and ratio of the essential fatty acids ω-3 and ω-6. Fats are not just source of energy and thermal insulator, but serve as a major component of cell membranes and the myelin sheath around the nerves, provide essential fatty acids, supply fat-soluble vitamins, participate in the manufacturing of hormones and eicosanoids, and help in nutrient absorption. Therefore, just lowering fat intake may not be the best strategy for a healthier life. In this paper we discuss the myths and realities, the health effects and the risks, of high- and low-fat diets.

Chapter IV – Lipids are essential nutrients for life development and maintenance. However, due to the current worldwide epidemiological context, adverse health effects have been attributed to high-fat diets, without consider dietary lipid composition and total calorie intake. Epidemiological and clinical studies have shown strong association between dietary fat intake and cardiovascular disease and various types of cancer.

High- and low-fat diets, do not necessarily equate to high- or low-calorie diets. When analyzing the health effects of high or low fat diets with an excess of calories, it should be noted that whatever the effect attributable to dietary lipids, there are negative effects of a positive energy imbalance. Therefore, it is incorrect to refer to dietary fat's effects in terms of "high and low fat" diets. It is necessary to consider intrinsic food variables, as well as extrinsic dietary conditions, such as physiological status and environmental and genetic factors.

In post-epidemiological-transition populations, the health effects of the proportion, amount and type of dietary fat cannot be isolated. Interaction with other energetic nutrients, proteins and carbohydrates can significantly modulate the metabolism of lipids according to their proportions and origins in diet. Under certain conditions, all dietary lipid components can be harmful, favoring the development and progression of various diseases. However while the intake of some lipids is considered unhealthy in most cases, other lipids will promote diseases only under very specific circumstances. In the development of non-communicable chronic diseases, deterioration of tissue functionality derived from lipotoxicity is associated with several causes including oxidative stress, inflammation, cell death and uncontrolled proliferation. Lipotoxicity is mainly mediated by two major groups of fats, cholesterol derivatives and saturated free fatty acids. Low-fat diets with high-calorie content could have harmful effects due to an excess of circulating lipids derived from an endogenous lipogenesis derived from other energy nutrients, especially carbohydrates. The most important benefits of high-fat diets at population level are associated with marine omega-3 LCPUFA.

In conclusion the proportion of dietary fat is not the only variable to be considered when analyzing the lipid impact on health. The major type of fat in the diet, the proportions of different types of lipids and fatty acids families, the interaction with other nutrients and total calories consumed also primarily determines the effects that a high- or low-fat diet will have on health.

Chapter V – The dramatic increase in obesity worldwide remains a public health challenge and underscores the urgent need to test the effectiveness and safety of several widely used weight-loss diets, especially in children. Dietary guidelines recommend a reduction in total dietary fat to less than 30% of energy intake to help reduce the prevalence of obesity, cardiovascular disease (CVD) and certain cancers. Which diets result in safe weight loss, have positive long-term effects on chronic disease risk factors, and are sustainable? This question has been only partially answered. Numerous cross-sectional studies have clearly demonstrated a positive correlation between the proportion of total energy intake provided by fat and obesity. Subjects exposed to high-fat foods tend to overconsume energy. This effect depends largely on the high energy density of high-fat foods. A large body of short-term studies on appetite and energy intake unequivocally shows that fat is less satiating than carbohydrate and protein and that high-fat foods are more likely to induce passive overconsumption and weight gain than low-fat foods. Reducing the consumption of saturated fatty acids is one of the basis of international dietary recommendations to reduce the risk of cardiovascular disease. Recent studies of healthy individuals indicate that a single meal high in saturated fat causes immediate increases in triglycerides, oxidative stress, and inflammation. In general, the most efficient triggers of postprandial inflammatory response appear to be triglycerides and saturated fatty acids. On the other hand, the most important modulators of postprandial immune response appear to be polyunsaturated fatty acids (PUFA), and the n-3 to n-6 ratio is especially important. In general, n-3 PUFAs suppress postprandial inflammation, whereas n-6 PUFAs promote it. However, several critical questions remain regarding the relationship between saturated fatty acids consumption and cardiovascular risk. First, the health effects of reducing saturated fatty acids consumption can vary depending on whether the replacement nutrient is a carbohydrate, monounsaturated fat, or polyunsaturated fat. In this sense, another type of low-fat diet is the so called "high-protein diet," of which there are several variations. The diets are based on reduced carbohydrate and fat intake and high protein intake. These diets are effective for short-term weight loss, but this efficacy is counteracted by the negative effects on kidney function, both short and long term, and other secondary effects, such as hypercalciuria and osteopenia. Macrobiotic and vegetarian diets are also low-fat diets. Macrobiotic diets are characterized by reducing the percentage of fat and increasing complex carbohydrate and fiber intake. Macrobiotic diets also replace animal protein with vegetable protein. The composition of vegetarian diets depends on the type: vegan, lacto-vegetarian, ovo-vegetarian, lacto-ovo-vegetarian or semivegetarian. These diets may be deficient in vitamins and minerals (calcium, protein, iron, zinc, vitamins D and B12, riboflavin) and essential fatty acids that are necessary for growing children. In this way, considerable concerns have been raised about the safety of long-term low-fat diets in children.

Chapter VI – We investigated with LC-MS techniques, measuring approximately 109 lipid compounds, in mouse brain and liver tissue after 48 hours of starvation and a High-Fat Diet if brain and liver lipid composition changed. We measured Cholesterolesters (ChE), Lysophosphatidyl-cholines (LPC), Phosphatidylcholine (PC), Sphingomyelin (SPM) and Triacylglycerols (TG's) for liver tissue while for brain tissue we had an extra lipid compound the Plasmalogens. In addition, dynamics of hepatic steatosis were determined in an *in vivo* mouse model with localized non-invasive Magnetic Resonance Spectroscopy (^{1}H-MRS) techniques. In the experimental design Male C57bl6 mice (age 8-12 weeks) were exposed to three treatments: A: They were fed a chow Diet for a period of approximately 40 days (Control group); B: They were fed a High-Fat Diet, containing 0.25% cholesterol (Ch) and 24% energy from bovine lard for a period of approximately 40 days, C: Or they were exposed to 48 hours of starvation. For whole brain tissue of these mice groups the LC-MS techniques indicated that the brain was rather invulnerable to Dietary intervention. The (phospho-) lipid-composition of the brain was unchanged in the starvation group but the cholesterol-ester content was significantly increased in the high High-Fat Diet group. These observations suggest that the brain lipid composition is insensitive to starvation but can be affected by a high High-Fat Diet. In contrast, for liver tissue both 24 h starvation and the 40 day High-Fat Diet resulted in exponential hepatic fat accumulation, although their time course (measured with ^{1}H MRS) techniques was distinctly different. Mass spectrometry (LC-MS) demonstrated for liver tissue remarkable differences in lipid profiles between treatments. ^{1}H-MRS proved to be a reliable method for frequent, repetitive determination of hepatic fat *in vivo* and a noninvasive alternative to biopsy. Moreover, LC-MS and Principal Component Analysis (PCA) demonstrated that in liver tissue different lipid end products are formed as result of Dietary composition Apparently, for liver tissue starvation and a High-Fat Diet result in a process called hepatic steatosis which is regulated under both conditions via different metabolic pathways. In addition, ^{1}H-MRS techniques demonstrated for liver that the relative amount of unsaturated bindings is significantly higher in the High-Fat Diet group ($P \leq 0.001$), which can be deducted from the relative intensities of the (CH=CH) elements and their conjugated unsaturated elements (C-CCH$_2$C=C). We conclude, comparing brain *vs.* liver tissue that both tissues have a totally different metabolic response to both treatments. The brain is insensitive to starvation but can be affected by a High-Fat Diet while in liver tissue both treatments result paradoxically in a hepatic steatosis. However, for the liver, the dynamics and the lipid profiles of this process of this hepatic steatosis under starvation or a High-Fat Diet are totally different.

In: Low and High-Fat Diets: Myths vs. Reality
Editors: J. E. Ferreira and N. Muniz
ISBN: 978-1-62257-797-2

Chapter I

New Insights into High-fat Diets and Metabolic Disorders

A. M. Baviera, C. M. B. Andrade and N. H. Kawashita*
Department of Chemistry, Federal University of Mato Grosso,
Cuiabá, Mato Grosso, Brazil

Abstract

It has been recognized that one major risk factor present in current lifestyle that contributes to the development of metabolic dysfunctions like obesity, type II diabetes mellitus and other associated diseases is the long-term ingestion of high-fat diets. However, the relationship between high-fat diet and the mechanisms involved in the pathogenesis of these metabolic disorders has been subject of extensive studies and seems to involve a broad range of physiological changes that affects several tissues. Initial investigations to comprehend these changes showed that the central feature of insulin-resistant state installation in obese animals is the chronic low-grade inflammation promoted by a pro-inflammatory cytokine tumor necrosis factor-alpha (TNF-α), synthesized and released by white adipose tissue. After that, new areas of research have been arising in the understanding of several other alterations that explain the relationship between the high-fat diet ingestion and various pathologies. In this way, lipid accumulation and mitochondrial dysfunction in skeletal muscle, changes in the gut microbiota and impairment in hypothalamic and hippocampus neuronal remodeling have been pointed as new candidates to the development of metabolic disturbances as a consequence of high-fat diet ingestion. In this chapter will be described the most recent scientific evidence about the mechanisms of the changes promoted by a high-fat diet in the development of metabolic disorders.

* Address for correspondence: Nair Honda Kawashita; Department of Chemistry, Federal University of Mato Grosso, Brazil. 78060-900 Cuiabá, Mato Grosso, Brazil. Phone: +55 (65) 3615 8765; Fax: +55 (65) 3615 8798/8799; E-mail address: nairhonda@terra.com.br.

Introduction

According to the National Research Council, the recommended Reference Intakes of Energy in lipids for adult humans is within the range of 20-35%. Studies in humans have shown that diets containing 30% or more of these calories from fat can contribute to obesity (Schrauwen & Westerterp, 2000; Hariri & Thibault, 2010), depending on the different types of fat found in the diet. Some studies have shown that the profile of fatty acids in the diet is more important than the amount, because not all fats are obesogenic (Bell et al., 1997; Storlien et al., 2001). On the other hand, other authors do not show differences in animals consuming different kinds of fatty acids (Su & Jones, 1993). Other factors, such as overconsumption of energy, increased meal size, decreased meal frequency and sensorial characteristics are fundamental to determine obesity induced by diet (Hariri & Thibault, 2010).

According to a report from the World Health Organization, cases of human overweight and obesity are increasing significantly around the world. These health disorders have not been considered a problem restricted only to high-income countries, since they are now increasingly present in low- and middle-income countries, thus reaching an epidemic proportion. Estimative data from the World Health Organization pointed out that in 2008 one tenth of the adult population was obese and that in 2010 more than 40 million children were overweight. In addition, the increased incidence of type 2 diabetes mellitus (T2DM), ischemic heart diseases and some cancer types has been closely attributable to overweight and obesity. The association of increased ingestion of high-energy foods (mainly represented by foods with elevated quantity of fats, carbohydrates and salt) and diminished physical activity can be cited as an important cause for the pathogenesis of these metabolic disturbances in modern society (World Health Organization, 2012).

For these reasons, a worldwide effort to decrease the amount of fat in human diet and an increase in the number of studies using animals submitted to high-fat diet were observed in the last decades, once diets rich in fat not only induce obesity in humans but also in other animals. Fenton & Dowling (1953) induced obesity in weanling mice using a diet containing fat at 50% of the total calories. After this initial success in achieving obesity in animals by high-fat diet administration, many other preparations with different amounts and types of fat have been administered to rodents as an experimental model to study obesity, dyslipidemia and insulin resistance, although the damage to health promoted by chronic high-fat diet ingestion is associated with other impairments, such as renal dysfunction, hypertension, liver steatosis and others. The percentage of lipids in the composition of high-fat diet used experimentally has been between 30-78% (Buettner et al., 2006) and different lipid sources have been used according to the objectives of the study (olive oil, palm oil, rapeseed oil, sunflower oil, coconut, lard, beef tallow, milk fat). The proportion of the other macronutrients (proteins and carbohydrates) in the composition of the high-fat diet is determinant for the alterations caused by its administration.

Despite the numerous metabolic and physiological disturbances in the course of long-term ingestion of high-fat diets, this chapter will approach new insights about: *i*) lipid accumulation and mitochondrial dysfunction in skeletal muscle; *ii*) changes in the gut microbiota; *iii*) impairment in hypothalamic and hippocampus neuronal remodeling.

Skeletal Muscle Lipid Accumulation, Active Lipid Metabolites and Mitochondrial Dysfunction: Role in the Development of Insulin Resistance

Insulin resistance is characterized by a reduction in the ability of insulin to stimulate glucose uptake by peripheral tissues, leading to hyperglycemia that accounts for the subsequent hyperinsulinemia after a compensatory insulin production and secretion by pancreatic beta cells. Both hyperglycemia and hyperinsulinemia are clinical indicators of insulin resistance, which has been playing a central role in the development of obesity, T2DM and other metabolic disturbances. Although it can be observed in many tissues, insulin resistance in skeletal muscles deserves an especial attention, because skeletal muscle contributes to a major uptake of postprandial glucose, through a mechanism that involves the insulin-stimulated redistribution of vesicles that contain the glucose transporter 4 (GLUT4) in this tissue, promoting their translocation and fusion to the plasma membrane. The translocation of GLUT4-containing vesicles depends on the insulin binding to the insulin receptor (IR) that promotes phosphorylation of the insulin receptor substrate-1 (IRS-1) and recruits the intermediate phosphatidylinositol 3-kinase (PI3 kinase), which in turn produces phosphatidylinositol 3,4,5-trisphosphate (PIP3) in plasma cell membranes. Increased PIP3 content recruits the serine/treonine protein kinase B (PKB or AKT) to the plasma membrane, leading to the phosphorylation of this kinase; the activation of AKT after phosphorylation in threonine-308 and serine-473 residues is crucial for the insulin control of diverse metabolic actions. Among the several intracellular AKT substrates, protein AS160 is the main one among those involved in the glucose uptake by skeletal muscles, because its phosphorylation by AKT allows the GLUT4 trafficking to the plasma membrane (see reviews in Rowland et al., 2011; Bogan, 2012). The increased phosphorylation of IRS-1 on several serine residues (Gual et al., 2005) and the hydrolysis of PIP3 by specific phosphatases (Ijuin & Takenawa, 2012) are examples of intracellular events that abrogate the insulin signaling pathway related to PI3 kinase/AKT activation. Disruptions in this orchestrated intracellular cascade during the installation and maintenance of insulin resistant states may occur at several levels, and different mechanisms have contributed in the development of these signaling disturbances. However, the pathogenesis of insulin resistance is far from being completely understood, because it involves a large, multi-faceted interaction between numerous impaired intracellular processes of several tissues that participate in the body energy control, interplayed by either acquired (environmental factors such as increased food consumption, low physical activity) or inherent (genetic individual predisposition) metabolic disturbances.

The rates of obesity, metabolic syndrome and T2DM have been increasing at an alarming rate, reaching epidemic proportions worldwide (Hossain et al., 2007; Misra & Khurana, 2008) and can be attributed, at least in part, to an excess in energy intake, mainly represented by high-fat foods. According to a review by Schrauwen (2007), the availability of food products characterized by low price, good palatability and high fat content has increased in the last decades, justifying the growing consumption of these foods by the current population. Therefore, the increased levels of circulating glucose and triacylglycerol (promoted by nutrient excess) and of fatty acids (from the increased adiposity of obese individuals) are closely associated with the onset and maintenance of insulin resistance. However, the relationship between long-term high-fat diet ingestion, development of overweight and the appearance of insulin resistance, T2DM and other metabolic disturbances involves the concomitant participation of several mechanisms. The involvement of skeletal muscle impairments in the pathogenesis of metabolic disturbances promoted by high-fat diet ingestion will be described next.

Intramyocellular Lipid Accumulation and Toxicity of Lipid Metabolites in Skeletal Muscles

Accumulated evidence has substantiated that high-fat diet ingestion followed by long-term exposition to circulating lipids, exceeding the capacity of uptake and storage by white adipose tissues, leads to ectopic lipid deposition in organs with low capacity for this, such as skeletal muscles (Schrauwen-Hinderling et al., 2006; Schrauwen, 2007), generating intramyocellular lipid (IMCL) deposits; IMCLs are small lipid droplets preferentially located close to mitochondria, suggesting its role in the rapid fuel disposal for mitochondrial adenosine triphosphate (ATP) production used during muscle contraction. Studies from Schrauwen-Hinderling et al. (2005) demonstrated that the ingestion of a high-fat diet for 7 days promoted an increase in the IMCL content in healthy subjects. Although the increase in the IMCL content has also been observed in healthy conditions, such as in endurance-trained athletes (Dubé et al. 2008), an inverse correlation has been mentioned between the IMCL content and insulin sensitivity in conditions of physical inactivity and/or fat overfeeding (Machann et al. 2004; Schrauwen-Hinderling et al., 2006). Increased muscle triacylglycerol content has been pointed as an early step for the installation of insulin resistance in type 2 diabetic and physically non-active individuals (Jacob et al., 1999; Roden, 2005). Corroborating this relationship, normal insulin sensitivity has been found in overweight individuals that presented IMCL content similar to leaner subjects (Perseghin et al., 2002). However, it is important to clarify that IMCL accumulation itself is not sufficient to explain the impairments in the muscle insulin sensitivity. Thus, in an oversupply of dietary fats, the IMCL will be involved in the development of insulin resistance only if the oxidation of fatty acids released from the lipid droplets is not accompanied by an increase in IMCL, as observed in individuals under regular physical activity. Thus, it can be concluded that the muscle lipid oxidative capacity is a better determinant of changes in the insulin sensitivity if compared with IMCL content (Bruce et al., 2003). The use of lipids as fuel by skeletal muscles depends on the generation of acyl-CoA derivatives, mainly the long-chain fatty acyl-CoA molecules, which are translocated to the mitochondrial matrix via carnitine acyltransferases, where beta-oxidation occurs. However, the accumulation of IMCL that is not proportionally oxidized by mitochondria expose the skeletal muscles to the deleterious consequences of the lipotoxicity processes (Schmitz-Peiffer, 2000), since long-chain fatty acyl-CoA will then be preferentially used as a source of monoacylglycerol (MAG), diacylglycerol (DAG), phosphatidic acid and ceramides; some of these lipid metabolites have been strongly related to promoting disturbances in muscle insulin sensitivity, much more than the accumulation of IMCL in this tissue. In fact, many studies have demonstrated that both human and rodents feeding on high-fat diets show increased levels of DAG (Schmitz-Peiffer et al., 1997; Stefanyk et al., 2011) and ceramide (Zendzian-Piotrowska et al., 2006; Frangioudakis et al., 2010) in skeletal muscles, conditions which are always associated with insulin resistant states.

The mechanisms by which DAG and ceramide can disrupt insulin intracellular signaling have been extensively investigated. Thus, the appearance of muscle insulin resistance through a DAG-dependent mechanism is conditioned to the activation of serine-threonine kinases that belong to the protein kinase C (PKC) family, composed of several isoforms divided into atypical, classical and novel PKCs. Both classical (cPKC) and novel (nPKC) PKCs are activated by a DAG-dependent mechanism. Once activated, these PKC isoforms are able to promote phosphorylation of IRS-1 on serine-307, a crucial residue in the inhibition of this component, because this phosphorylation interferes in the tyrosine stimulatory phosphorylation of IRS-1, thus failing in the subsequent activation of PI3 kinase, as well as in the next insulin intracellular intermediates (see review in Corcoran et al., 2007). Corroborating this, rats fed a high-fat diet for 3 weeks presented decreased muscle insulin sensitivity associated with increased triacylglycerol and DAG levels and activation of PKC isoenzymes, mainly nPKC θ and ε isoforms (Schmitz-Peiffer et al., 1997). Concomitant increase in DAG levels and activation of PKC has also been found in other conditions of impaired muscle insulin signaling, as observed in humans and rodents under obesity or T2DM conditions (Avignon et al., 1996; Itani et al., 2002; Bergman et al., 2012). Similar to DAG, increased levels of ceramide in skeletal muscles can also promote diminished insulin sensitivity and the mechanism by which this sphingolipid promotes this disturbance seems to be related to direct inhibition of AKT. Holland et al. (2007) observed that rats receiving a lard-oil infusion into the bloodstream presented an increase in the skeletal muscle ceramide levels, as well as DAG, followed by a decrease in the insulin-stimulated AKT phosphorylation and in the glucose uptake. In this same study, rats pre-treated with myriocin, a ceramide synthesis blocker, presented no inhibitory lard-oil effects on muscle glucose uptake and AKT phosphorylation, demonstrating the pivotal role of ceramide on the development of insulin resistance after higher fat circulating levels.

In addition to the negative effects of DAG and ceramide metabolites on muscle insulin sensitivity, many studies have postulated that long-chain fatty acyl-CoA also affects insulin signaling (Kraegen & Cooney, 2008; Hirabara et al., 2010; Martins et al., 2012). Furthermore, several studies have demonstrated that saturated fatty acids, rather than monounsaturated (MUFAs) or polyunsaturated fatty acids (PUFAs), play an important role in the development of insulin resistance in skeletal muscles (Lee et al., 2006; Xiao et al., 2006). Unfortunately, the feeding pattern of modern society stimulates the consumption of high-fat, saturated fatty acids-enriched diets (Manco et al., 2004), which directly influences the composition of the lipid depots in skeletal muscles (Andersson et al., 2002). Studies from Hundal and collaborators have demonstrated that the incubation of L6 myotubes in the presence of palmitate (a saturated fatty acid) led to an inhibition of AKT phosphorylation on serine-473 residue and decrease of glucose uptake, showing that palmitate desensitizes L6 cells to insulin (Powell et al., 2004); in another study, the same group observed that incubation of L6 cells with palmitoleate and oleate (MUFAs) or with linoleate and linoleneate (PUFAs) promoted an increase in the basal glucose uptake (Dimopoulos et al., 2006). The mechanisms by which saturated fatty acids disrupt insulin signaling in skeletal muscles seem to involve the activation of PKCs, JNK (c-jun NH_2-terminal kinase), IKK (IκB kinase), among others, because these kinases phosphorylate IRS-1 at serine sites (Griffin et al., 1999; Gao et al., 2004; Herschkovitz et al., 2007), avoiding the activation of subsequent intracellular intermediates of the insulin cascade. The activation of IKK (Yaspelkis et al., 2009), JNK

(Ropelle et al., 2006) and PKC (Kim et al., 2004) kinases in association with an insulin-resistant state has been found in skeletal muscles from animals fed a high-fat diet.

Mitochondrial Dysfunction in Skeletal Muscles

Considering all these findings, the question that rises at this point is: why is fatty acid oxidation decreased in skeletal muscles after the exposition to elevated fat circulating levels, leading to the deleterious effects of fatty acyl-CoA, DAG and ceramides on muscle insulin sensitivity? In fact, it seems reasonable to infer that the increased uptake of fatty acids is an important factor involved in the cytosolic lipid accumulation in muscles from individuals that were fed a high-fat diet for long periods. However, several studies have proposed that a decrease in the fatty acid oxidation also contributes to the lipid accumulation (and consequently insulin resistance) in skeletal muscles (Kraegen & Cooney, 2008; Pagel-Langenickel et al., 2010). Currently, it has been widely accepted that mitochondrial disturbances have a crucial participation in the development of metabolic disorders, affecting many organs involved in the energy metabolism control, such as liver (Rector et al., 2010; Choudhury et al., 2011), pancreas (Newsholme et al., 2007; Ma et al., 2012), adipose tissue (Kaaman et al., 2007) and also skeletal muscles (this issue will be detailed further on). In this way, the mitochondrial dysfunction has been defined as a group of defects in the mitochondrial oxidative capacity or a reduction in the organelle number, or both, contributing to the etiology of different pathological conditions, including those characterized by insulin resistant states.

Although it is practically impossible to attribute the responsibility for the onset of insulin signaling disruptions to a single factor, because insulin resistance may occur in such different contexts, at least one interesting proposal was described by Schrauwen & Hesselink (2004) to explain the consequences of fatty acids oversupply beyond the mitochondrial oxidative capacity, which in turn could lead to several impairments of this organelle, triggering the subsequent failure in mitochondrial oxidative process. According to these authors, the oversupply of fatty acids that cannot be oxidized (for example individuals feeding a high-fat diet during prolonged periods) will accumulate in muscle cells, which in turn will promote an overload of fatty acids in neighboring areas of the mitochondrial surface, leading to an unregulated diffusion of neutral fatty acids into the inner mitochondrial membrane, reaching the matrix (Hamilton & Kamp, 1999). Because only the fatty acyl-CoA form can be oxidized by mitochondrial processes, these neutral fatty acids will be deprotonated, generating fatty acid anion species into the mitochondrial matrix, which will accumulate in this organelle because mitochondrial membranes are impermeable to fatty acid anions (Ho et al., 2002). In the mitochondrial matrix, where the production of reactive oxygen species (ROS) is constant, these fatty acid anions will undergo lipid peroxidation; since lipid peroxides are highly reactive, they could therefore react with several components, for example proteins, DNA, RNA, leading to mitochondrial damage. Ultimately, after installed, mitochondrial dysfunction also promotes IMCL accumulation, demonstrating that is difficult to state, in fact, the real sequence of events that precedes the onset of muscle insulin resistance, whether mitochondrial dysfunction is the cause or the consequence of IMCL accumulation, contributing to the excessive production of DAG and ceramide in skeletal muscles.

Several functional defects have been found in mitochondria of skeletal muscles from animals fed high-fat diet. Impaired mitochondrial respiratory activity and decreased activity of electron transport chain complexes I and III have been observed in skeletal muscles from mice fed a high-fat diet for 8 weeks; these mice also presented increased blood glucose levels in the glucose tolerance test (Yokota et al., 2009). Reduced activity of citrate synthase, carnitine palmitoyltransferase-1 (CPT-1) and of beta-oxidation enzymes in skeletal muscles from obese individuals and from high-fat diet fed animals (Kim et al., 2000; Chen et al., 2011) can be also cited as examples of mitochondrial dysfunction associated with insulin resistance conditions.

Despite the fact that insulin resistance installation depends on several factors, it has been widely accepted that ROS overproduction has an important role in the onset and maintenance of insulin resistant related diseases, mainly T2DM (Newsholme et al., 2007). In fact, increased ROS generation has been widely observed in obese and type 2 diabetic individuals (Mogensen et al., 2007; Kelishadi et al., 2008). In addition, Montero et al. (2012) recently demonstrated that the increased oxidative stress has an important role in the pathogenesis of obesity in children and adolescents, consequently the authors proposed that lifestyle interventions attempting to avoid this increased ROS generation seems to be useful to prevent the initiation and progression of obesity-related metabolic diseases. Several studies with experimental animal models have demonstrated the relationship between high-fat diet ingestion and the promotion of oxidative stress, accompanied by a decreased muscle mitochondrial oxidative capacity and an insulin resistant profile. Yokota et al. (2009) reported that mice fed a high-fat diet for 8 weeks were obese, showed increased insulin resistance and reduced O_2 consumption in mitochondria isolated from skeletal muscle, in association with oxidative stress installation, since muscle superoxide anion ($O_2^{\bullet-}$) production was increased. In another study, mice feeding a high-fat, high-sucrose diet for 16 weeks presented hyperglycemia and hyperinsulinemia, indicating an insulin resistant state; they also showed diminished muscle mitochondrial oxidative capacity, associated with an increased oxidative stress in these muscles, evaluated by the increase in the protein carbonylation levels (a marker of protein oxidative damage) and in the activity of caspase-3 (a marker of apoptosis), as well as in plasma H_2O_2 levels. Taken together, these findings indicate that ROS-induced mitochondrial dysfunction could be involved in the decrease of muscle insulin sensitivity after long periods of high-fat diet ingestion (Bonnard et al., 2008).

In addition to the intrinsic defects of mitochondria, there is growing evidence showing that the lower mitochondrial density in skeletal muscles also plays an important role in the development of insulin-resistant states (Morino et al., 2006). Among the factors that control mitochondrial biogenesis, the peroxisome proliferator-activated receptor-γ coactivator-1α (PGC-1α) can be cited. PGC-1α is a nuclear transcriptional factor that responds to extracellular stimuli, such as cold and physical exercise, increasing the mitochondrial biogenesis in many tissues, including skeletal muscles (St-Pierre et al., 2003). Increased mitochondrial biogenesis is closely related to higher oxidative capacity, since many PGC-1α target genes lead, ultimately, to the expression of proteins involved in the glucose and fatty acid oxidation; thus, PGC-1α activity results in an increased expression of the nuclear respiratory factor 1 (NRF-1), a transcription factor that activates some promoters of mitochondrial genes, including respiratory subunit components, factors involved in the replication and transcription of mitochondrial DNA, among others (Andersson & Scarpulla, 2001; Shao et al., 2010).

Several studies have observed a significant decrease in the expression of PGC-1α and NRF-1 in skeletal muscles of obese and type 2 diabetic individuals (Patti et al., 2003; Heilbronn et al., 2007; Mensink et al., 2007). An interesting study by Sparks and collaborators (2005) investigated the changes in the expression of several genes related to mitochondrial function in skeletal muscles from healthy young individuals who ate a 50% fat diet during 3 days. Although the ingestion of a high-fat diet for 3 days did not change the fasting blood glucose, insulin and free fatty acids levels in comparison with baseline values (i.e., before the high-fat diet), this short-term high-fat diet ingestion was sufficient to promote a decrease in the expression of genes involved in the electron transport chain, as well as in the genes involved in the mitochondrial biogenesis, mainly PGC-1α. Finally, the decreased mitochondrial biogenesis may also be cited as an example of mitochondrial dysfunction that is involved in the increased risk of individual's offspring from parents with T2DM to develop insulin-resistant diseases. Morino et al. (2005) demonstrated that the reduced mitochondrial activity in muscles from young, insulin-resistant offspring of parents with T2DM is associated with a lower mitochondrial density, together with higher IMCL content in comparison to insulin-sensitive control subjects. Insulin-resistant offspring also presented an increase in the basal IRS-1 serine inhibitory phosphorylation (serine-312 and serine-636 residues) and diminished phosphorylation of AKT on serine-473 residue, leading to the molecular characterization of insulin resistance in these subjects.

It must be highlighted that the search for compounds derived from natural products that attenuate or even avoid the installation of insulin resistance has been a current trend. In this way, recent studies have demonstrated that resveratrol (Chen et al., 2011), berberine (Gomes et al., 2012), epigallocatechin-3-gallate (Li et al., 2011) and quercetin (Ahn et al., 2008) improve insulin resistance in skeletal muscles from animals fed a high-fat diet; the beneficial effects of these natural compounds are associated with an increase in the mitochondrial biogenesis by a mechanism that involves a stimulation in the expression of PGC-1α and NRF-1 factors, leading to an increase in muscle glucose uptake and to a decrease in IMCL accumulation.

Impact of High-fat Diets on Gut Microbiota Composition: Consequences for Energy Harvest, Endotoxemia and Inflammatory Status

The gastrointestinal tract contains a diverse microbial community which is predominantly bacterial and collectively known as the gut microbiota. The human gut hosts a large variety of microorganisms, including at least 10^{14} bacterial cells and up to 500-1000 different species, representing more than 100 times the human genome (Vrieze et al., 2010). The majority of bacteria in the human and mouse intestine belong to only four major phyla: the Firmicutes (including gram-positive genera, such as *Clostridium*, *Eubacterium*, *Ruminococcus*, *Butyrivibrio, Anaerostipes*, *Roseburia*, *Faecalibacterium*), the Bacteroidetes (including the gram-negative genera *Bacteroides*, *Porphyromonas*,and *Prevotella*), Actinobacteria (including the gram-positive genus *Bifidobacterium*), and Proteobacteria (including the gram-negative *Enterobacteriaceae*) (Steve et al., 2011; Blaut & Klaus, 2012).

The gut microbiota provides important metabolic and biological functions that cannot be performed by our human metabolism, including the conversion of otherwise indigestible components of our diet such as plant polysaccharides to short-chain fatty acids (SCFAs), transformation of bile acids, the provision of a barrier against pathogenic bacteria, and modulation of the innate and the adaptive immune systems. Studies have highlighted the role of the gut microbiota in the regulation of energy homeostasis, in the pathogenesis of insulin resistance, in fatty liver, in lipid and amino acid metabolism and as a modulator of host fatty acid composition (Murphy et al., 2010; Delzenne & Cani, 2011).

The composition and functionality capabilities of intestinal bacteria may change in response to a variety of intrinsic and environmental factors, such as age, host physiology and genotype, the diet being one of the most important among those factors (Flint et al., 2007; Bernstein & Shanahan, 2008). Diet plays an important role in modulating the gut microbiota and thus has an impact on weight gain, fat deposition and metabolic health. These diet-induced changes can foster significant shifts in the gut microbiota at phylum, class, and family levels. Nowadays, great attention has been focused on the role of the gut microbiota in the regulation of host energy homeostasis and its interaction with hyper-caloric diets because of its influence the development of metabolic disorders, including obesity and insulin resistance (Patrone et al. 2012; Flint, 2011). Obesity is the result of a complex interaction between genetic and environmental factors. Ingestion of diets high in fat and calories leads to hyperphagia and obesity, which is associated with changes in the gut microbiota and chronic "low-grade" systemic inflammation (La Serre et al., 2010).The interplay between diet, gut microbiota and energy homeostasis has been further investigated in rodent models of diet-induced obesity. It has been proposed that changes in gut microbiota composition in response to high-fat diets affect the provision of additional energy by the conversion of dietary fiber to SCFAs, increasing the intestinal permeability, and thus causing elevated systemic levels of lipopolysaccharides (LPS) and inflammatory status, as well as the endocannabinoid system tone (Cani et al., 2007a; Bäckhed et al., 2007; Muccioli et al., 2010; Zang et al., 2012).

The literature evidence further suggests that diet, specifically dietary fat, is a highly potential modulator of the gut microbiota composition. Cani et al. (2007b) demonstrated that high-fat diet deeply affects gut microbiota composition. More precisely, the study showed that diet-induced obesity strongly altered gut microbiota composition compared with normal chow-fed control mice, since high-fat feeding significantly reduced intestinal Gram-negative and Gram-positive bacteria including bifidobacteria, a dominant member of the intestinal microbiota. Several other studies have characterized the gut microbiota composition of diet-induced obese mice and all of these studies are relatively consistent regarding gut microbiota modulation in mice fed a high-fat diet; Firmicutes become more abundant, and Bacteroidetes decrease in number. More specifically, Hildebrandt et al. (2009) showed decreased Bacteriodetes and increased Firmicutes and Proteobacteria in mice fed a high-fat diet. Murphy et al. (2010) found an increased proportion of Firmicutes and a reduction in Bacteroidetes in similar dietary conditions. More recently, Ravussin et al. (2012) confirmed that mice on a high-fat diet had increased levels of Firmicutes. These data support the influence of the diet composition in the diversity and profiles of the gut microbiota.

While the host genotype has been proven to affect microbiota, the effect of diet also plays an important role in determining bacterial composition. It was found that diet explained 57%

of the bacterial variation in the gut while genetic background only accounted for 12% of the variation in animals, which suggests the primacy of diet in determining the composition of the gut microbiota. Within the context of obesity, it appears that genetics may determine initial gut composition, but dietary fat is a potent modulator (Zhang et al., 2010; Harris et al., 2012).

The composition of the gut microbiota is also significantly altered in obesity and diabetes in both animal and human subjects, presenting differences in quantity and proportion of two dominant gut bacteria: Bacteroidetes and Firmicutes (Larsen et al., 2010). It has been suggested that this alteration in microbial composition increases the risk of obesity because of enhanced energy harvest from dietary intake (Turnbaugh et al., 2006). Studies have demonstrated that in murine models, changes in the gut microbiota in response to diet and obesity are dissociated from markers of energy harvest over time, suggesting that mechanisms other than energy harvest may contribute to microbiota-induced susceptibility to obesity and metabolic diseases (Bajzer & Seeley, 2006; Murphy et al., 2010). In this regard, the gut microbiota and associated products such as LPS and SCFAs, have been reported to regulate gene expression, and thereby alter energy expenditure and storage through host related mechanisms (Cani & Delzenne, 2007; Samuel et al., 2008).

It has been suggested that the mechanism by which the gut microbiota affects body weight is by increasing energy harvesting from dietary fibers. The intestinal microbiota breaks down indigestible polysaccharides to SCFAs, especially acetate, propionate and butyrate, which in turn can be oxidized by the host and thus provide additional energy. This may represent 80 to 200 kcal per day or about 4-10% of daily energy intake in normal adults (Sanz et al., 2010). SCFAs are ligands for the G-protein-coupled receptors (GPCRs) Gpr41 and Gpr43. These receptors are expressed in epithelial and endocrine cells and in adipocytes. Gpr41 inactivation is associated with decreased expression of peptide YY (PYY), increased intestinal transit rate, reduced energy uptake from the diet and decreased hepatic lipogenesis (Steve et al., 2011). Thus, the formation of SCFA has been associated with increased expression and production of glucagon-like peptide-1 (GLP-1) and PYY, two anorexigenic peptides in the intestine, resulting in slow intestinal transit, which in turn leads to a more complete absorption of intestinal nutrients including SCFA (Zhou et al., 2008). Altogether, the data imply that excessive calories taken in the form of SCFAs from microbiota metabolism of fiber may be a contributing factor to the development of diet-induced obesity. However, this contribution to the host energy demand is highly dependent on the amount and type of dietary fiber consumed (Murphy et al., 2010; Blaut & Klaus, 2012).

Gut microbiota-derived LPS was recently defined as a factor involved in the onset and progression of inflammation and metabolic diseases. Endotoxin or lipopolysaccharide is a major glycolipid component of the cell wall of gram-negative bacteria and, if absorbed into the circulation, activates the release of host-derived inflammatory mediators to induce a systemic inflammatory response (Raetz & Whitfield, 2002). Previous studies have shown that a fat-enriched diet facilitates the development of metabolic endotoxemia (e.g., increased plasma LPS levels). Furthermore, chronic endotoxemia commonly occurs in obesity and is associated with low-grade systemic inflammation and is an important factor leading to the metabolic syndrome. Endotoxemia can be triggered by physiological mechanisms, such as the transport of LPS from the gut lumen toward target tissues by newly synthesized chylomicrons from epithelial intestinal cells in response to fat feeding. This phenomenon could contribute to higher plasma LPS levels and low-grade inflammation, as is observed with a high-fat diet, suggesting that metabolic endotoxemia could be linked to the gut microbiota (Cani et al., 2007a; 2012).

The LPS molecule is structurally divided into three parts: lipid A, the oligosaccharide core and the O-antigen (Raetz & Whitfield, 2002). Lipid A is the portion of the LPS molecule that is responsible for endotoxicity. Toll-Like Receptors (TLRs) are a family of pattern-recognition receptors that play a critical role in innate immunity by integrating signals from microbiota-host interactions. The innate immune system detects LPS via its interaction with specific proteins that complex with TLR4 (CD14/TLR4 complex). The recognition of a LPS molecule by Toll-like receptor-4 (TLR4) is mediated by the LPS-binding protein, the CD14 co-receptor of TLR4. CD14 is present in soluble form (sCD14), which is derived from both the secretion of CD14 and the enzymatic cleavage of the membrane form of CD14. TLR4 is present on the membrane surface of immune cells and other cells, including adipocytes, hepatocytes and endothelial cells. Upon recognition of LPS, TLR4 undergoes oligomerisation and leads to the activation of downstream signaling pathways, such as NF-kB and mitogen-activated protein kinase (MAPK), which can lead to inflammation (Cani & Delzenne, 2011; Manco et al., 2010). The translocation of NF-kB to the nucleus promotes the activation of genes that codify proteins involved in the inflammatory response, such as TNF-α, IL-6, inducible NO synthase and monocyte chemotactic protein-1 (Song et al., 2006). The signaling pathways activated by MAPK include JNK, p38 MAPK and extracellular signal-regulated kinases (ERK) that can induce insulin resistance via different mechanisms (Moreira & Alfenas, 2012; Moreira et al., 2012).

The components of the diet, such as fatty acid profile can contribute to the modulation of the onset of low-grade inflammation by influencing the type of endotoxin receptors and transporters. Recently, Laugerette et al. (2012) investigated the effects of dietary oil composition on endotoxin metabolism and inflammation. In this study, mice were fed for 8 weeks with chow or isocaloric-isolipidic diets enriched with oils differing in fatty acid composition: milk fat, palm oil, rapeseed oil, or sunflower oil. LPS-binding protein is used as a marker of metabolic endotoxemia because it is a major LPS transporter in plasma, while sCD14 seems to provide protective effects against the LPS response, buffering the inflammatory signals by avoiding LPS exposure to the cell-anchored membrane form of CD14. The higher inflammatory response observed in the palm oil group was correlated with a greater ratio of LPS-binding protein/sCD14 in plasma. Rapeseed oil intake resulted in higher levels of sCD14 than the intake of palm oil and was associated with less inflammation in plasma. The authors conclude that dietary fat composition can contribute to modulate the onset of low-grade inflammation through plasma endotoxin receptors, and transporters sCD14 and LBP oriented toward TLR4 and CD14 activation rather than being directly correlated with gut-derived plasma endotoxemia.

The observed increase in plasma LPS in response to high-fat diets was suggested as resulting from increased gut permeability. High-fat diet feeding modulates the gut microbiota composition by decreasing the prevalence of specific gut barrier-protecting bacteria and increasing the prevalence of opportunistic pathogens that can release free antigens such as LPS. This imbalance may be associated with higher gut permeability, leading to higher plasma levels of endotoxin, and the development of metabolic endotoxemia (Cani et al., 2007a; Zhang et al., 2010). Cani et al. (2008; 2009; 2012) showed that a high-fat diet contributes to the disruption of the tight-junction proteins (Zonula Occludens-1(ZO-1) and Occludin) involved in the gut barrier function, whose expression was lower in mice fed a high-fat diet than in mice fed a normal diet. Antibiotic treatment of the high-fat diet-fed mice normalized the expression of ZO-1, suggesting that the gut microbiota modifies the permeability of the gut epithelial layer. In accordance with this hypothesis, the authors also found that the specific modulation of the gut microbiota composition with non-digestible carbohydrates improves gut barrier integrity, reduces metabolic endotoxemia, and lowers inflammation and glucose intolerance. In this context, studies have shown that while the high-fat diet led to a reduction in the concentration of most bacterial groups, including the bifidobacteria, mice fed the high-fat diet supplemented with oligofructose had normal bifidobacteria concentrations just like mice fed a control diet. Importantly, *Bifidobacterium* spp. has been shown to reduce intestinal endotoxin levels in rodents and improve mucosal barrier function. In conjunction with these effects on the gut microbiota, oligofructose supplementation lowered the endotoxin levels and improved glucose tolerance and glucose-induced insulin secretion. Consequently, cell numbers of bifidobacteria correlated negatively with various parameters of endotoxemia and positively with improved glucose tolerance and insulin secretion. Therefore, it has been proposed that stimulating the growth of intestinal bifidobacteria may minimize the pathophysiological consequences of endotoxemia and thereby prevent the occurrence of diabetes and obesity.

Another proposed system involved in energy homeostasis potentially mediates the influence of microbiota on gut permeability, namely, the endocannabinoid system. This system includes the endocannabinoid receptors CB1 and CB2, which belong to the family of the G protein-coupled receptors (Scherer & Buettner, 2009). A role in the regulation of energy metabolism has been attributed to CB1. Physiological ligands of the CB1 receptor are lipid signals derived from polyunsaturated fatty acids known as endocannabinoids (ECs). Studies involving specific antagonists and agonists demonstrated that the endocannabinoid system controls the gut permeability and metabolic endotoxemia via CB1 receptor dependent mechanisms. Endocannabinoids increase mRNA expression of the tight junction protein occludin-1 and decrease expression of claudin-1, further supporting a hypothetical role of these in the regulation of intestinal permeability (Muccioli et al., 2010; Tilg & Kaser, 2011). These data corroborate with studies of Cani and Delzenne, which show that high-fat feeding reduced the expression of epithelial tight junction proteins occludin and ZO-1, leading to increased intestinal permeability and LPS levels, suggesting that intestinal fat absorption and secretion may have a predominant role in LPS entry into the portal blood (Cani et al., 2007b; 2009; Delzenne & Cani, 2011).

In summary, gut microbiota alterations have been shown to be associated and causally linked to metabolic diseases such as T2DM and obesity in both animals and humans. A high-fat diet is able to unbalance the gut microbiota and impair the gut barrier resulting in increased endotoxemia, subclinical inflammation and its metabolic effects.

Effects of the High-fat Diet on Central Nervous System

In addition to peripheral effects, the high-fat diet alters many functions of the central nervous system. It has been reported by several authors that high-fat diet is responsible for cognitive decline and neurodegenerative diseases, impairing learning and memory (Del Parigi et al., 2006). Recent works have showed that the dentate gyrus of the hippocampus is an area in the brain that contributes to cognitive function and it is one of the most plastic areas. It is the area where the neurogenesis from neural progenitor cells, necessary for the reposition of dying cells, continues into adulthood maintaining functional synapses (Park & Lee, 2011). Studies show impairment in neurogenesis in adult rats and mice submitted to high-fat diet as well as offspring of female mice submitted to the same diet (Lindquist et al., 2006; Hwang et al., 2008; Tozuka et al., 2009). The brain-derived neurotrophic factor (BDNF) is a potent modulator of synaptic plasticity, involved in neurogenesis and neuronal differentiation. The expression, release and neuromodulatory activity of the BDNF can be mediated by epigenetic and/or post-translational mechanisms (Cowansage et al., 2010; LeDoux & Monfils, 2010). Park et al. (2010) demonstrated that C57BL/6 mice, after seven weeks of high-fat diet, show impairment in the hippocampus neurogenesis and in the proliferation of the progenitor cells, as well as an increase of lipid peroxidation and a reduction of BNDF level. Wu et al. (2004) found similar results and additional data that show that malondialdehyde, a product of lipid peroxidation, also impairs the proliferation of the hippocampus progenitor cells. One other important function impaired in central nervous system by high-fat diet is the control of energetic balance and body weight by the hypothalamus, an area in the brain which plays a key role in the control of food intake and energetic expenditure. Thus, models of high-fat diet administration in rats and mice have been used as an experimental strategy to obtain models of obesity and other consequences related to it. More recently, obesity has been associated with a state of moderate and chronic inflammation characterized by an increase in cytokines in tissue and blood. Evidences have shown that immune cell-mediate inflammation occurs, not only in peripheral tissues, but also in central nervous system, more exactly in hypothalamus (Yi et al., 2012). In 2005, it was demonstrated that in animals after 16 weeks of high-fat diet the proinflammatory cytokines IL-1β, TNF-α and IL-6 represent the largest class of genes with increased hypothalamic expression levels (De Sousa et al., 2005).

The saturated fat, seems to be an important factor for the onset of the process through the Toll-like receptor 4 (TLR4), a receptor of the immune system, (Velloso, 2012; Lee & Gao, 2003). The activation of the receptor can induce endoplasmatic reticulum stress and damage the protein folding and consequently its function. The leptin, synthesized mainly in adipose tissue, is the most important factor to regulate long-term body energy stores, by a feedback mechanism, mainly by its action on hypothalamus. These effects are mediated via cytokine-like receptor isoforms distributed in the central nervous system and peripheral tissues. The loss of hypothalamic response to this cytokine is known as hyphotalamic leptin resistance (Thaler & Schwartz, 2010). The secretion of leptin by adipose tissue is directly proportional to adipose mass and the highest levels of expression of its receptor are found in neurons of the nuclei of the basomedial hypothalamus, including the arcuate (ARC), dorsomedial and ventromedial hypothalamic (VMH) nucleus (Elmquist et al., 1998). The leptin receptors (Ob-R) are encoded by the diabetes gene (db), that generate at least six leptin receptor. There are short and long forms of receptors containing about 30-40 and 302 citoplasmatic residues, respectively. The long-form receptor (Ob-Rb) is an isoform that has a pivotal role in the control of obesity. Leptin binding to Ob-Rb activates janus tyrosine kinases (JAK2) and proteins are phosphorylated followed by the activation of several signaling pathways, including insulin receptor substrate protein (IRS) and the p85 subunit of PI3-kinase, which is a common target downstream of IRS-1. The signal transducers and activators of transcription factors (STAT) can also be activated by JAKs. In vivo, intravenous administration of leptin in the hypothalamus activates STAT3 leading to nuclear translocation and the transcriptional activation of genes. Leptin can also induce expression of SOCS-3 (suppressor of cytokine receptor signaling) in the hypothalamus, which is important for the feedback mechanism to control leptin receptor signaling. SOCS seems to bind to phosphorylated tyrosine residues on JAKs, to suppress cytokine receptor signaling. Thus, SOCS3 can physically block the leptin receptor signal transduction (Harvey & Ashford, 2003; Kille & Alexandre, 2001; Velloso, 2012; Rother et al., 2012; Cottrell & Mercer, 2012).

Within the ARC, the leptin receptor is found in two different populations of neurons: *i*) neurons that express neuropeptide Y (NPY) and agouti-related peptide (AgRP); *ii*) neurons that express pro-opiomelanocortin (POMC) which is processed to α-melanocyte stimulating hormone (αMSH) which mediates the appetite-suppressing signal, via activation of melanocortin receptors. The binding of leptin in its receptor activates the POMC neuron and stimulates its expression. Leptin also acts via its receptors inhibiting the NPY/AgRP neurons. AgRP is an antagonist of αMSH signaling and NPY is itself an orexigenic (Bates & Myers, 2004). Thus leptin stimulates the production of anorectic neuropeptides and suppresses levels of orexigenic peptides.

Persistent hyperleptinaemia, when obesity is induced by high-fat diet, leptin resistance develops, and signalling through of the leptin receptor is curtailed, conducting to body weight gain. Leptin resistance promotes reduction in leptin signaling proteins, hypothalamic inflammation by TNF-α and an increase in the expression of SOCS3 (negative regulators of cytokine signaling). One important difference between peripheral and central inflammation in obese rats observed by Thaler et al. (2012) is that the first one develops after a long-term exposition to high-fat diet, while markers of hypothalamic inflammation are observed after 24 hours of high-fat diet administration. In the first week, injury markers also become evident in the arcuate nucleus and median eminence. Together with an increase in injury markers, reactive gliosis involving recruitment of microglia and astrocytes was observed in this period.

It seems clear that hypothalamic inflammation is an event that occurs before peripheral inflammation and also precedes leptin resistance which involves several leptin signaling targets. When leptin resistance is installed in an early life phase, studies show that the inflammation seems to be restricted to the hypothalamus although the consequence of the central inflammation can alter the expression PGC1α by sympathetic stimulus in peripheral tissues, changing the expression of specific proteins in these organs (Mouihate & Galic, 2010; Liang & Ward, 2006). The control of the hypothalamic hormones corticotrophin-releasing hormone (CRH) and thyrotropin-releasing hormone (TRH) by leptin, also explains how the high-fat diet can regulate other endocrine systems by hypothalamus-pituitary-adrenal and hypothalamus-pituitary-thyroid axis (Vrang et al., 2002; Flier et al., 2000), although the results about the alterations in hypothalamus- pituitary- adrenal axis by high-fat diet are not conclusive because different experimental conditions are used in the studies found in literature (Auvinem et al., 2011).

Chronic high-fat diet ingestion also alters the brain neurotransmitter system that regulates hunger and satiety, increasing hypothalamic dopamine. Fat and sucrose are stimuli that increase dopamine release in the nucleus accumbens area in the hypothalamus, promoting food intake. The alterations in the dopaminergic system have been identified in both obese animals and humans, and they seem to occur by an epigenetic mechanism, having been shown vulnerable to maternal diet in prenatal and early post-natal period of offspring (Chen et al., 1997; Teegarden et al., 2009). DNA methylation was identified within the promoter region on the first enzyme of the catecholamine synthesis genes tyrosine hydroxilase by high-fat diet administration (Vucetic et al., 2012).

It can be concluded, according to data in literature, that high-fat diet triggers changes in the cerebral metabolism, promoting hypothalamic inflammation; alteration in the brain neurotransmitter system and hippocampus impairment; and that maternal feeding can also promote central epigenetic alterations in pre-natal or early post-natal offspring.

References

Ahn J, Lee H, Kim S, Park J, Ha T. The anti-obesity effect of quercetin is mediated by the AMPK and MAPK signaling pathways. *Biochem Biophys Res Commun.* 2008; 373(4): 545-9.

Andersson A, Nälsén C, Tengblad S, Vessby B. Fatty acid composition of skeletal muscle reflects dietary fat composition in humans. *Am J Clin Nutr.* 2002; 76(6): 1222-9.

Andersson U, Scarpulla RC. Pgc-1-related coactivator, a novel, serum-inducible coactivator of nuclear respiratory factor 1-dependent transcription in mammalian cells. *Mol Cell Biol.* 2001; 21(11): 3738-49.

Auvinen HE, Romijn JA, Biermasz NR, Havekes LM, Smit JW, Rensen PC, Pereira AM. Effects of high fat diet on the Basal activity of the hypothalamus-pituitary-adrenal axis in mice: a systematic review. *Horm Metab Res.* 2011; 43(13): 899-906.

Avignon A, Yamada K, Zhou X, Spencer B, Cardona O, Saba-Siddique S, Galloway L, Standaert ML, Farese RV. Chronic activation of protein kinase C in soleus muscles and other tissues of insulin-resistant type II diabetic Goto-Kakizaki (GK), obese/aged, and obese/Zucker rats. A mechanism for inhibiting glycogen synthesis. *Diabetes.* 1996; 45(10): 1396-404.

Bäckhed F, Manchester JK, Semenkovich CF, Gordon JI. Mechanisms underlying the resistance to diet-induced obesity in germ-free mice. *Proc Natl Acad Sci U S A.* 2007; 104(3): 979-84.

Bajzer M, Seeley RJ. Physiology: obesity and gut flora. *Nature.* 2006; 444 (7122): 1009-10.

Bates SH, Myers MG. The role of leptin-->STAT3 signaling in neuroendocrine function: an integrative perspective. *J Mol Med (Berl).* 2004; 82(1): 12-20.

Bell RR, Spencer MJ, Sherriff JL. Voluntary exercise and monounsaturated canola oil reduce fat gain in mice fed diets high in fat. *J Nutr.* 1997; 127(10): 2006-10.

Bergman BC, Hunerdosse DM, Kerege A, Playdon MC, Perreault L. Localisation and composition of skeletal muscle diacylglycerol predicts insulin resistance in humans. *Diabetologia.* 2012; 55(4): 1140-50.

Bernstein CN, Shanahan F. Disorders of a modern lifestyle: reconciling the epidemiology of inflammatory bowel diseases. *Gut.* 2008; 57(9): 1185-91.

Blaut M, Klaus S. Intestinal microbiota and obesity. *Handb Exp Pharmacol.* 2012; (209): 251-73.

Bogan JS. Regulation of glucose transporter translocation in health and diabetes. *Annu Rev Biochem.* 2012; 81: 507-32.

Bonnard C, Durand A, Peyrol S, Chanseaume E, Chauvin MA, Morio B, Vidal H, Rieusset J. Mitochondrial dysfunction results from oxidative stress in the skeletal muscle of diet-induced insulin-resistant mice. *J Clin Invest.* 2008; 118(2): 789-800.

Bruce CR, Anderson MJ, Carey AL, Newman DG, Bonen A, Kriketos AD, Cooney GJ, Hawley JA. Muscle oxidative capacity is a better predictor of insulin sensitivity than lipid status. *J Clin Endocrinol Metab.* 2003; 88(11): 5444-51.

Buettner R, Parhofer KG, Woenckhaus M, Wrede CE, Kunz-Schughart LA, Schölmerich J, Bollheimer LC. Defining high-fat-diet rat models: metabolic and molecular effects of different fat types. *J Mol Endocrinol.* 2006; 36(3): 485-501.

Cani PD, Amar J, Iglesias MA, Poggi M, Knauf C, Bastelica D, Neyrinck AM, Fava F, Tuohy KM, Chabo C, Waget A, Delmée E, Cousin B, Sulpice T, Chamontin B, Ferrières J, Tanti JF, Gibson GR, Casteilla L, Delzenne NM, Alessi MC, Burcelin R. Metabolic endotoxemia initiates obesity and insulin resistance. *Diabetes.* 2007a; 56(7): 1761-72.

Cani PD, Bibiloni R, Knauf C, Waget A, Neyrinck AM, Delzenne NM, Burcelin R. Changes in gut microbiota control metabolic endotoxemia-induced inflammation in high-fat diet-induced obesity and diabetes in mice. *Diabetes.* 2008; 57(6): 1470-81.

Cani PD, Delzenne NM. Gut microflora as a target for energy and metabolic homeostasis. *Curr Opin Clin Nutr Metab Care.* 2007; 10(6): 729-34.

Cani PD, Delzenne NM. The gut microbiome as therapeutic target. *Pharmacol Ther.* 2011; 130(2): 202-12.

Cani PD, Delzenne NM. The role of the gut microbiota in energy metabolism and metabolic disease. *Curr Pharm Des.* 2009; 15(13): 1546-58.

Cani PD, Neyrinck AM, Fava F, Knauf C, Burcelin RG, Tuohy KM, Gibson GR, Delzenne NM. Selective increases of bifidobacteria in gut microflora improve high-fat-diet-induced diabetes in mice through a mechanism associated with endotoxaemia. *Diabetologia.* 2007b; 50(11): 2374-83.

Cani PD, Osto M, Geurts L, Everard A. Involvement of gut microbiota in the development of low-grade inflammation and type 2 diabetes associated with obesity. *Gut Microbes.* 2012; 3(4): 1-10.

Chen LL, Zhang HH, Zheng J, Hu X, Kong W, Hu D, Wang SX, Zhang P. Resveratrol attenuates high-fat diet-induced insulin resistance by influencing skeletal muscle lipid transport and subsarcolemmal mitochondrial β-oxidation. *Metabolism.* 2011; 60(11): 1598-609.

Chen LL, Zhang HH, Zheng J, Hu X, Kong W, Hu D, Wang SX, Zhang P. Resveratrol attenuates high-fat diet-induced insulin resistance by influencing skeletal muscle lipid transport and subsarcolemmal mitochondrial β-oxidation. *Metabolism.* 2011; 60(11): 1598-609.

Choudhury M, Jonscher KR, Friedman JE. Reduced mitochondrial function in obesity-associated fatty liver: SIRT3 takes on the fat. *Aging* (Albany NY). 2011; 3(2): 175-8.

Corcoran MP, Lamon-Fava S, Fielding RA. Skeletal muscle lipid deposition and insulin resistance: effect of dietary fatty acids and exercise. *Am J Clin Nutr* 2007; 85(3): 662-77.

Cottrell EC, Mercer JG. Leptin receptors. *Handb Exp Pharmacol.* 2012; (209): 3-21.

Cowansage KK, LeDoux JE, Monfils MH. Brain-derived neurotrophic factor: a dynamic gatekeeper of neural plasticity. *Curr Mol Pharmacol.* 2010; 3(1): 12-29.

De La Serre CB, Ellis CL, Lee J, Hartman AL, Rutledge JC, Raybould HE. Propensity to high-fat diet-induced obesity in rats is associated with changes in the gut microbiota and gut inflammation. *Am J Physiol Gastrointest Liver Physiol.* 2010; 299(2): G440-8.

De Souza CT, Araujo EP, Bordin S, Ashimine R, Zollner RL, Boschero AC, Saad MJ, Velloso LA. Consumption of a fat-rich diet activates a pro-inflammatory response and induces insulin resistance in the hypothalamus. *Endocrinology* 2005; 146: 4192-4199.

Del Parigi A, Panza F, Capurso C, Solfrizzi V. Nutritional factors, cognitive decline, and dementia. *Brain Res Bull.* 2006; 69(1): 1-19.

Delzenne NM, Cani PD. Interaction between obesity and the gut microbiota: relevance in nutrition. *Annu Rev Nutr.* 2011; (21) 31: 15-31.

Dimopoulos N, Watson M, Sakamoto K, Hundal HS. Differential effects of palmitate and palmitoleate on insulin action and glucose utilization in rat L6 skeletal muscle cells. *Biochem J.* 2006; 399(3): 473-81.

Dubé JJ, Amati F, Stefanovic-Racic M, Toledo FG, Sauers SE, Goodpaster BH. Exercise-induced alterations in intramyocellular lipids and insulin resistance: the athlete's paradox revisited. *Am J Physiol Endocrinol Metab.* 2008; 294(5): E882-8.

Elmquist JK, Bjørbaek C, Ahima RS, Flier JS, Saper CB. Distributions of leptin receptor mRNA isoforms in the rat brain. *J Comp Neurol.* 1998; 395(4): 535-47.

Esteve E, Ricart W, Fernández-Real JM. Gut microbiota interactions with obesity, insulin resistance and type 2 diabetes: did gut microbiote co-evolve with insulin resistance? *Curr Opin Clin Nutr Metab Care.* 2011; 14(5): 483-90.

Fenton PF, Dowling MT. Studies on obesity. I. Nutritional obesity in mice. *J Nutr.* 1953; 49(2): 319-31.

Flier JS, Harris M, Hollenberg AN. Leptin, nutrition, and the thyroid: the why, the wherefore, and the wiring. *J Clin Invest.* 2000; 105(7): 859-61.

Flint HJ, Duncan SH, Scott KP, Louis P. Interactions and competition within the microbial community of the human colon: links between diet and health. *Environ Microbiol.* 2007; 9(5): 1101-11.

Flint HJ. Obesity and the gut microbiota. *J Clin Gastroenterol.* 2011; 45 Suppl: S128-32.

Frangioudakis G, Garrard J, Raddatz K, Nadler JL, Mitchell TW, Schmitz-Peiffer C. Saturated- and n-6 polyunsaturated-fat diets each induce ceramide accumulation in mouse skeletal muscle: reversal and improvement of glucose tolerance by lipid metabolism inhibitors. *Endocrinology.* 2010; 151(9): 4187-96.

Gao Z, Zhang X, Zuberi A, Hwang D, Quon MJ, Lefevre M, Ye J. Inhibition of insulin sensitivity by free fatty acids requires activation of multiple serine kinases in 3T3-L1 adipocytes. *Mol Endocrinol.* 2004; 18(8): 2024-34.

Gomes AP, Duarte FV, Nunes P, Hubbard BP, Teodoro JS, Varela AT, Jones JG, Sinclair DA, Palmeira CM, Rolo AP. Berberine protects against high fat diet-induced dysfunction in muscle mitochondria by inducing SIRT1-dependent mitochondrial biogenesis. *Biochim Biophys Acta.* 2012; 1822(2): 185-95.

Griffin ME, Marcucci MJ, Cline GW, Bell K, Barucci N, Lee D, Goodyear LJ, Kraegen EW, White MF, Shulman GI. Free fatty acid-induced insulin resistance is associated with activation of protein kinase C theta and alterations in the insulin signaling cascade. *Diabetes.* 1999; 48(6): 1270-4.

Gual P, Le Marchand-Brustel Y, Tanti JF. Positive and negative regulation of insulin signaling through IRS-1 phosphorylation. *Biochimie.* 2005 Jan; 87(1): 99-109.

Hamilton JA, Kamp F. How are free fatty acids transported in membranes? Is it by proteins or by free diffusion through the lipids? *Diabetes*. 1999; 48(12): 2255-69.

Hariri N, Thibault L. High-fat diet-induced obesity in animal models. *Nutr Res Rev*. 2010; 23(2): 270-99.

Harris K, Kassis A, Major G, Chou CJ. Is the gut microbiota a new factor contributing to obesity and its metabolic disorders? *J Obes*. 2012; 2012: 879151.

Harvey J, Ashford ML. Leptin in the CNS: much more than a satiety signal. *Neuropharmacology*. 2003; 44(7): 845-54.

Heilbronn LK, Gan SK, Turner N, Campbell LV, Chisholm DJ. Markers of mitochondrial biogenesis and metabolism are lower in overweight and obese insulin-resistant subjects. *J Clin Endocrinol Metab*. 2007; 92(4): 1467-73.

Herschkovitz A, Liu YF, Ilan E, Ronen D, Boura-Halfon S, Zick Y. Common inhibitory serine sites phosphorylated by IRS-1 kinases, triggered by insulin and inducers of insulin resistance. *J Biol Chem*. 2007; 282(25): 18018-27.

Hildebrandt MA, Hoffmann C, Sherrill-Mix SA, Keilbaugh SA, Hamady M, Chen YY, Knight R, Ahima RS, Bushman F, Wu GD. High-fat diet determines the composition of the murine gut microbiome independently of obesity. *Gastroenterology*. 2009; 137(5): 1716-24.

Hirabara SM, Curi R, Maechler P. Saturated fatty acid-induced insulin resistance is associated with mitochondrial dysfunction in skeletal muscle cells. *J Cell Physiol*. 2010; 222(1): 187-94.

Ho JK, Duclos RI Jr, Hamilton JA. Interactions of acyl carnitines with model membranes: a (13)C-NMR study. *J Lipid Res*. 2002; 43(9): 1429-39.

Holland WL, Brozinick JT, Wang LP, Hawkins ED, Sargent KM, Liu Y, Narra K, Hoehn KL, Knotts TA, Siesky A, Nelson DH, Karathanasis SK, Fontenot GK, Birnbaum MJ, Summers SA. Inhibition of ceramide synthesis ameliorates glucocorticoid-, saturated-fat-, and obesity-induced insulin resistance. *Cell Metab*. 2007; 5(3): 167-79.

Hossain P, Kawar B, El Nahas M. Obesity and diabetes in the developing world--a growing challenge. *N Engl J Med*. 2007; 356(3): 213-5.

HR, Park M, Choi J, Park KY, Chung HY, Lee J. A high-fat diet impairs neurogenesis: involvement of lipid peroxidation and brain-derived neurotrophic factor. *Neurosci Lett*. 2010; 482(3): 235-9.

Hwang IK, Kim IY, Kim DW, Yoo KY, Kim YN, Yi SS, Won MH, Lee IS, Yoon YS, Seong JK. Strain-specific differences in cell proliferation and differentiation in the dentate gyrus of C57BL/6N and C3H/HeN mice fed a high fat diet. *Brain Res*. 2008; 1241: 1-6.

Ijuin T, Takenawa T. Regulation of insulin signaling and glucose transporter 4 (GLUT4) exocytosis by phosphatidylinositol 3,4,5-trisphosphate (PIP3) phosphatase, skeletal muscle, and kidney enriched inositol polyphosphate phosphatase (SKIP). *J Biol Chem*. 2012; 287(10): 6991-9.

Itani SI, Ruderman NB, Schmieder F, Boden G. Lipid-induced insulin resistance in human muscle is associated with changes in diacylglycerol, protein kinase C, and IkappaB-alpha. *Diabetes*. 2002; 51(7): 2005-11. *J Neurosci*. 2010; 30(23): 7975-83.

Jacob S, Machann J, Rett K, Brechtel K, Volk A, Renn W, Maerker E, Matthaei S, Schick F, Claussen CD, Häring HU. Association of increased intramyocellular lipid content with insulin resistance in lean nondiabetic offspring of type 2 diabetic subjects. *Diabetes*. 1999; 48(5): 1113-9.

Kaaman M, Sparks LM, van Harmelen V, Smith SR, Sjölin E, Dahlman I, Arner P. Strong association between mitochondrial DNA copy number and lipogenesis in human white adipose tissue. *Diabetologia.* 2007; 50(12): 2526-33.

Kelishadi R, Hashemi M, Mohammadifard N, Asgary S, Khavarian N. Association of changes in oxidative and proinflammatory states with changes in vascular function after a lifestyle modification trial among obese children. *Clin Chem.* 2008; 54(1): 147-53.

Kim JK, Fillmore JJ, Sunshine MJ, Albrecht B, Higashimori T, Kim DW, Liu ZX, Soos TJ, Cline GW, O'Brien WR, Littman DR, Shulman GI. PKC-theta knockout mice are protected from fat-induced insulin resistance. *J Clin Invest.* 2004; 114(6): 823-7.

Kim JY, Hickner RC, Cortright RL, Dohm GL, Houmard JA. Lipid oxidation is reduced in obese human skeletal muscle. *Am J Physiol Endocrinol Metab.* 2000; 279(5): E1039-44.

Kraegen EW, Cooney GJ. Free fatty acids and skeletal muscle insulin resistance. *Curr Opin Lipidol.* 2008; 19(3): 235-41.

Larsen N, Vogensen FK, van den Berg FW, Nielsen DS, Andreasen AS, Pedersen BK, Al-Soud WA, Sørensen SJ, Hansen LH, Jakobsen M. Gut microbiota in human adults with type 2 diabetes differs from non-diabetic adults. *PLoS One.* 2010; 5(2): e9085.

Laugerette F, Furet JP, Debard C, Daira P, Loizon E, Géloën A, Soulage CO, Simonet C, Lefils-Lacourtablaise J, Bernoud-Hubac N, Bodennec J, Peretti N, Vidal H, Michalski MC. Oil composition of high-fat diet affects metabolic inflammation differently in connection with endotoxin receptors in mice. *Am J Physiol Endocrinol Metab.* 2012; 302(3): E374-86.

Lee JS, Pinnamaneni SK, Eo SJ, Cho IH, Pyo JH, Kim CK, Sinclair AJ, Febbraio MA, Watt MJ. Saturated, but not n-6 polyunsaturated, fatty acids induce insulin resistance: role of intramuscular accumulation of lipid metabolites. *J Appl Physiol.* 2006; 100(5): 1467-74.

Li Y, Zhao S, Zhang W, Zhao P, He B, Wu N, Han P. Epigallocatechin-3-O-gallate (EGCG) attenuates FFAs-induced peripheral insulin resistance through AMPK pathway and insulin signaling pathway in vivo. *Diabetes Res Clin Pract.* 2011; 93(2): 205-14.

Liang H, Ward WF. PGC-1alpha: a key regulator of energy metabolism. *Adv Physiol Educ.* 2006; 30(4): 145-51.

Lindqvist A, Mohapel P, Bouter B, Frielingsdorf H, Pizzo D, Brundin P, Erlanson-Albertsson C. High-fat diet impairs hippocampal neurogenesis in male rats. *Eur J Neurol.* 2006;13(12):1385-8.

Ma ZA, Zhao Z, Turk J. Mitochondrial dysfunction and β-cell failure in type 2 diabetes mellitus. *Exp Diabetes Res.* 2012, Article ID 703538, 11 pages.

Machann J, Häring H, Schick F, Stumvoll M. Intramyocellular lipids and insulin resistance. *Diabetes Obes Metab.* 2004; 6(4): 239-48.

Manco M, Calvani M, Mingrone G. Effects of dietary fatty acids on insulin sensitivity and secretion. *Diabetes Obes Metab.* 2004; 6(6): 402-13.

Manco M, Putignani L, Bottazzo GF. Gut microbiota, lipopolysaccharides, and innate immunity in the pathogenesis of obesity and cardiovascular risk. *Endocr Rev.* 2010; 31(6): 817-44.

Martins AR, Nachbar RT, Gorjao R, Vinolo MA, Festuccia WT, Lambertucci RH, Cury-Boaventura MF, Silveira LR, Curi R, Hirabara SM. Mechanisms underlying skeletal muscle insulin resistance induced by fatty acids: importance of the mitochondrial function. *Lipids Health Dis.* 2012; 11: 30.

Mensink M, Hesselink MK, Russell AP, Schaart G, Sels JP, Schrauwen P. Improved skeletal muscle oxidative enzyme activity and restoration of PGC-1 alpha and PPAR beta/delta gene expression upon rosiglitazone treatment in obese patients with type 2 diabetes mellitus. *Int J Obes* (Lond). 2007; 31(8): 1302-10.

Misra A, Khurana L. Obesity and the metabolic syndrome in developing countries. *J Clin Endocrinol Metab.* 2008; 93(11 Suppl 1): S9-30.

Mogensen M, Sahlin K, Fernström M, Glintborg D, Vind BF, Beck-Nielsen H, Højlund K. Mitochondrial respiration is decreased in skeletal muscle of patients with type 2 diabetes. *Diabetes*. 2007; 56(6): 1592-9.

Montero D, Walther G, Perez-Martin A, Roche E, Vinet A. Endothelial dysfunction, inflammation, and oxidative stress in obese children and adolescents: markers and effect of lifestyle intervention. *Obes Rev.* 2012; 13(5): 441-55.

Moreira AP, Teixeira TF, Ferreira AB, do Carmo Gouveia Peluzio M, de Cássia Gonçalves Alfenas R. Influence of a high-fat diet on gut microbiota, intestinal permeability and metabolic endotoxaemia. *Br J Nutr.* 2012; 16: 1-9.

Moreira APB, Alfenas RGG. The influence of endotoxemia on the molecular mechanisms of insulin resistance. *Nutr Hosp.* 2012; 27(2): 382-90.

Morino K, Petersen KF, Dufour S, Befroy D, Frattini J, Shatzkes N, Neschen S, White MF, Bilz S, Sono S, Pypaert M, Shulman GI. Reduced mitochondrial density and increased IRS-1 serine phosphorylation in muscle of insulin-resistant offspring of type 2 diabetic parents. *J Clin Invest.* 2005; 115(12): 3587-93.

Morino K, Petersen KF, Shulman GI. Molecular mechanisms of insulin resistance in humans and their potential links with mitochondrial dysfunction. *Diabetes.* 2006; 55 Suppl 2: S9-S15.

Mouihate A, Galic MA, Ellis SL, Spencer SJ, Tsutsui S, Pittman QJ. Early life activation of toll-like receptor 4 reprograms neural anti-inflammatory pathways. *J Neurosci.* 2010; 30(23): 7975-83.

Muccioli GG, Naslain D, Bäckhed F, Reigstad CS, Lambert DM, Delzenne NM, Cani PD. The endocannabinoid system links gut microbiota to adipogenesis. *Mol Syst Biol.* 2010; 6: 392.

Murphy EF, Cotter PD, Healy S, Marques TM, O'Sullivan O, Fouhy F, Clarke SF, O'Toole PW, Quigley EM, Stanton C, Ross PR, O'Doherty RM, Shanahan F. Composition and energy harvesting capacity of the gut microbiota: relationship to diet, obesity and time in mouse models. *Gut.* 2010; 59(12): 1635-42.

Newsholme P, Haber EP, Hirabara SM, Rebelato EL, Procopio J, Morgan D, Oliveira-Emilio HC, Carpinelli AR, Curi R. Diabetes associated cell stress and dysfunction: role of mitochondrial and non-mitochondrial ROS production and activity. *J Physiol.* 2007; 583(Pt 1): 9-24.

Pagel-Langenickel I, Bao J, Pang L, Sack MN. The role of mitochondria in the pathophysiology of skeletal muscle insulin resistance. *Endocr Rev.* 2010; 31(1): 25-51.

Panchal SK, Poudyal H, Iyer A, Nazer R, Alam MA, Diwan V, Kauter K, Sernia C, Campbell F, Ward L, Gobe G, Fenning A, Brown L. High-carbohydrate, high-fat diet-induced metabolic syndrome and cardiovascular remodeling in rats. *J Cardiovasc Pharmacol.* 201; 57(5): 611-24.

Park HR, Lee J. Neurogenic contributions made by dietary regulation to hippocampal neurogenesis. *Ann N Y Acad Sci.* 2011; 1229:23-8.

Patrone V, Ferrari S, Lizier M, Lucchini F, Minuti A, Tondelli B, Trevisi E, Rossi F, Callegari ML. Short-term modifications in the distal gut microbiota of weaning mice induced by a high-fat diet. *Microbiology.* 2012; 158(Pt 4): 983-92.

Patti ME, Butte AJ, Crunkhorn S, Cusi K, Berria R, Kashyap S, Miyazaki Y, Kohane I, Costello M, Saccone R, Landaker EJ, Goldfine AB, Mun E, DeFronzo R, Finlayson J, Kahn CR, Mandarino LJ. Coordinated reduction of genes of oxidative metabolism in humans with insulin resistance and diabetes: Potential role of PGC1 and NRF1. *Proc Natl Acad Sci U S A.* 2003; 100(14): 8466-71.

Perseghin G, Scifo P, Danna M, Battezzati A, Benedini S, Meneghini E, Del Maschio A, Luzi L. Normal insulin sensitivity and IMCL content in overweight humans are associated with higher fasting lipid oxidation. *Am J Physiol Endocrinol Metab.* 2002; 283(3): E556-64.

Powell DJ, Turban S, Gray A, Hajduch E, Hundal HS. Intracellular ceramide synthesis and protein kinase C-zeta activation play an essential role in palmitate-induced insulin resistance in rat L6 skeletal muscle cells. *Biochem J.* 2004; 382(Pt 2): 619-29.

Raetz CR, Whitfield C. Lipopolysaccharide endotoxins. *Annu Rev Biochem.* 2002; 71: 635-700.

Ravussin Y, Koren O, Spor A, LeDuc C, Gutman R, Stombaugh J, Knight R, Ley RE, Leibel RL. Responses of gut microbiota to diet composition and weight loss in lean and obese mice. *Obesity (Silver Spring).* 2012; 20(4): 738-47.

Rector RS, Thyfault JP, Uptergrove GM, Morris EM, Naples SP, Borengasser SJ, Mikus CR, Laye MJ, Laughlin MH, Booth FW, Ibdah JA. Mitochondrial dysfunction precedes insulin resistance and hepatic steatosis and contributes to the natural history of non-alcoholic fatty liver disease in an obese rodent model. *J Hepatol.* 2010; 52(5): 727-36.

Roden M. Muscle triglycerides and mitochondrial function: possible mechanisms for the development of type 2 diabetes. *Int J Obes (Lond).* 2005; 29 Suppl 2: S111-5.

Ropelle ER, Pauli JR, Prada PO, de Souza CT, Picardi PK, Faria MC, Cintra DE, Fernandes MF, Flores MB, Velloso LA, Saad MJ, Carvalheira JB. Reversal of diet-induced insulin resistance with a single bout of exercise in the rat: the role of PTP1B and IRS-1 serine phosphorylation. *J Physiol.* 2006; 577(Pt 3): 997-1007.

Rother E, Kuschewski R, Alcazar MA, Oberthuer A, Bae-Gartz I, Vohlen C, Roth B, Dötsch J. Hypothalamic JNK1 and IKKβ activation and impaired early postnatal glucose metabolism after maternal perinatal high-fat feeding. *Endocrinology.* 2012; 153(2): 770-81.

Rowland AF, Fazakerley DJ, James DE. Mapping insulin/GLUT4 circuitry. *Traffic.* 2011; 12(6): 672-81.

Samuel BS, Shaito A, Motoike T, Rey FE, Backhed F, Manchester JK, Hammer RE, Williams SC, Crowley J, Yanagisawa M, Gordon JI. Effects of the gut microbiota on host adiposity are modulated by the short-chain fatty-acid binding G protein-coupled receptor, Gpr41. *Proc Natl Acad Sci U S A.* 2008; 105(43): 16767-72.

Sanz Y, Santacruz A, Gauffin P. Gut microbiota in obesity and metabolic disorders. *Proc Nutr Soc.* 2010; 69(3): 434-41.

Scherer T, Buettner C. The dysregulation of the endocannabinoid system in diabesity-a tricky problem. *J Mol Med (Berl).* 2009; 87(7): 663-8.

Schmitz-Peiffer C, Browne CL, Oakes ND, Watkinson A, Chisholm DJ, Kraegen EW, Biden TJ. Alterations in the expression and cellular localization of protein kinase C isozymes epsilon and theta are associated with insulin resistance in skeletal muscle of the high-fat-fed rat. *Diabetes.* 1997; 46(2): 169-78.

Schmitz-Peiffer C. Signalling aspects of insulin resistance in skeletal muscle: mechanisms induced by lipid oversupply. *Cell Signal.* 2000; 12(9-10): 583-94.

Schrauwen P, Hesselink MK. Oxidative capacity, lipotoxicity, and mitochondrial damage in type 2 diabetes. *Diabetes.* 2004; 53(6): 1412-7.

Schrauwen P, Westerterp KR. The role of high-fat diets and physical activity in the regulation of body weight. *Br J Nutr.* 2000; 84(4): 417-27.

Schrauwen P. High-fat diet, muscular lipotoxicity and insulin resistance. *Proc Nutr Soc.* 2007; 66(1): 33-41.

Schrauwen-Hinderling VB, Hesselink MK, Schrauwen P, Kooi ME. Intramyocellular lipid content in human skeletal muscle. *Obesity* (Silver Spring). 2006; 14(3): 357-67.

Schrauwen-Hinderling VB, Kooi ME, Hesselink MK, Moonen-Kornips E, Schaart G, Mustard KJ, Hardie DG, Saris WH, Nicolay K, Schrauwen P. Intramyocellular lipid content and molecular adaptations in response to a 1-week high-fat diet. *Obes Res.* 2005; 13(12): 2088-94.

Shao D, Liu Y, Liu X, Zhu L, Cui Y, Cui A, Qiao A, Kong X, Liu Y, Chen Q, Gupta N, Fang F, Chang Y. PGC-1 beta-regulated mitochondrial biogenesis and function in myotubes is mediated by NRF-1 and ERR alpha. *Mitochondrion.* 2010; 10(5): 516-27.

Song MJ, Kim KH, Yoon JM, Kim JB. Activation of Toll-like receptor 4 is associated with insulin resistance in adipocytes. *Biochem Biophys Res Commun.* 2006; 346(3): 739-45.

Sparks LM, Xie H, Koza RA, Mynatt R, Hulver MW, Bray GA, Smith SR. A high-fat diet coordinately downregulates genes required for mitochondrial oxidative phosphorylation in skeletal muscle. *Diabetes.* 2005; 54(7): 1926-33.

Stefanyk LE, Gulli RA, Ritchie IR, Chabowski A, Snook LA, Bonen A, Dyck DJ. Recovered insulin response by 2 weeks of leptin administration in high-fat fed rats is associated with restored AS160 activation and decreased reactive lipid accumulation. *Am J Physiol Regul Integr Comp Physiol.* 2011; 301(1): R159-71.

Storlien LH, Huang XF, Lin S, Xin X, Wang HQ, Else PL. Dietary fat subtypes and obesity. *World Rev Nutr Diet.* 2001; 88: 148-54.

St-Pierre J, Lin J, Krauss S, Tarr PT, Yang R, Newgard CB, Spiegelman BM. Bioenergetic analysis of peroxisome proliferator-activated receptor gamma coactivators 1alpha and 1beta (PGC-1alpha and PGC-1beta) in muscle cells. *J Biol Chem.* 2003; 278(29): 26597-603.

Su W, Jones PJ. Dietary fatty acid composition influences energy accretion in rats. *J Nutr.* 1993 Dec; 123(12): 2109-14.

Teegarden SL, Scott AN, Bale TL Early life exposure to a high fat diet promotes long-term changes in dietary preferences and central reward signaling. *Neuroscience.* 2009; 162(4): 924-32.

Thaler JP, Schwartz MW. Minireview: Inflammation and obesity pathogenesis: the hypothalamus heats up. *Endocrinology.* 2010; 151(9): 4109-15.

Thaler JP, Yi CX, Schur EA, Guyenet SJ, Hwang BH, Dietrich MO, Zhao X, Sarruf DA, Izgur V, Maravilla KR, Nguyen HT, Fischer JD, Matsen ME, Wisse BE, Morton GJ, Horvath TL, Baskin DG, Tschöp MH, Schwartz MW. Obesity is associated with hypothalamic injury in rodents and humans. *J Clin Invest.* 2012; 122(1): 153-62.

Tilg H, Kaser A. Gut microbiome, obesity, and metabolic dysfunction. *J Clin Invest.* 2011; 121(6): 2126-32.

Tozuka Y, Wada E, Wada K. Diet-induced obesity in female mice leads to peroxidized lipid accumulations and impairment of hippocampal neurogenesis during the early life of their offspring. *FASEB J.* 2009; 23(6):1920-34.

Turnbaugh PJ, Ley RE, Mahowald MA, Magrini V, Mardis ER, Gordon JI. An obesity-associated gut microbiome with increased capacity for energy harvest. *Nature.* 2006; 444 (7122): 1027-31.

Velloso LA. Maternal consumption of high-fat diet disturbs hypothalamic neuronal function in the offspring: implications for the genesis of obesity. *Endocrinology.* 2012; 153(2): 543-5.

Vrang N, Kristensen P, Tang-Christensen M, Larsen PJ. Effects of leptin on arcuate pro-opiomelanocortin and cocaine-amphetamine-regulated transcript expression are independent of circulating levels of corticosterone. *J Neuroendocrinol.* 2002; 14(11): 880-6.

Vrieze A, Holleman F, Zoetendal EG, de Vos WM, Hoekstra JB, Nieuwdorp M. The environment within: how gut microbiota may influence metabolism and body composition. *Diabetologia.* 2010; 53(4): 606-13.

Vucetic Z, Carlin JL, Totoki K, Reyes TM. Epigenetic dysregulation of the dopamine system in diet-induced obesity. *J Neurochem.* 2012; 120(6): 891-8.

World Health Organization. *Obesity and overweight, Fact sheet, number 311.* 2012.

Wu A, Ying Z, Gomez-Pinilla F. The interplay between oxidative stress and brain-derived neurotrophic factor modulates the outcome of a saturated fat diet on synaptic plasticity and cognition. *Eur J Neurosci.* 2004; 19(7): 1699-707.

Xiao C, Giacca A, Carpentier A, Lewis GF. Differential effects of monounsaturated, polyunsaturated and saturated fat ingestion on glucose-stimulated insulin secretion, sensitivity and clearance in overweight and obese, non-diabetic humans. *Diabetologia.* 2006; 49(6): 1371-9.

Yaspelkis BB 3rd, Kvasha IA, Figueroa TY. High-fat feeding increases insulin receptor and IRS-1 coimmunoprecipitation with SOCS-3, IKKalpha/beta phosphorylation and decreases PI-3 kinase activity in muscle. *Am J Physiol Regul Integr Comp Physiol.* 2009; 296(6): R1709-15.

Yi CX, Al-Massadi O, Donelan E, Lehti M, Weber J, Ress C, Trivedi C, Müller TD, Woods SC, Hofmann SM. Exercise protects against high-fat diet-induced hypothalamic inflammation. *Physiol Behav.* 2012; 106(4): 485-90.

Yokota T, Kinugawa S, Hirabayashi K, Matsushima S, Inoue N, Ohta Y, Hamaguchi S, Sobirin MA, Ono T, Suga T, Kuroda S, Tanaka S, Terasaki F, Okita K, Tsutsui H. Oxidative stress in skeletal muscle impairs mitochondrial respiration and limits exercise capacity in type 2 diabetic mice. *Am J Physiol Heart Circ Physiol.* 2009; 297(3): H1069-77.

Zendzian-Piotrowska M, Baranowski M, Zabielski P, Górski J. Effects of pioglitazone and high-fat diet on ceramide metabolism in rat skeletal muscles. *J Physiol Pharmacol.* 2006; 57 Suppl 10: 101-14.

Zhang C, Zhang M, Pang X, Zhao Y, Wang L, Zhao L. Structural resilience of the gut microbiota in adult mice under high-fat dietary perturbations. *ISME J.* 2012 Apr 12. doi: 10.1038/ismej.2012.27.

Zhang C, Zhang M, Wang S, Han R, Cao Y, Hua W, Mao Y, Zhang X, Pang X, Wei C, Zhao G, Chen Y, Zhao L. Interactions between gut microbiota, host genetics and diet relevant to development of metabolic syndromes in mice. *ISME J.* 2010; 4(2): 232-41.

Zhou J, Martin RJ, Tulley RT, Raggio AM, McCutcheon KL, Shen L, Danna SC, Tripathy S, Hegsted M, Keenan MJ. Dietary resistant starch upregulates total GLP-1 and PYY in a sustained day-long manner through fermentation in rodents. *Am J Physiol Endocrinol Metab.* 2008; 295(5): E1160-6.

In: Low and High-Fat Diets: Myths vs. Reality
Editors: J. E. Ferreira and N. Muniz

ISBN: 978-1-62257-797-2

Chapter II

Cactus Stems (*Opuntia spp.*): Anti-Hyperlipidemic, Cholesterol Lowering and Other Positive Health Benefit Effects

Hasna El Gharras[*]
Laboratoire de Chimie Organique et Analytique, Unité de Chimie Agroalimentaire,
Université Sultan Moulay Slimane. Faculté des Sciences et Techniques,
Béni-Mellal, Maroc

Dedication

Dedicated to the memory of my dear father.

Abstract

Recently, nutritional studies are focused on examining foods for their protective and disease preventing potential. Furthermore, consumers are increasingly becoming aware of diet related health problems, therefore demanding natural ingredients which are expected to be safe and health-promoting. The importance of functional foods, nutraceuticals and other natural health products has been well recognized in relation to health promotion, disease risk reduction and reduction in health care costs. In this line, recent studies on *Opuntia spp.* have demonstrated cactus pear fruit and vegetative cladodes to be excellent candidates for the development of healthy food. Experimental evidence suggests that cactus cladodes reduce cholesterol levels in human blood and modify low density lipoprotein (LDL) composition. Italian researchers have found that the cholesterol, LDL

[*] Corresponding author: Hasna El Gharras ; Laboratoire de Chimie Organique et Analytique, Unité de Chimie Agroalimentaire, Université Sultan Moulay Slimane, Faculté des Sciences et Techniques BP523, Béni-Mellal. Maroc. Personal Postal Address: Bloc 1, N°23, Lotissement AlQods. BP1825, Ouled Hamdane, BéniMellal, Maroc. Telephone: +212 6 61 79 70 78. E–mail: elgharrashasna@yahoo.fr.

and triglyceride plasma levels of rats were strongly reduced after 30 days of a daily administration (1 g/kg) of lyophilized cladodes of *Opuntia ficus-indica* L. Mill. While another stuff of researchers reported a reduction of total cholesterol, LDL, apolipoprotein levels, triglycerides, fibrinogen, blood glucose, insulin and urate, while body weight, high-density lipoprotein (HDL)-cholesterol, apolipoprotein A-1 and lipoproteinA levels were found to remain unchanged. The anti-hyperlipidemic effect after cladode ingestion was investigated in many studies. Other positive health effects were confirmed by various researchers. The purpose of this chapter is to highlight current knowledge on the beneficial health effects of cactus stems with particular emphasis on its use as food and medicine.

Keywords: Cactus stem, *Opuntia spp.*, anti-hyperlipidemic, cholesterol lowering, various effects

Introduction

There is an extensive list of disease that popular medicine (mainly Mexican) claims can be fought and cured with different parts of plants of *Opuntia* genus, mainly their cactus pad, pulp fruit, or flowers. This stimulated investigators to study the pharmacological actions of these plants. As with numerous fruits and vegetables [1-8], cactus plants have also been reported to be beneficial to health [9]. These effects are demonstrated in the treatment of several diseases. However, most accessible information on pharmacological studies deal with cactus stems rather than the fruit, the former being even less frequently encountered in non-producing countries.

Therefore, many pharmacological actions have been attributed to the cactus pad including antioxidant capacity and anti-cancer effect; anti-inflammatory, analgesic and antiulcerogenic effects; anti-diabetic, anti-hyperlipidemic and anti-hypercholesterolemic properties; anti-viral and antispermatogenic effects; and diuretic properties [10,11]. These interesting quality attributes suggest the use of cactus pad from *Opuntia* genus as a promising functional food or functional food ingredient.

Traditionally, cactus pads contributed considerably to the human diet in many countries, mainly in Latin American countries. They still serve as therapeutic agents and in folk medicine. Several cactus species, and mainly *Opuntia fuliginosa* and *Opuntia streptacantha*, have been used for the treatment of gastritis, fatigue, dyspnoe, and liver injury following alcohol abuse [12]. Traditionally, heated poltices were applied to treat rheumatic disorders, erythemas and chronic skin infections, but also to improve digestion and enhance the general "detoxification processes" [13].

Recently, positive effects of cladodes on hyperglycemia, acidosis, and arteriosclerosis were reported [14]. In Italy, a review on folk veterinary medicine compiles *Opuntia ficus-indica* as a plant species for ethnoveterinary [15]. The Aztecs used it for medicinal purposes as described in the Aztec Herbal of 1552. They referred to it as "nohpalli." Today the Mexicans still call the cactus plant "nopal". Parts of the cactus have been used in various ways throughout the world. The Aztecs extracted the milky juice from the plant and mixed it with honey and egg yolk to provide an ointment to treat burns. The Chinese dressed abscesses with the fleshy pad of the plant. The Indians used the fruit for food and also made syrup from it to treat whooping cough and asthma. In Mexican traditional medicine, prickly pear cactus (nopal) is used for the treatment of diabetes and high cholesterol. Today nopal is a commonly called upon herbal agent for the treatment of Type 2 Diabetes by Mexican Americans as well as American Indians. The blood sugar- lowering action of nopal has been documented in a number of studies.

Deep inside the African Kalahari desert, grows an ugly and bitter cactus called the Hoodia Gordonii. It thrives in extremely high temperatures, and takes years to mature. The San Bushmen of the Kalahari, one of the world's oldest and most primitive tribes, had been eating the Hoodia for thousands of years, to stave off hunger during long hunting trip.

When South African scientists were routinely testing it, they discovered the plant contained a previously unknown molecule, which has since been christened P 57. The license was sold to a Cambridgeshire bio-pharmaceutical company, Phytopharm, who in turn sold the development and marketing rights to the giant Pfizer Corporation.

In Italy, the flowers have served as a diuretic. A tea made from the blossoms has treated colitis. In Israel, researchers found that the dried flowers may be used to battle an enlarged prostate.

Antioxidant Capacity

The antioxidative action is one of many mechanisms by which fruit and vegetable substances might exert their beneficial health effects [16-20]. The presence of several antioxidants (ascorbic acid, carotenoids and flavonoids such as quercetin, kaempferol and isorhamnetin) has been detected in the fruits and vegetables of different varieties of cactus (Table 1) [20-23].

Lee and Kim (2002) [24] investigated *Opuntia ficus-indica* var Saboten (OFS), widely spread cactus in Southwestern Korea, and where is used as a functional food. The total phenols in an ethanolic cladode extract from lyophilized were held responsible for the radical scavenging activity towards superoxide and hydroxyl anions. In addition, a cell growth-regulating activity was noted [25].

Antioxidant activity of OFS is reported to correspond to well-known antioxidants, such as catalase, α-tocopherol, and ascorbic acid in a cell-free reactive oxygen species (ROS) generating system. It well established that oxidative stress may play a role in several diseases, such as heart disease, degenerative neuronal disease, and cancers. Many biochemical and clinical studies suggest that natural and synthetic antioxidant compounds are helpful in treating diseases mediated by oxidative stresses. Lee and Kim (2002) [24] demonstrated that cactus cladodes have excellent antioxidant activities. In another work, the same authors demonstrated that antioxidative flavonoids, quercetin, (+)-dihydroquercetin and quercetin 3-methyl ether, isolated from *Opuntia ficus-indica* var. Saboten have neuroprotective effects [25]. They evaluated their protective effects against oxidative neuronal injuries induced in primary cultured rat cortical cells and their antioxidant activities.

They found that quercetin inhibits H_2O_2- or xanthine (X)/xanthine oxidase (XO)-induced oxidative neuronal cell injury.

Moreover, quercetin 3-methyl ether potently and dramatically inhibited H_2O_2 and X/XO-induced neuronal injuries. All above mentioned three principles markedly inhibited lipid peroxidation and scavenged 1,1-diphenyl-2-picrylhydrazyl free radicals.

Table 1. Vitamin and antioxidant contents of both *Opuntia* spp. cladodes and fruit pulp [10,11]

Compounds	Fresh weight in cactus pear (per 100g)	
	Cladodes	Fruit pulps
Ascorbic acid	7-22 mg	12-81 mg
Niacin	0.46 mg	Trace amounts
Riboflavin	0.60 mg	Trace amounts
Thiamine	0.14 mg	Trace amounts
Total carotenoid	11.3-53.5 mg	0.29-2.37 g
Beta-carotene	Not available	1.2-3.0 μg
Total vitamin E	Not available	111-115 μg
Vitamin K1	Not available	53 μg
Flavonols:		
Kaempferol derivatives	Not available	0.11-0.38 g
Quercetin derivatives	Not available	0.98-9 g
Isorhamnetin derivatives	Not available	0.19-2.41 g

These results indicate that quercetin, (+)-dihydroquercetin, and quercetin 3-methyl ether are the active antioxidant principles in the fruits and cladodes of *Opuntia ficus-indica* var. Saboten. Furthermore, quercetin 3-methyl ether appears to be the most potent neuroprotectant of the three flavonoids isolated from this plant. The DPPH-assay proved that the 4'-hydroxy-substituted flavonoids, such as kaempferol, exhibited lower potency than their corresponding 3',4'-dihydroxy- derivatives (quercetin) (Figure 1). Moreover, hydroxyl substitution at positions 3' and 7 proved to be essential for antioxidant activity. In the superoxide anion assay, the 4'-hydroxy compounds were superior being additionally increased by 3-methoxyl-substitution [26]. In a parallel investigation, the presence of quercetin, (+)-dihydroquercetin and quercetin-3-methyl ether in fruits and cladodes from *Opuntia ficus-indica* var. saboten was reported which proved to be efficient radical scavengers towards the neuronal cell damage caused by H_2O_2 and xanthin/xanthinoxidase [27]. In the latter case, the methanolic cladode fraction was reextracted with ethyl acetate, dichloromethane, or n-butanol. Only the ethyl acetate fraction showed a higher activity than the methanol fraction.

Again, quercetin 3-methyl ether was more effective than quercetin or (+)-dihydroquercetin underlining the importance of the double bond at position 2 and 3 and methylation at 3 (Figure 1). A medical application of these compounds has been patented recently [28].

According to [29] the processing temperature also affected the antioxidant potency of cladodes which was mainly ascribed to an increased extraction of the carotenoids α-cryptoxanthin, ß-carotene, and lutein, respectively, while the phenolic contents were decreased.

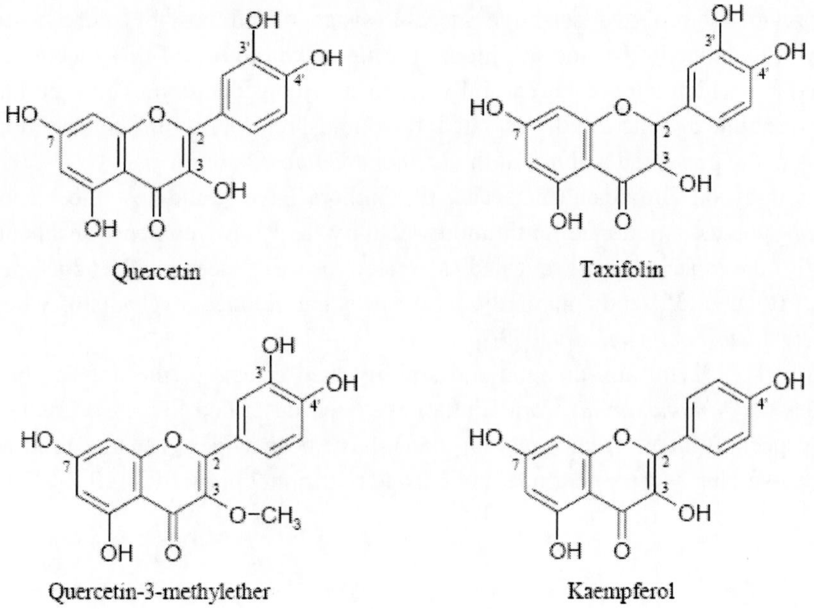

Quercetin

Taxifolin

Quercetin-3-methylether

Kaempferol

Figure 1. Chemical structures of the most bioactive phenolics from cactus stem tissue.

Antiradical Activity

Antioxidants and radical scavengers are considered important nutraceuticals exerting a protective effect in several diseases [10]. Moreover, it has been well documented that natural polyphenolic compounds have a close relationship within these properties [30-32]. The species *Opuntia monacantha* Haw. (Cactaceae) is native to Brazil, Argentina, Paraguay and Uruguay and it has been introduced and naturalized in Australia, China, Cuba, the Himalayas, India and South Africa.

In a recent work, Valente *et al.* (2010) [33] reported, as a continuation of their studies on the Brazilian *O. monacantha* Haw. (Cactaceae), the nutritional potential and the antiradical activity of its cladodes, as well as the isolation of kaempferol and isorhamnetin through activity-guided fractionation from its active MeOH extract. The study seeks to contribute to the knowledge of the chemical composition and bioactivity of this species and also of its potential use as a functional food. This work represents the first report on the antiradical activity, nutritional potential and isolation of the flavonoids of the cladodes of the Brazilian species *O. monacantha* [33]. It shows complex mixtures of antiradical compounds present sometimes in very low yields. The antioxidant activity of their MeOH extract and of its n-hexane, EtOAc and n-BuOH fractions was assessed by measuring the ability of the fractions to scavenge DPPH radical, showing an activity enhancement for the fractions in comparison to the crude MeOH extract. The activity-guided fractionation has led to the isolation of antiradical flavonoid glycosides that after acidic hydrolysis yielded the aglycones kaempferol and isorhamnetin. The nutritional profile of the cladodes of the species shows a close similarity to other *Opuntia* spp. including the Mexican species *O. ficus indica* widely used as food and forage thus showing the potential of *O. monacantha* as an alternative feed resource for humans and animals.

The previously reported selective insect resistance and possible defence mechanism together with its bioactivities and nutritional profile make the use of this species as a regular crop something which should be carefully taken into consideration. The well-known free-radical scavenging activity of the isolated flavonoids reinforces the contribution of these compounds to the presented activity of the *O. monacantha* cladodes.

In this study on Brazilian Cactaceae, the authors have found that the cladodes of *O. monacantha* possess moderate antitumour activity and low content of alkaloids [34]. Interestingly the species has revealed a selective resistance to the cochineal *Diapis echinocacti* Bouché [35] and apparently possesses some defence mechanisms when predated by the *Cactoblastis cactorum* larvae [36].

Recently, significant anti-diabetic and anti-glycated effects of the polysaccharides from the cladodes of *O. monacantha* from China have been described [37; 38]. Cactus fruits and cladodes, especially those from *Opuntia* genus, have been widely used as food and in folk medicine, possessing several pharmacological and nutritional properties [10, 11, 39-41].

Anti-Inflammatory and Analgesic Properties

Numerous studies have evocated the anti-inflammatory and analgesic actions of the genus *Opuntia* by using either the fruit extract from *Opuntia dillenii* [42], the lyophilized cladodes [43], or the phytosterols from fruit and stem extracts [23].

Anti-Inflammatory Properties

Park *et al.* (2001) [44] identified beta-sitosterol as the active anti-inflammatory principle from the stem extract. Reduction of acute inflammation by ethanolic *O. ficus indica* stem extracts was ascribed to a lower leucocyte migration. In contrast to nonsteroidal inflammation inhibitors, no adverse effects were noted. Therefore, cladode extracts were proposed for inflammation treatment [23]. In further experiments with a methanolic extract from *O. ficus-indica* cladodes, the fractions obtained after re-extraction with hexane and ethyl acetate were most efficient to accelerate the healing process [45]. A follow-up study identified b-sitosterol to be the active principle [44]. Galati *et al.* (2003) [46] tested a wound-healing topical preparation containing 15% cladode extract. A fast regeneration of the tissue was ascribed to inflammation inhibition, stimulation of the fibroblast migration with accelerated collagen formation and faster angio-genesis. Again, a low-molecular-weight compound was held responsible for the observed effect. Gastric lesions in rat animal studies were reduced both by stem and fruit powders [25,47]. *Opuntia ficus-indica* cladodes contain a polysaccharide fraction that can retain water. The cladodes are used in Sicilian folk medicine as cicatrizant. Evidently, the *Opuntia ficus-indica* treatment accelerates wound healing, probably by involving the proliferation and migration of the keratinocytes in the healing process. In an earlier work, the same authors demonstrated in 2000 the anti-inflammatory activity of *Opuntia ficus-indica* cladodes, and the correlation between the two phenomena is possible. Also, the angiogenesis is an essential process in wound healing, and these activators could be a low-molecular weight component of the cladodes as monosaccharide residues, polyphenols or b-sitosterol, that is the predominant sterol in cactacea [48]. Reduction of acute inflammation by ethanolic *O. ficus-indica* stem extracts was ascribed to a lower leucocytes migration. In contrast to non steroidal inflammation inhibitors, no adverse effects were noted. Therefore, cladode extracts were proposed for inflammation treatment. In further experiments with a methanolic extract from *O. ficus-indica* cladodes, the fractions obtained after reextraction with hexane and ethyl acetate were most efficient to accelerate the healing process [49]. A follow-up study identified beta-sitosterol to be the active principle. An ethanolic extract of the cladodes (300–600 mg/kg body weight) from *O. ficus-indica* var. saboten showed a similar analgesic effect as acetylsalicylic acid (200 mg/kg body weight) without toxic effects in mice (LD50 > 2 g/kg body weight) even at high dosages.

Analgesic Action

An ethanolic extract of the cladodes (300–600 mg/kg body weight) from *O. ficus-indica* var. saboten showed a similar analgesic effect as acetylsalicylic acid (200 mg/kg body weight) [23] without toxic effects in mice (LD50 > 2 g/kg body weight) even at high dosages.

Antiulcerogenic Effect and Healing Properties

Opuntia ficus-indica cladodes are used in traditional medicine of many countries for their cicatrisant activity. The major components of cladodes are carbohydrate-containing polymers, which consist of a mixture of mucilage and pectin. In Sicily folk medicine *Opuntia ficus-indica* (L.) Mill. cladodes are used for the treatment of gastric ulcer.

Furthermore, Lee et al. [25,47] postulated an antiulcerogenic effect of the cladode or fruit powder from *O. ficus indica* var. saboten Makino. Stomach lesions triggered by hydrochloric acid/ethanol or hydrochloric acid/acetylsalicylic acid were reduced, but no anti-inflammatory effect could be proven. The secretion rate of both gastric juice as well as the pH value remained constant. Galati *et al.* (2001,202) [43,50] confirmed these results. However, the protective effect was ascribed to the cladodes hydrocolloid acting as a buffer, spreading out on the gastric mucosa and increasing mucus production by enhancing the number of secretory cells. Galati *et al.* (2002) [50] studied the effect of administration of lyophilized cactus cladodes on experimental ethanol-induced ulcer in rat. The ultrastructural changes were monitored by transmission electronic microscopy (TEM) confirming the protective effect induced by administration of lyophilized cladodes, and revealed a protective action against ethanol-induced ulcer. This protective effect is probably due to the mucilage.

Indeed, the major components of cladodes are carbohydrate-containing polymers, which consist of a mixture of mucilage and pectin. The OFI cladodes administration gives rise to cytoprotection phenomena by breaking up the epithelial cells and stimulating an increase in mucus production. When OFI cladodes are administered as a preventive therapy, keep the gastric mucosa under normal condition by preventing mucus dissolution caused by ethanol and favouring mucus production. An increase of mucus production is also observed during the course of the curative treatment. The treatment with OFI cladodes provokes an increase in the number of secretory cells. Probably, the gastric fibroblasts are involved in the antiulcer activity [50]. Additionally, Lee *et al.* [25,47] postulated an antiulcerogenic effect of the cladode or fruit powder from *O. ficus-indica* var. saboten Makino. Stomach lesions triggered by hydrochloric acid/ethanol or hydrochloric acid/acetylsalicylic acid were reduced, but no anti-inflammatory effect could be proven. The secretion rate of both gastric juice as well as the pH value remained constant, which has been confirmed by Galati *et al.* (2001) [43].

However, the protective effect was ascribed to the cladodes' hydrocolloid acting as a buffer, spreading out on the gastric mucosa and increasing mucus production by enhancing the number of secretory cells.

Hypoglycemic and Antidiabetic (Type II) Effect

The antihyperglycemic activity of cactus pads and pulp fruit of species of *Opuntia* genus has been documented; however, the mechanism of action has not yet been clarified. The use of cactus stems in the treatment of the diabetes mellitus type 2 is particularly interesting. The prickly pear cactus stems have been used traditionally to treat diabetes in Mexico [51].

Nowadays, *Opuntia spp.* is amongst the majority of products recommended by Italian herbalists that may be efficacious in reducing glycemia [52]. Some studies have demonstrated the hypoglycemic activity of the prickly pear cactus extract on non-diabetics and diabetic-induced rats or diabetic humans [53-57].

Although there are some controversies [58,59], most investigators [10,11,60,61] have suggested or demonstrated the association between cactus pad consumption of *Opuntia* species and hypoglycemic activity in non-diabetic and diabetic rats or diabetic humans. However, the component responsible for therapeutic effect and its mechanism of action have not yet been established. The high percentage of pectin and soluble fiber present in cactus pad and pulp fruit [37,62] can increase fecal mass and intestinal motility [63], which in turn decreases the intestinal absorption and the glucose and cholesterol plasma levels [64-66]. However, Trejo-González *et al.* (1996) [57] concluded that the magnitude of the glucose control in diabetic rats could be achieved by a small amount of *Opuntia* extract (1 mg/kg bodyweight per day) that precludes a predominant role for dietary fiber for hypoglycemia activity. Analogously, Frati, Jiménez, and Ariza (1990) [55] found that the hypoglycemic effect of cladodes in non-insulin dependent diabetes could not be ascribed to the functional properties of the hydrocolloids of soluble fibers. Other plausible mechanism of action could also be due to improvement of insulin sensitivity in peripheral insulin target tissues and suppression of hepatic glucose output [55, 67]. Some authors have hypothesized that the anti-diabetic component could be a gastric enterohormone [68] or a saponin of steroidal nature [13]. Recently, Luo *et al.* (2010) [69] found that an ether extract separated from edible *Opuntia Milpa* Alt is the major hypoglycemic part of the plant and it may be developed to a potential natural hypoglycemia functional ingredient. In this study, we studied the antihyperglycemic activity of cactus pad and fruit pulp of *Opuntia dillenii* in healthy rats by oral consumption. We hypothesized the role of the high concentrations of chromium (III) in the cactus pad and pulp fruit, as a possible explanation of this antihyperglycemic activity.

In a study on rats, the combination of insulin and purified extract of cactus (*Opuntia fuliginosa* Griffiths) was found to reduce blood glucose and glycated hemoglobin levels to normal [57]. In this study, the oral dose of extract (1 mg/kg body weight per day) necessary to control diabetes contrast with the high quantities of insulin required for an equivalent hypoglycemic effect. A recent study has shown that a supplementation of rats' diets with cactus seed oil (25 mg/kg) decreases the serum glucose concentration, which is associated with a glycogen formation in the liver and skeletal muscle [70]. These observations were explained by a potential induction of insulin secretion, converting glucose to glycogen. Except for one study [71], similar research on fruit components are lacking. In the future, it should be remembered that a clear differentiation between stem and fruit components are required to pin down the most pharmacologically active plant parts.

The cactus cladodes have been used traditionally to treat diabetes in Mexico [51]. Nowadays, *Opuntia* spp. is amongst the majority of products recommended by Italian herbalists that may be efficacious in reducing glycemia [52]. Human studies in the 80es demonstrated glucose and insulin levels in healthy fasting subjects were stable when eating cladodes. The positive contribution to overall health in diabetes mellitus type II (noninsulin-dependent diabetes) patients was assumed to be due to reduced postprandial sugar absorption. Following a glucose challenge test, the increase in insulin and glucose were retarded.

Also, the glucose and insulin plasma levels were reduced. After 10 days of cladode ingestion prior to meals, a significant reduction of the serum glucose level was noticed [72]. Since these effects did not depend on glucagon, cortisone, and human growth hormone levels, which are closely interrelated with glucose metabolism, a gastric enterohormone was held responsible for the hypoglycemic effect [13].

To assess the hypoglycemic effect of the *Opuntia streptacantha* Lemaire cladodes, Frati-Munari *et al.* (1988) [56] conducted an experiment with patients with non-insulin-dependent diabetes mellitus. After the intake of *O.streptacantha* Lem., serum glucose and serum insulin levels decreased significantly. Authors did not identify the mechanism responsible of this action, but suggest increased insulin sensitivity. Wolfram *et al.* (2002) [73] reached quite similar conclusions. Indeed, they demonstrate that cladodes have an anti-hyperglycemic effect that was proposed as alternative to oral antidiabetics, thereby preventing insulin resistance. The hypoglycemic effect seemed to be related to improved sensibility of the pancreatic cells with a concomitant improved glucose usage [73]. These effects deserve special attention since the populations of developed countries are increasingly suffering from obesity and diabetes symptoms urgently requiring effective countermeasures.

The efficiency of cactus cladodes in lowering blood sugar was observed in both fried and raw materials. Interspecific variations of the plant material, harvest time, and application modes (oral, intravenous) should be considered. Some studies have demonstrated the hypoglycemic activity of the cactus pear extract on non-diabetics and diabetic-induced rats or diabetic humans [74,75]; the same observations as reported in other studies [57,70] were confirmed [74,75]. Wolfram and collaborators (2003) [76] from the University of Vienna, Austria, suspected a soluble fibre in lowering cholesterol levels in both animals and man with hyperlipidemia as well as being able to slow carbohydrate absorption and hence reduce the postprandial rise in blood glucose and serum insulin in patients with type-II diabetes. The aim of their work was to investigate the effect of cactus consumption on glucose and lipid metabolism. Cactus consumption leads to a decrease of total cholesterol (12%), low-density lipoproteincholesterol (15%), apolipoprotein B (9%), triglycerides (12%), fibrinogen (11%), blood glucose (11%), insulin (11%) and uric acid (10%), while body weight, high-density lipoprotein-cholesterol, apolipoprotein A-I, and lipoprotein(a) remained unchanged.

Authors conclude that the hypocholesterolemic action of cactus may be partly explained by the fiber (pectin) content, but the hypoglycaemic actions (improvement of insulin sensitivity) in the nonobese, non-diabetic need further investigation to get more insights on the potential advantage of treating the metabolic syndrome. An amazing effect of cacti in controlling appetite has been recently reported in several media and it may change the life of people suffering from obesity. It is perceived as a new miracle diet ingredient. Imagine an organic pill that kills the appetite and attacks obesity. It has no known side-effects, and contains a molecule that fools your brain into believing you are full. This pill is already sold through internet and it is manufactured from a cactus ugly plant with a bitter taste named Hoodia gordonii. This unattractive plant which sprouts about 10 tentacles, and is the size of a long cucumber is growing in the Kalahai desert. Each tentacle is covered in spikes which need to be carefully peeled. Inside is a slightly unpleasant-tasting, fleshy plant. The plant is said to have a feel-good almost aphrodisiac quality. The San bushmen have eaten this plant for years, which help to suffer hunger and starvation when hunting. Trials were conducted on animals and human. When offered Hoodia plant, rats, a species that will eat literally anything, stopped eating completely. Trials on human with two groups, one half were given Hoodia, and the other half placebo. Fifteen days later, the Hoodia group had reduced their calorie intake by 1000 a day." What the Hoodia seems to contain is a molecule that is about 10,000 times as active as glucose. "It goes to the mid-brain and actually makes those nerve cells fire as if you were full. But you have not eaten. Nor do you want to. When South African scientists were routinely testing the plant, they discover that it contains unknown molecule, which has since been named P57. The licence was sold to a Cambridgeshire bio-pharmaceutical company, Phytopharm, who in turn sold the development and marketing rights to the giant Pfizer Corporation. In a very recent study, cactus pad and pulp fruit extracts of *Opuntia dillenii* were used to evaluate their effects on blood glucose concentration and glycemic curve of Sprague–Dawley rats [77]. After acute administration, no significant differences were observed in the glycemic curve among cactus pad, pulp fruit and control groups. However, the glycemic peaks and glycemic curves obtained in the groups corresponding to both cactus pad and pulp fruit as well as the Cr(III) group were less pronounced than in the control group after 8 days of daily intake. Besides, a slight decrease of fasting blood glucose was observed, maintaining within the normal levels, after 8 days of daily intake of cactus pad extract [77]. Therefore, the possible role of Cr(III) present in high amounts in these vegetable foods was suggested, for the first time, to explain their antihyperglycemic activity.

Anti-Hyperlipidemic and Cholesterol-Lowering Actions

Anti-Hyperlipidemic Effects

The anti-hyperlipidemic effect after cladode ingestion was investigated only in recent studies [64,65,73,76,78-80]. In general, a prolonged period of satiety was registered after cladode consumption. In a series of studies with Guinea pigs, Fernandez *et al.* (1992,1994,1990) [64,65,79] demonstrated that the reduction of blood lipids triggered by isolated pectin from *Opuntia* was due to the enhanced binding of bile acid. It was concluded that through reduced bile absorption in the colon the enterohepatic circle was disrupted [64,79]. In a follow up study, the same authors presented evidence that the low density lipoprotein (LDL)-catabolism was considered to be more important than the modulation and de novo synthesis in the liver [65]. The same pectic-like substances were held responsible for a decreased lipid absorption, lower blood lipid levels, and finally weight reduction [12].

Cholesterol-Lowering Properties

Experimental evidence suggest that cactus pear reduces cholesterol levels in human blood and modify low density lipoprotein (LDL) composition [11,64,81-83]. Galati *et al.* (2003) [84] have found that the cholesterol, LDL and triglyceride plasma levels of rats were strongly reduced after 30 days of a daily administration (1 g/kg) of lyophilized cladodes of *Opuntia ficus indica L. Mill.* Sterols which comprise the bulk of the unsaponifiables in many oils are of interest due to their ability to lower blood LDL-cholesterol by approximately 10–15% as part of a healthy diet [85]. Recently, Ennouri *et al.* (2006) [70] observed a decrease in plasma total cholesterol and LDL (VLDL) cholesterol with no effect on HDL-cholesterol concentrations after addition of seed oil (25 g/kg) to the diet in rats.

Overall, the effects of cactus are generally attributed to the high fiber content of the cladodes, although other active ingredients (such as beta-carotenes, vitamin E and beta-sitosterol) may be involved.

In a recent study it was shown that a daily consumption of 250 g of prickly pear pulp reduced the risk of thrombosis in patients suffering from hyperlipidemia and diabetes [76]. The authors did not disclose whether the observed effects were due to fruit or cladode ingestion. In addition, the botanical origin of the plant material was not provided, however, *O. robusta* had been used by this group in earlier studies [73,78,80]. Wolfram *et al.* [73] reported a reduction of total cholesterol, LDL, apolipoprotein levels, triglycerides, fibrinogen, blood glucose, insulin and urate, while body weight, high-density lipoprotein (HDL)-cholesterol, apolipoprotein A-1 and lipoprotein A levels were found to remain unchanged. The anti-hyperlipidemic effects were ascribed to the pulp pectin, which both reduced lipid absorption and increased fecal sterol excretion, thus disrupting the enterohepatic circle. Since the level of 3-hydroxy-3-methyl-glutaryl-coenzyme A, the key enzyme of cholesterol biosynthesis, did not exhibit any activity changes, the reduced LDL levels and modified LDL composition were ascribed to an enhanced hepatic apo-B/Ereceptor [80]. These results were proven by the same authors when an enhanced activity of the apo-B/E-receptor in the human liver was found, resulting in an enhanced LDL degradation [80]. The exact mechanisms, however, still need to be elucidated.

The use of cactus may also lower blood lipid levels. In a recent study, the daily consumption of 250 grams of cooked cactus cladodes lowered total cholesterol and LDL cholesterol levels (but not HDL cholesterol or triglyceride levels) in 15 young patients with familial hypercholesterolemia. Although there are many species of *Opuntia*, few varieties have been positively shown to be effective in normalizing blood sugar or blood lipid levels [10]. The anti-hyperlipidemic effect after cladode ingestion was investigated only in many studies [73,76]. In general, a prolonged period of satiety was registered after cladode consumption.

Anti-Viral Power

An interesting study by Ahmad *et al.* [86] demonstrated that administration of a cactus stem extract (*Opuntia streptacantha*) to mice, horses, and humans inhibits intracellular replication of a number of DNA- and RNA-viruses such as Herpes simplex virus Type 2, Equine herpes virus, pseudorabies virus, influenza virus, respiratory syncitial disease virus and HIV-1.

The active principle was located in the outer noncuticular tissue and ascribed to a protein with unknown mechanisms of action [86]. Both the replication of DNA and RNAviruses was inhibited while the extract from the parenchyma acted both preventively and post-infectionary. In security tests on mice, horses (27 g/day over the period of 2–4 weeks) and finally humans (6 g/day for 1 month or 3 g/d over 6 months), all dosages were well tolerated [86]. An inactivation of extra-cellular viruses was also reported by the same authors. However, the active inhibitory component(s) of the cactus extract used in this study was not investigated, and as of yet, no further study dealt with this specific topic.

Anti-Cancer Effect

Most recent studies suggests that the cactus pear fruit extract (i) inhibits the proliferation of cervical, ovarian and bladder cancer cell lines *in vitro,* and (ii) suppresses tumor growth in the nude mice ovarian cancer model *in vivo* [87]. These experiments showed that inhibition was dose- (1, 5, 10 and 25% cactus pear extract) and time- (1, 3 or 5 days treatment) dependent on *in vitro*-cultured cancer cells. The intra-peritoneal administration of cactus extract solution into mice did not affect the animal body weight, which indicated that cactus did not have a significant toxic effect in animals. More importantly, tumor growth inhibition was comparable to the synthetic retinoid N-(4-hydroxyphernyl) retinamide (4-HPR), which is currently used as a chemopreventive agent in ovarian cancer chemoprevention [88-90].

Growth inhibition of cultured-cancer cells was associated with an increase in apoptotic cells and the cell cycle arrest at the G1-phase. Moreover, the induced growth inhibition seems dependent on the P53 pathway, which is the major tumor suppressor. Annexin IV was increased and the VEGF decreased in the tumor tissue obtained from animals having received the cactus solution [87].

The mechanism of action as well as the component(s) by which cactus pear extract exerts these effects is not yet elucidated. However, first an extrinsic effect through an activation of membrane death receptors such as tumor necrosis factor, nuclear factor kappa B, Fas appears to be feasible. Secondly, intrinsic actions via the mitochondria, playing a pivotal role by releasing a number of molecules favorable to the induction of apoptosis such as Bax, AIF, cytochrome C, reactive oxygen species such anion superoxide may be considered. Further investigations are needed to identify the potential active component(s) and the respective underlying mechanisms.

It has been noted that Native Americans have a lower cancer rate when compared to white and African Americans [91]. Both cactus fruits and cladodes which contain multiple antioxidants have been used as a dietary supplement for centuries by Native Americans. The goal of cancer prevention is to delay or block the processes of initiation and progression from pre-cancerous cells into cancer. Cancer chemoprevention, which targets normal and high risk populations, involves the use of drugs or other chemical agents to inhibit, delay, or reverse cancer development [92]. Medical benefits from plant forms have been recognized for centuries. Herbs have been used in Chinese medicine for thousands of years to cure diseases and heal wounds. As rule, herbs and natural products lack much of the toxicity that is present in synthetic chemicals, thus, enhancing their appeal for long term preventive strategies.

Although hundreds of agents have been developed in the United States during the past decade, only a few new drugs have actually been approved [92]. The development of chemopreventive agents is slow and inefficient. More effective and less toxic agents, including natural products, are needed if we are to reach the goal of cancer prevention, both primary and secondary. The development of effective and safe agents for prevention and treatment of cancer remains slow, inefficient, and costly. The key to effective chemoprevention is the identification of a chemopreventive agent(s) that can effectively inhibit cancer development without toxic side effects. In an Italian 4-HPR trial, retinoids showed the preventive effect on ovarian cancer only during the period while the drug was taken. After cessation of treatment, the incidence of ovarian cancer increased to the level that was observed in the untreated control group [89]. Therefore, chemopreventive agents may need to be used for a long period of time to be effective. As a result, identification of agents with little or no toxicity becomes important.

The anti-carcinogenic properties of natural and synthetic retinoids have been suggested to be due, in part, to the antioxidant effect, increased consumption of fruit and vegetables is associated with prevention of various human diseases, and the oxidative damage is an important etiologic risk factor for many diseases, including cancer and heart disease.

Anti-Atherogenic Effect

Recently, Stintzing and Carle (2005) reported in their review on cactus stems [11] that decreasing isoprostane levels in urine, serum and plasma as an indicator for oxidative stress and generally improved blood parameters levels, were held responsible for the antiatherogenic effect of broiled *O. robusta* pulp [78].

Diuretic Effect and Impact on Uric Acid Metabolism

An ethanolic extract from *Opuntia* megacantha was reported to decrease blood glucose but also affect kidney function in rats [93]. While sodium excretion was enhanced, potassium levels in urine decreased.

In contrast, sodium, calcium, and magnesium levels in the plasma dropped, but phosphate, creatinine, and urea concentrations increased [93]. Both observations were related to the hormonal regulatory mechanisms of the kidney. In rats, uric acid excretion was enhanced and lower uric acid levels were detected in the serum after administration of an *Opuntia megacantha* extract.

These results show cactus potential for gout treatment as claimed by Bwititi *et al.* [94]. In this context, oxalic acid needs to be taken into consideration since calcium availability was found to be decreased due to sequestration by oxalic acid and high oxalic acid contents resulted in an enhanced urinary calcium oxalate excretion [95].

After *Opuntia* extract ingestion, the water intake rose and the urine volume was increased [94]. Galati *et al.* (2002) [96] investigated the diuretic effect of a 15% extract from flowers, fruits, and peeled cladodes from *Opuntia ficus-indica*, respectively. The latter showed the highest diuretic effect while urea levels in blood and urine remained unchanged. The diuretic effect was chiefly ascribed to the high potassium content of *Opuntia* cladodes amounting to 548 mg/kg.

Antispermatogenic Properties

A methanolic extract from *O. dillenii* Haw. defatted with chloroform and petroleum ether exerted antispermatogenic effects in animal tests on rats. According to [97], the flavones derivatives vitexin and myricetin (Figure 2) were found to be the active principles.

When 250 mg extract per kg body weight was applied, the weight of testis, epididymis, seminal vesicle, and ventral prostate were reasonably, that of Sertoli cells, Leydig cells, and gametes considerably reduced. The motility of the sperms was also diminished [97]. Unfortunately, data about the solvent used for extraction are missing.

Monoamino-Oxidase Inhibition

Besides catecholmethyltransferases, the monoamino-oxidases (MAOs) are usually involved in the catabolism of catecholamines, thus regulating the overall amine pool [98]. In cladodes and fruits from the Korean *O. ficus-indica* var. saboten Makino, methyl esters derived from organic acids were identified as MAO inhibitors [99].

The aqueous extracts showed least inhibitory activity, followed by the nbutanol fraction and the hexane extract whereas the ethyl acetate fraction exerted the highest inhibitory action. The active agents were identified as 1-methyl malate, 1-monomethyl citrate, 1,3-dimethylcitrate, and 1,2,3-trimethylcitrate.

The purified components showed MAO-A inhibitory action with increasing number of methyl substituents, whilst the MAO-B inhibitory action was superior for 1-methylmalate compared to the mono- and dimethylcitrates. However, 1,2,3-trimethylcitrate exerted the strongest inhibition on both MAOs. When citrate was compared with its corresponding methyl derivatives, the methoxy moiety proved to be the effective moiety [99]. However, the authors did not disclose the extraction procedure applied.

Since prolonged storage, especially under acidic conditions, may result in free carboxylic group derivatization, the formation of these derivatives during sample workup needs to be ruled out prior to further pharmacological testing.

Further Positive Health Effects

Cactus fruits, cladodes or flower infusions have been traditionally used as folk medicine to treat other ailments such as ulcers [25,84,100], allergies [101], fatigue and rheumatism, and as an antiuric and diuretic agent [96]. Amongst the flavonoids extracted from either the cactus stem or fruit, quercetin 3-methyl appears to be the most potent neuroprotector [27]. Recent work [Lee *et al.*, 2006] showed that *Opuntia ficus-indica* may have a neuroprpotective activity. Indeed, activated microglia by neuronal injury or inflammatory stimulation overproduce nitric oxide (NO) by inducible nitric oxide synthase (iNOS) and reactive oxygen species (ROS) such as superoxide anion, resulting in neurodegenerative diseases. The toxic peroxynitrite (ONOO-), the reaction product of NO and superoxide anion further contributes to oxidative neurotoxicity. A butanol fraction obtained from 50% ethanol extracts of *Opuntia ficus-indica* var. Saboten (Cactaceae) stem and its hydrolysis product inhibited the production of NO in LPS-activated microglia in a dose dependent manner (IC50 15.9, 4.2 μg/ml, respectively). They also suppressed the expression of protein and mRNA of iNOS in LPS-activated microglial cells at higher than 30 μg/ml as observed by western blot analysis and RT-PCR experiment. Moreover, they showed strong activity of peroxynitrite scavenging in a cell free bioassay system. These results imply that *Opuntia ficus-indica* may have neuroprotective activity through the inhibition of NO production by activated microglial cells and peroxynitrite scavenging activity.

The cactus flower extract was able to exert an effect on benign prostatic hyperplasia (BPH) through the inhibition of aromatase and 5a reductase activities, both of which are involved in androgen aromatization and testosterone reduction [102]. A diuretic effect was reported to be promoted by ingestion of flower, cladode and especially fruit infusions in a rat feeding trial [96]. Though *Opuntia spp.* glochids may induce dermal irritations, peeled *Opuntia* fruits or cladodes appear to be nonallergenic [103]. More recently, Galati *et al.* [104] reported a protective effect of cactus juice against carbon hydrochloride (CCl4)-induced hepato-toxicity in rats. Alleviating effects towards alcohol hangover symptoms have been addressed recently [10,105] and were associated with reduced inflammatory responses after excessive alcohol consumption.

Conclusion

“Let food be your medicine” Hippocrates recommended as far as 2,500 years ago. The so-called “nutraceuticals” and the “functional food” make this old tenet a new reality. Coined in Japan in the eighties, these terms refer to natural mostly vegetal products. In this line, interdisciplinary efforts on a molecular basis are required to integrate nutrition-related health and disease research.

The present review focused on the documented beneficial effects of the cactus stems. Many pharmacological actions have been attributed to the cactus pad including antioxidant capacity and anti-cancer effect; anti-inflammatory, analgesic and antiulcerogenic effects; anti-diabetic, anti-hyperlipidemic and anti-hypercholesterolemic properties; anti-viral and antispermatogenic effects; and diuretic properties. These interesting quality attributes suggest the use of cactus pad from *Opuntia* genus as a promising functional food or functional food ingredient. In this context, interest and studies on phytochemicals and their biological effects have increased immensely during the past decade. Sophisticated analytical approaches and innovative processing technologies will open new avenues to further promote the use of cactus pear stems, fruits and flowers in food, medicine, cosmetic, and pharmaceutical industries. In summary, the constituents of *Opuntia* cladodes are only partly known and often not quantitatively determined. Investigations were mostly performed 20 years ago and need to be validated with up-to-date methods. Furthermore, data stem from all kinds of different *Opuntia* spp. and it is open to question whether the botanical classification has properly been assessed in each case. Beside a sound systematic classification, the background of cladode physiology needs to be considered. Based on additional data, a reliable nutritional evaluation can be performed. The technofunctional properties of the respective extracts can be efficiently exploited for manifold food, cosmetic and medicinal applications. Whether isolated substances or rather a concerted action of several components in the complex plant matrix are responsible for the big variety of biological activities remains unknown, let alone the underlying mechanisms of the traditional curative treatments being still little understood.

In conclusion, we demonstrated vegetative cladodes to be an important source of natural antioxidants and nutraceuticals and excellent candidates for the development of healthy food.

References

[1] Rice-Evans, C. A. and Miller, N. J. (1985). Antioxidants: the case of fruit and vegetables in the diet. *British Food Journal*, 97, 35-40.

[2] Ames, B. N, M. Shigenaga, K. and Hagen, T. M. (1993). Oxidants, antioxidants and the degenerative disease of aging. *Proceeding of the National Academy of Sciences*, 90, 7915-7922.

[3] Lampe, J. W. (1999). Health effects of vegetables and fruits: assessing mechanism of action in human experimental studies. *American Journal of Clinical Nutrition*, 70, 475-490.

[4] Hertog, M. G. L., Feskens, E. J. M., Hollman, P. C. H., Katan, M. B., and Kromhout, D. (1993). Dietary antioxidants, flavonoids and the risk of coronary heart disease: the Zutphen eldery study. *Lancet*, 342, 1007-1011.

[5] Rice-Evans, C. A., Miller, N. J. and Paganga, G. (1997). Antioxidant properties of phenolic compounds. *Trends in Plant Science*, 2, 152-159.

[6] Peterson, J and Dwyer. J. (1998). Flavonoids: dietary occurrence and biochemical activity. *Nutrition Research*, 12, 1995-2018.

[7] Block, G., Patterson, B., Subar, A. (1992). Fruit, vegetables, and cancer prevention: a review of the epidemiological evidence. *Nutrition Cancer*, 18, 1-29.

[8] Donaldson, M. S. (2004). Nutrition and cancer: A review of the evidence for an anti-cancer Diet. *Nutrition Journal*, 3:19.

[9] El Kossori, R. L., Villaume, C., El Boustani, E., Sauvaire, Y., and Mejean, L. (1998). Composition of pulp, skin and seeds of prickly pears fruits (Opuntia ficus indica sp.). *Plant Foods Human Nutrition*, 52, 263-270.

[10] Feugang, J. M., Konarski, P., Zou, D., Stintzing, F. C., and Zou, C. (2006). Nutritional and medicinal use of cactus (Opuntia spp.) cladodes and fruits. *Frontiers in Bioscience*, 11, 2574-2589.

[11] Stintzing, F. C. and Carle, R. (2005). Cactus stems (Opuntia spp.): A review on their chemistry, technology, and uses. *Molecular Nutrition and Food Research,* 49, 175-194.

[12] Shapiro, K., Gong, W. C. (2002). Natural products used for diabetes. *Journal of the American Pharmaceutical Association*, 42, 217–226.

[13] Muñoz de Chavez, M., Chavez, A., Valles, V., and Rodlan, J. A. (1995). The nopal : a plant of manifold qualities. *World Review of Nutrition and Dietetics*, 77, 109-134.

[14] Hegwood, D. A. (1990). Human health discoveries with Opuntia sp. (prickly pear) indica (L.) Mill. cladodes in the wound-healing process. *Journal of Horticultural Science*, 25, 1315–1316.

[15] Viegi, L., Pieroni, A., Guarrera, P. M., and Vangelisti, R. (2003). A review of plants used in folk veterinary medicine in Italy as basis for a databank. *Journal of Ethnopharmacology*, 89, 221-244.

[16] Tesoriere, L., Fazzari, M., Allegra, M., and Livrea. M. A. (2005). Biothiols, taurine, and lipid-soluble antioxidants in the edible pulp of Sicilian cactus pear (Opuntia ficus-indica) fruits and changes of bioactive juice components upon industrial processing. *Journal of Agricultural and Food Chemistry,* 53, 7851-7855.

[17] Steinmetz, K. A. and Potter, J. D. (1996). Vegetables, fruit, and cancer prevention: a review. *Journal of the American Dietetic Association*, 96, 1027- 1039.

[18] Leenen, R., Roodenburg, A. J., Tijburg, L. B., and Wiseman, S. A. (2000). A single dose of tea with or without milk increases plasma antioxidant activity in humans. *European Journal of Clinical Nutrition*, 54, 87–92.

[19] Martinez, J. and Moreno, J. J. (2000). Effect of resveratrol, a natural polyphenolic compound, on reactive oxygen species and prostaglandin production. *Biochemical Pharmacology*, 59, 865–870.

[20] Tesoriere, L., Butera, D., Pintaudi, A. M., Allegra, M., and Livrea, M. A. (2004). Supplementation with cactus pear (Opuntia ficus-indica) fruit decreases oxidative stress in healthy humans: a comparative study with vitamin C. *American Journal of Clinical Nutrition*, 80, 391-395.

[21] Tesoriere, L., Butera, D., Allegra, M., Fazzari, M., and Livrea, M. A. (2005). Distribution of betalain pigments in red blood cells after consumption of cactus pear fruits and increased resistance of the cells to ex vivo induced oxidative hemolysis in humans. *Journal of Agricultural and Food Chemistry*, 53, 1266-1270.

[22] Kuti, J. O. (2004). Antioxidant compounds from four Opuntia cactus pear fruit varieties. *Food Chemistry*, 85, 527-533.

[23] Park, E.-H., Kahng, J. H. and Paek, E.-A. (1998). Studies on the pharmacological actions of cactus: identification of its anti-inflammatory effect. *Archives of Pharmacal Research*, 21, 30–34.

[24] Lee, J.-C., Kim, H. R., Kim, J., Jang, Y.-S. (2002). Antioxidant property of an ethanol extract of the stem of Opuntia ficus indica var. saboten. *Journal of Agricultural and Food Chemistry*, 50, 6490– 6496.

[25] Lee, B., Hyun, J. E., Li, D. W., and Moon, Y. I. (2002). Effects of Opuntia ficus-indica var. Saboten stem on gastric damages in rats. *Archives of Pharmacal Research*, 25, 67–70.

[26] Qiu, Y., Chen, Y., Pei, Y., Matsuda, H., Yoshikawa, M. (2002). Constituents with radical scavenging effect from Opuntia dillenii, Structures of new a-pyrones and flavonolglycoside. *Chemical and Pharmaceutical Bulletin*, 50, 1507–1510.

[27] Dok-Go, H., Lee, K. H., Kim, H. J., Lee, E. H., Lee, J., Song, Y. S. Lee,Y.-H., Jin, C., Lee, Y. S., and Cho, J. (2003). Neuroprotective effects of antioxidative flavonoids, quercetin, (+)- dihydroquercetin and quercetin 3-methyl ether, isolated from Opuntia ficus-indica var. saboten. *Brain Research*, 965, 130-136.

[28] Lee, Y. S., Park, H., Jin, C., Kim, H. J., Cho, J., Park, M., Song, Y. (2003). Use of an Opuntia ficus-indica extract and compounds isolated therefrom for protecting nerve cells. *WO Patent* 03/037324 A1 (08. 05. 2003).

[29] Jaramillo-Flores, M. E., González-Cruz, L., Cornejo-Mazón, M., Dorantes-Àlvarez, L., Gutiérrez-López, G. F., Hernández-Sánchez, H. (2003). Effect of thermal treatment on the antioxidant activity and content of carotenoids and phenolic compounds of cactus pear cladodes (Opuntia ficus-indica). *Food Science Technology International.*, 9, 271–278.

[30] Heim, K. E., Tagliaferro, A. R. and Bobilya, D. J. (2002). Flavonoid antioxidants: chemistry, metabolism and structure-activity relationships. *The Journal of Nutritional Biochemistry*, 13(10), 572–584.

[31] Pinent, M., Castell, A., Baiges, I., Montagut, G., Arola, L., and Ardévol, A. (2008). Bioactivity of flavonoids on insulin-secreting cells. *Comprehensive Reviews in Food Science and Food Safety*, 7(4), 299–308.

[32] Seyoum, A., Asres, K. and El-Fiky, F. K. (2006). Structure-radical scavenging activity relationship of flavonoids. *Phytochemistry*, 67, 2058–2070.

[33] Ligia, M. M., Valente, Djavan da Paixão., Adriana C. do Nascimento, Priscila, F. P. dos Santos, Leia A. Scheinvar, Mirian, R. L. Moura, Luzineide W. Tinoco, Luiz Nelson F. Gomes, Joaquim, F. M. da Silva. (2010). Antiradical activity, nutritional potential and flavonoids of the cladodes of Opuntia monacantha (Cactaceae). *Food Chemistry*, 123 1127–1131.

[34] Valente, L. M., Scheinvar, L., Da Silva, G. C., Antunes, A. P., Dos Santos, F. A. L., Oliveira, T. F., Tappin, M. R. R., Aquino Neto, F. R., Pereira, A. S., Cavalhaes, S. F., Siani,A. C., Dos Santos, R. R., Soares, R. O. A., Ferreira, E. F., Bozza, M., and Gibaldi, C. Stutz y D. (2007). Evaluation of the antitumor and trypanocidal activities and alkaloid profile in species of Brazilian Cactaceae. *Pharmacognosy Magazine*, 3(11), 167–172.

[35] Lima, I. M. M. and Gama, N. S. (2001). Record of host plants (Cactaceae) and new dissemination strategy of Diaspis echinocacti (Bouché) (Hemiptera: Diaspididae), prickly-pear-scale, in the states of Pernambuco and Alagoas, Brazil. *Neotropical Entomology*, 30(3), 479–481.

[36] Lenzi, M., Soares, J. and Orth, A. I. (2006). Predation of Opuntia monacantha (Willd.) Haw. (Cactaceae) by Cactoblastis cactorum (Lepidoptera: Pyralidae) in a sand bank area of Santa Catarina island, south Brazil. *Biotemas*, 19(3), 35–44.

[37] Yang, N., Zhao, M., Zhu, B., Yang, B., Chen, C., Cui, C., and Jiang, Y. (2008). Antidiabetic effects of polysaccharides from Opuntia monacantha cladode in normal and streptozotocin-induced diabetic rats. *Innovative Food Science and Emerging Technologies*, 9(4), 570–574.

[38] Zhao, M.,Yang, N., Yang, B., Jiang, Y., and Zhang, G. (2007). Structural characterization of water-soluble polysaccharides from Opuntia monacantha cladodes in relation to their anti-glycated activities. *Food Chemistry*, 105, 1480–1486.

[39] Kim, J. H., Park, S. M., Ha, H. J., Moon, C. J., Shin, T. K., and Kim, J. M. (2006). Opuntia ficus indica attenuates neuronal injury in in vitro and in vivo models of cerebral ischemia. *Journal of Ethnopharmacology*, 104, 257–262.

[40] Saleem, R., Ahmad, M., Azmat, A., Ahmad, S. I., Faizi, Z., Abidi, L., and Faizi, S. (2005). Hypotensive activity, toxicology and histopathology of Opuntioside-I and methanolic extract of Opuntia dillenii. *Biological and Pharmaceutical Bulletin*, 28(10), 1844–1851.

[41] Stintzing, F. C. and Carle, R. (2007). Betalains – emerging prospects for food scientists. *Trends in Food Science and Technology*, 18, 514–525.

[42] Loro, J. F., del Rio, I. and Pérez-Santana, L. (1999). Preliminary studies of analgesic and anti-inflammatory properties of Opuntia dillenii aqueous extract. *Journal of Ethnopharmacology*, 67, 213-218.

[43] Galati, E. M., Monforte, M. T., Tripodo, M. M., d'Aquino, A., and Mondello, M. R. (2001). Antiulcer activity of Opuntia ficus-indica (L.) Mill. (Cactaeceae): ultrastructural study. *Journal of Ethnopharmacology*, 76, 1–9.

[44] Park, E. H., Kahng, J. H., Lee, S. H., and Shin, K. H. (2001). An anti-inflammatory principle from cactus. *Fitoterapia*, 72, 288-90.

[45] Park, E.-H., Chun, M.-J. (2001). Wound healing activity of Opuntia ficus-indica. *Fitoterapia*, 72, 165–167.

[46] Galati, E. M., Mondello, M. R., Monforte, M. T., Galluzo, M., Miceli, N., Tripodo, M. M. (2003). Effect of Opuntia ficus indica (L.) Mill. cladodes in the wound-healing process. *Professional Association for Cactus Development,* 5, 1–16.

[47] Lee, E. B., Hyun, J. E., Li, D. W., and Moon, Y. I. (2001). The effect of Opuntia ficus-indica var. saboten fruit on gastric lesion and ulcer in rats. *Natural Product Sciences*, 7, 90-93.

[48] Salt, T. A., Tocker, J. E., Adler, J. H. (1987). Dominance of D^5-sterols in eight species of the Cactaceae. *Phytochemistry*, 26, 731–737.

[49] Clark, W. D. and Parfitt, B. D. (1980). Flower flavonoids of Opuntia series Opuntiae. *Phytochemistry*, 19, 1856-1857.

[50] Galati, E. M., Pergolizzi, S., Miceli, N., Monforte, M. T., Tripodo, M. M. (2002). Study on the increment of the production of gastric mucus in rats treated with Opuntia ficus indica (L.) Mill. cladodes. *Journal of Ethnopharmacology*, 83, 229 –233.

[51] Domínguez López, A. (1995). Use of the fruits and stems of the prickly pear cactus (Opuntia spp.) into human food. *Food Science and Technology International,* 1, 65–69.

[52] Cicero, A. F. G., Derosa, G. and Gaddi. A. (2004). What do herbalists suggest to diabetic patients in order to improve glycemic control? Evaluation of scientific evidence and potential risks. *Acta Diabetologica*, 41, 91-98.

[53] Ibanez-Camacho, R. and Roman-Ramos, R. (1979). Hypoglycemic effect of Opuntia cactus. *Archivos de Investigacion Médica* (México) 10, 223–230.

[54] Ibanez-Camacho, R., Meckes-Lozoya, M. and Mellado-Campos, V. (1983). The hypoglycemic effect of Opuntia streptaeantha studied in different animal experimental models. *Journal of Ethnopharmacology*, 7, 175-181.

[55] Frati, A. C., Jimenez, E. and Ariza, C. R. (1990). Hypoglycemic effect of Opuntia ficus-indica in non insulin-dependent diabetes mellitus patients. *Phytotherapy Research*, 4, 195–197.

[56] Frati-Munari, A. C., Gordillo, B. E., Altamirano, P., and Ariza. C. R. (1988). Hypoglycemic effect of Opuntia streptaeantha Lemaire in NIDDM. *Diabetes Care* 11, 63-66.

[57] Trejo-González, A., Gabriel-Ortiz, G., Puebla-Pérez, A. M., Huízar-Contreras, M. D., del Rosario Munguía-Mazariegos, M., Mejía-Arreguín, S., and Calva, E. (1996). A purified extract from prickly pear cactus (Opuntia fuliginosa) controls experimentally induced diabetes in rats. *Journal of Ethnopharmacology*, 55, 27-33.

[58] Cárdenas Medellín, M., Serna Saldívar, S. and Velazco de la Garza, J. (1998). Efecto de la ingestión de nopal crudo y cocido (Opuntia ficus indica) en el crecimiento y perfil de colesterol total, lipoproteína y glucosa en sangre de ratas. *Archivos Latinoamericanos de Nutrición*, 48, 316–323.

[59] Romero Cerecero, O., Reyes-Morales, H., Aguilar-Santamaría, L., Huerta-Reyes, M., and Tortoriello-García, J. (2009). Use of medicinal plants among patients with diabetes mellitus type 2 in Morelos, Mexico. *Boletín Latinoamericano y del Caribe de Plantas Medicinales y Aromáticas*, 8, 380–388.

[60] Ramírez, G. and Aguilar, C. (1995). The effect of Opuntia in lowering serum glucose among NIDDM patients. A systematic reviewpreliminary findings. In Proceedings of I conference of the professional association for cactus development. *Firsts annual conference* (pp. 71–78). San Antonio, TX.

[61] Yeh, G. Y., Eisenberg, D. M., Kaptchuk, T. D., and Phillips, R. S. (2003). Systematic review of herbs and dietary supplements for glycemic control in diabetes. *Diabetes Care*, 26, 1277–1294.

[62] Goycoolea, F. M. and Cárdenas, A. (2003). Pectins from Opuntia spp.: A short review. *Journal of the Professional Association for Cactus Development*, 17–29.

[63] Rosado, J. L. and Díaz, M. (1995). Physicochemical properties related to gastrointestinal effects of six dietary fibers. *Revista de Investigación Clínica*, 47, 283–289.

[64] Fernández, L. M., Lin, E. C. K., Trejo, A., and McNamara, D. J. (1992). Prickly pear (Opuntia spp.) pectin reverses low lo density lipoprotein receptor suppression induced by a hypercholesterolemic diet in guinea pigs. *Journal of Nutrition*, 122, 2330–2340.

[65] Fernández, L. M., Lin, E. C. K., Trejo, A., and McNamara, D. J. (1994). Prickly pear (Opuntia spp.) pectin alters hepatic cholesterol metabolism without affecting cholesterol absorption in guinea pigs fed a hypercholesterolemic diet. *Journal of Nutrition*, 124, 817–824.

[66] Geil, P. and Shane-McWhorter, L. (2008). Dietary supplements in the management of diabetes: Potential risks and benefits. *Journal of American Dietetic Association*, 108, S59–S65.

[67] Lutz, T. A., Estermann, A., Haag, S., and Scharrrer, E. (2001). Depolarization of the liver cell membrane by metformin. *Biochimica et Biophysica Acta*, 1513, 176–184.

[68] Cruse, R. R. (1973). Desert plant chemurgy: A current review. *Economic Botany*, 27, 210–230.

[69] Luo, C. A., Zhang, W. N., Sheng, C. Q., Zheng, C. J., Yao, J. Z., and Miao, Z. Y. (2010). Chemical composition and antidiabetic activity of Opuntia Milpa Alta extracts. *Chemistry and Biodiversity*, 7, 2869–2879.

[70] Ennouri, M., Fetoui, H., Bourret, E., Zeghal, N., F., Attia, H., 2006. Evaluation of some biological parameters of Opuntia ficus-indica 1. Influence of a seed oil supplemented diet on rats. *Bioresource Technology* 97, 1382–1386.

[71] Lee Y.-C., Pyo,Y.-H., Ahn, C.-K., and Kim, S.-H. (2005). Food functionality of Opuntia ficus-indica var. cultivated in Jeju Island. *Journal of Food Sciences and Nutrition*, 10, 103-110.

[72] Meckes-Lozoya, M., Ibáñez-Camacho, R. (1989). Hypoglucaemic activity of Opuntia streptacantha throughout the annual cycle. American *Journal of Chinese Med.*, 17, 221–224.

[73] Wolfram, R. M., Kritz, H., Efthimiou, Y., Stomatopoulos, J., Sinzinger, H. (2002). Effect of prickly pear (Opuntia robusta) on glucose- and lipid-metabolism in non-diabetics with hyperlipidemia – a pilot study. Wiener Klin. *Wochenschr*, 114, 840 –846.

[74] Enigbokan, M. A., Felder, T. B., Thompson, J. O., Kuti, J. O., Ekpenyong, K. I. (1996). Hypoglycaemic effects of Opuntia ficus indica Mill., Opuntia lindheimeri Engelm. and Opuntia robusta Wendl. in streptozotocin-induced diabetic rats. *Phytotherapy Research*, 10, 379–382.

[75] Laurenz, J. C., Collier, C. C., Kuti, J. O. (2003). Hypoglycaemic effect of Opuntia lindheimeri Englem. in a diabetic pig model. *Phytotherapy Research*, 17, 26–29.

[76] Wolfram, R. M., Budinsky, A., Efthimiou, Y., Stomatopoulos, J., Oguogho, A., and Sinzinger, H. (2003). Daily prickly pear consumption improves platelet function. *Prostagland. Leukotr. Essential Fatty Acids*, 69, 61 –66.

[77] Díaz-Medinaa, Elena. M., Martín-Herrerab, Domingo, Rodríguez-Rodrígueza, Elena M., and Díaz-Romeroa, Carlos. (2012). Chromium (III) in cactus pad and its possible role in the antihyperglycemic activity. *Journal of functional foods*, 4, 311 –314.

[78] Budinsky, A., Wolfram, R., Oguogho, A., Efthimiou, Y., Stamatopoulos, Y., and Sinziger, H. (2001). Regular ingestion of Opuntia robusta lowers oxidation injury. Prostagland. Leukotr. *Essential Fatty Acids*, 65, 45 –50.

[79] Fernández, M. L., Trejo, A. and McNamara, D. J. (1990). Pectin isolated from prickly pear (Opuntia sp.) modifies low density lipoprotein metabolism in cholesterol-fed guinea pigs. *Journal of Nutrition*, 120, 1283 –1290.

[80] Palumbo, B., Efthimiou, Y., Stamatopoulos, J., Oguogho, A., Budinsky, A., Palumbo, R., and Sinziger, H. (2003). Prickly pear induces upregulation of liver LDL binding in familial heterozygous hypercholesterolemia. *Nuclear Medicine Review*, 6, 35–39.

[81] Stintzing F. C., Schieber, A. and Carle. R. (2001). Phytochemical and nutritional significance of cactus pear. *European Food Research and Technology*, 212, 396-407.

[82] Gurbachan, S. and Felker. P. (1998). Cactus: new world foods. *Indian Horticulture,* 43, 29–31.

[83] Frati, A. (1992). Medical implication of prickly pear cactus. In: *Proc. 3rd Annual Texas prickly pear council.* Eds: Felkar, P., Moss, L. R., 24–25 July, Kingsville, Texas, 29-34.

[84] Galati, E. M., Tripodo, M. M., Trovato, A., D'Aquino, A., and Monforte, M. T. (2003). Biological activity of Opuntia ficus indica cladodes II: Effect on experimental hypercholesterolemia in rats. *Pharmaceutical Biology*, 41 (3): 175-179 .

[85] Jones, P., Raeini-Sarjaz, M., Ntanios, F., Vanstone, C., Feng, J., and Parsons, W. (2000). Modulation of plasma lipid levels and cholesterol kinetics by phytosterol versus phytostanol esters. *Journal of Lipid Research*, 41, 697–705.

[86] Ahmad, A., Davies, J., Randall, S., and Skinner, G. R. B. (1996). Antiviral properties of extract of Opuntia streptacantha. *Antiviral Research*, 30, 75-85.

[87] Zou, D. M., M. Brewer, Garcia, F., Feugang, J. M., Wang, J., Zang, R., Liu, H., and Zou, C. (2005). Cactus Pear - a Natural Product in Cancer Chemoprevention. *Nutrition Journal*, 4: 25.

[88] Supino, R., Crosti, M., Clerici, M., Warlters, A., Cleris, L., Zunino, F., and Formelli, F. (1996). Induction of apoptosis by Fenretinide (4-HPR) in human ovarian carcinoma cells and its association with retinoic acid receptor expression. *International Journal of Cancer* 65, 491–497.

[89] Veronesi, U., De Palo, G., Marubini, E., Costa, A., Formelli, F., Mariani, L., Decensi, A., Camerini, T., Del Turco, M. R., Di Mauro, M. G., Muraca, M. G., Del Vecchio, M., Pinto, C., D'Aiuto, G., Boni, C., Campa, T., Magni, A., Miceli, R., Perloff, M., Malone W. F., and Sporn, M. B. (1999). Randomized trial of fenretinide to prevent second breast malignancy in women with early breast cancer. *Journal National Cancer Institute,* 91, 1847–1856.

[90] De Palo, G., Mariani, L., Camerini, T., Marubini, E., Formelli, F., Pasini, B., Decensi, A., and Veronesi, U. (2002). Effect of fenretinide on ovarian carcinoma occurrence. *Gynecologic Oncology*, 86, 24–27.

[91] Cancer statistics, 2004. American cancer society.

[92] Kelloff, G. J., Sigman, C. C. and Greenwald, P. (1999). Cancer chemoprevention: progress and promise. *European Journal of Cancer*, 35: 2031-2038.

[93] Bwititi, P., Musabayane, C. T., Nhachi, C. F. B. (2000). Effects of Opuntia megacantha on blood glucose and kidney function in streptozotocin diabetic rats. *Journal of Ethnopharmacology*., 69, 247 –252.

[94] Bwititi, P., Zamurawo, M., Mabhachi, G., Mashanga, N. (1997). Toxic and hypericaemic effects of Opuntia megacantha extract in rats. *Phytotherapy Research*, 11, 389–391.

[95] Nerd, A., Dumoutier, M. and Mizrahi, Y. (1997). Properties and post-harvest behavior of the vegetable cactus Nopalea cochenillifera. *Postharvest Biology and Technology*, 10, 135-143.

[96] Galati, E. M,. Tripodo, M. M., Trovato, A., Miceli, N., and Monforte, M. T. (2002). Biological effects of Opuntia ficus indica (L.) Mill. (Cactaceae) waste matter. Note I: diuretic activity. *Journal of Ethnopharmacology*, 79, 17-21.

[97] Gupta, R. S., Sharma, R., Sharma, A., Chaudhudery, R., Bhatnager, A. K., Dobha, M. P., Joshi, Y. C., and Sharma, M. C. (2002) Antispermatogenic effect and chemical investigation of Opuntia dillenii. *Pharmaceutical Biology*, 40, 411–415.

[98] Eisenhofer, G., Kopin, I. J. and Goldstein, D. S. (2004) Catecholamine metabolism: a contemporary view with implications for physiology and medicine. *Pharmacological Reviews*, 56, 331 –349.

[99] Han, Y. N., Choo, Y., Lee, Y.-C., Moon, Y.-I., Kim, S.-D., Choi, J.-W. (2001). Monoamine oxidase B inhibitors from the fruits of Opuntia ficus-indica var. saboten. *Archives of Pharmacal Research*, 24, 51–54.

[100] Galati, E. M., Monforte, M. T., Tripodo, M. M., D'Aquino, A., and Mondello, M. R. (2001). Antiulcer activity of Opuntia ficus-indica (L.) Mill. (Cactaeceae): ultrastructural study. *Journal of Ethnopharmacology*, 76, 1–9.

[101] Lee, H., Yoon, J.-S., Lee, B. H., Choi, B. W., and Park, K. H. (2000). Screening of the radical scavenging effects, tyrosinase inhibition, and anti-allergic activities using Opuntia ficus indica. *Korean Journal of Pharmacogn.*, 31, 412–415.

[102] Jonas, A., Rosenblat, G., Krapf, D., Bitterman, W., and Neeman, I. (1998). Cactus flower extracts may prove beneficial in benign prostatic hyperplasia due to inhibition of 5 alpha reductase activity, aromatase activity and lipid peroxidation. *Urological Research*, 26, 265-270.

[103] Yoon, H. J., Won, C. H. and Moon. S. E. (2004). Allergic contact dermatitis due to Opuntia ficus-indica var. saboten. *Contact Dermatitis*, 51, 311-312.

[104] Galati, E. M., Mondello,M. R., Lauriano, E. R., Taviano, M. F., Galluzzo, M., and Miceli. N. (2005). Opuntia ficus indica (L.) Mill. Fruit Juice Protects Liver from Carbon Tetrachlorideinduced Injury. *Phytotherapy Research*, 19, 796–800.

[105] Wiese, J., McPherson, S., Odden, M. C., and Shlipak, M. G. (2004). Effect of Opuntia ficus indica on symptoms of the alcohol hangover. *Archives of Internal Medicine*, 164, 1334-1340.

In: Low and High-Fat Diets: Myths vs. Reality
Editors: J. E. Ferreira and N. Muniz
ISBN: 978-1-62257-797-2

Chapter III

The Importance of Dietary Fats

Cristiane de Oliveira*[1,*]*, Ana Barbosa Marcondes De Mattos*[2]*,
***João Felipe Mota*[3] *and Karina Vieira de Barros*[4]**
[1]Systemic Inflammation Laboratory, Trauma Research,
St. Joseph's Hospital and Medical Center, Phoenix, AZ, US
[2]Nutrition and Development Physiology Laboratory,
Federal University of Rio de Janeiro State (UFRJ), Rio de Janeiro, Brazil
[3]Nutrition College, Federal University of Goias (FANUT), Goiânia, Brazil
[4]Nutrition Physiology Unit, Federal University of São Paulo (UNIFESP),
São Paulo, Brazil

Abstract

Dietary fat intake (more specifically the type of fat consumed) together with a sedentary lifestyle, have been considered responsible for the increase in the prevalence of obesity and co-morbidities of obesity. While high-fat diets (>30% of energy from fat) have been shown to contribute to obesity and to a number of diseases including type 2 diabetes, hypertension and cardiovascular disease, low-fat diets (≤20% from fat), especially those low in saturated fat and cholesterol, have been promoted as healthier and recommended for weight loss and to reduce cardiovascular risk. However, doubts have been raised with regard to the effectiveness of this type of diet. Low-fat diets have been associated with an increase in carbohydrate intake from plant-based foods. Furthermore, there is the possibility of deficiencies in the amount and ratio of the essential fatty acids ω-3 and ω-6. Fats are not just source of energy and thermal insulator, but serve as a major component of cell membranes and the myelin sheath around the nerves, provide essential fatty acids, supply fat-soluble vitamins, participate in the manufacturing of hormones and eicosanoids, and help in nutrient absorption. Therefore, just lowering fat intake may not be the best strategy for a healthier life. In this paper we discuss the myths and realities, the health effects and the risks, of high- and low-fat diets.

[*] E-mail: crioliva@uol.com.br.

Introduction

Fatty acids are not just a source of energy and thermal insulator, but are biologically active molecules throughout the body. Fats serve as important component of the cell membranes and the myelin sheath around the nerves, provide the essential fatty acids ω-3 and ω-6, supply the fat-soluble vitamins A, D, E and K, participate in the manufacturing of hormones and eicosanoids and aide nutrient absorption. The nature of fatty acids into membrane phospholipids contributes to its fluidity and is believed to play a regulatory role in the activity of proteins present in this membrane. Phospholipids also serve as sources of second messengers such as diacylglycerol, phosphatidic acid, inositol triphosphate (IP3), ceramide and arachidonic acid, which are responsible for signaling events that are originally from the membrane to the cytosol and the nucleus (Calder et al., 1997; 2007). Also, fatty acids modulate immunologic and inflammatory mechanism, lipoprotein composition, metabolic parameters and insulin resistance (Calder et al., 1996; 2007; 2012; Hite et al., 2011).

Dietary fat intake is considered a risk factor for obesity development and co-morbidities of obesity like coronary heart disease, hypertension and stroke, certain types of cancer and diabetes mellitus. Consequently, there is a worldwide effort to decrease the amount of fat consumed with an emphasis in the concept that a low-fat diet is healthier and helps to avoiding weight gain. Whether there is a causal relationship between dietary fat and the current high levels of obesity continues to be debated. But, fat in diets have benefits and just lowering fat intakes may not be the best strategy for a healthier life. Several weight loss diets, including low-fat diet, with focus on improve physical appearance instead of health reasons emerged without consider the potential side effects associated with these dietary programs. Food is complex and when one macronutrient of the diet is altered, many others components can be altered.

In this paper we discuss some of the myths and reality, health effects and risks about high and low-fat diets.

Myths vs Reality in Low and High Fat Diets

All diets aren't without their faults but the conventional dietary recommendations for weight-loss, caloric restriction and an increased intake of complex carbohydrate from whole grain products, fruits and vegetables, still remains the best method to maintain a healthy weight and to reduce the incindence of obesity metabolic disorders. However, lack of population compliance makes necessary other methods for obesity treatment (Hite et al., 2011). Calorie restriction can achieve short-term weight loss, but weight loss has not been shown to be sustainable long-term. Reduction in the motivation to keep into the restrictive regimens and the activation of biological adaptations in response to weight loss, like decline in energy expenditure and increase in hunger, contribute to lack of long term sustainability (Leibel et al., 1995; Sumithran et al., 2011).

An alternative approach to calorie restriction is to lower or modify the fat content of diet. High-fat diets have been associated with weight gain and obesity and a low-fat/high carbohydrate, fiber, grains, and protein diet has been considered the best diet for weight loss

(Bray and Popkin, 1998; McManus et al., 2001; Wing and Hill, 2001; Astrup et al., 1997, 2002, 2005). With regard to fat content, diets can be classified as follows; high-fat diet (55%–65% daily caloric intake from fat; are low in carbohydrates); moderate fat diet (20–30% from fat; high in carbohydrates), low fat diet (11–19% from fat, high in carbohydrate) and very low fat diet (<10% from fat, high in carbohydrate) (Fleming, 2002; Ness-Abramof & Apovian, 2006). In this context, besides of a variety of studies published with diet and weigh loss, the correct amount and the composition of dietary fat remain unclean. The long-term effects of fat-restricted diets on weight loss are also unclear. Short-term dietary intervention studies show that low-fat diets lead to weight loss but were no better than other calorie restricted diets in achieving long-term weight loss (Pirosso et al., 2002; Brehm et al., 2003; Samaha et al., 2003; Foster et al., 2003; Yancy et al., 2004; Stern et al., 2004; Volek et al., 2004; Brinkworth et al., 2009). Moreover, Low- and very-low-fat diets are less palatable diets and therefore more difficult to keep a long-term adherence.

In a recent clinical trial by Ebbeling et al. (2012), overweight and obese patients under a low-fat diet program (20% of energy from fat, 60% from carbohydrate and 20% from protein) for 4 weeks had the same final body weight that patients under a low–glycemic index diet (40% from fat, 40% from carbohydrate and 20% from protein) or a very low-carbohydrate diet (60% from fat, 10% from carbohydrate and 30% from protein). Also, patients under the low-fat diet had the highest serum leptin levels and the highest decrease in the resting energy expenditure (REE) compared to patients under other weigh loss diets, what would predict weigh regain. According to some studies, high baseline serum leptin can predict weight regain after dieting weight loss (Crujeiras et al., 2010; Erez et al., 2011).

A high-fat/high-protein/low-carbohydrate diets, i.e. ketogenic, that force the body to burn fats rather than carbohydrates, in some cases, have been prescribed as promoter of a rapid weight loss and decreased hunger (Bravata et al., 2003; Bray, 2003; Crowe, 2005) through decrease in insulin levels that induces lipolysis and fat mobilization, and increase in protein levels and ketosis generated during fat metabolism that will promote satiety (Ness-Abramof and Apovian, 2006). The rapid weight loss due to this diet is caused by diuresis due to depletion of glycogen stores in the liver and muscle together with a lower caloric intake (Bray, 2003). But a low-carbohydrate diet is nutritional inadequate (low in fiber, micronutrients and minerals) and the increase in saturated fat levels has adverse effects on cardiovascular risk factors like increased LDL-C, triglycerides and total cholesterol and decreased HDL-C (Fleming, 2002; Blake et al., 2002), raising the risk of heart disease, strokes, peripheral vascular disease and blood clots.

Regarding to the correlation between fat consumption and coronary heart disease (CHD), early studies showed positive correlation between fat and saturated fat intake and coronary heart disease (Dayton et al., 1969; Kris-Etherton et al., 2003) but more recent reviews did not confirm these correlations (Skeaff and Miller, 2009; Baum et al., 2012). In a randomized controlled trial with postmenopausal women, a reduction of total fat intake to 20% of calories and increase intake of vegetables, fruits and grains showed that in ± 8 years of dietary intervention did not significantly reduce the risk of CHD, stroke or CVD in and achieved only modest effects on CVD risk factors: LDL-cholesterol levels, diastolic blood pressure and factor VIIc (coagulation factor) levels were significantly reduced but levels of HDL-cholesterol, triglycerides, glucose and insulin did not significantly differ between low-fat and control group (Howard et al., 2006). There are strong evidences that *trans* fats is positively associate with increase in both coronary heart disease events and deaths, and that total PUFA and ω-3 fats decrease them (Skeaff and Miller, 2009; Baum et al., 2012).

The western diet with high amount of saturated and *trans* fatty acids and lower in ω-3/ω-6 ratio and PUFA/saturated fat has been associated with coronary and chronic diseases such diabetes, metabolic syndrome, renal diseases and arthritis (Hu et al., 2001; Cordain et al., 2005; Moussavi et al., 2007; Siri-Tarino et al., 2010a, 2010b). It is clear that obesity is related to chronic disease development, however, in animal models, HF diets, even those with high percentage of fat as 60% are not always the main cause. For example, White et al. (2012), evaluating mice with pancreatic cancer that received for 19 weeks high-fat diet (60%) or low-fat diet (10%) showed that the tumor weight correlated positively with body weight, but not with the high-fat diet. However, they did not mentioned about the quality of lipid supplied in the diet.

Health Effects and Risks of Low and High Fat Diets

The role of fat in diet has long been debated. In the last century, fats were considered harmful to health. The first Food Guide Pyramid created by the U.S. Department of Agriculture (USDA, 1992) showed fat and oils on top of the pyramid, indicating that their consumption should be reduced. Policy markers aimed to prevent heart diseases since high-fat diets were associated with elevated cholesterol levels and heart diseases. The effort to decrease fat intake had little impact on the incidence of heart diseases, but it may have contributed to the current epidemics of obesity and diabetes, as people replaced fats with fast-burning carbohydrates. People also consumed fewer healthy fats such monounsaturated (MUFA) and polyunsaturated (PUFA) (Willet et al., 1995).

In 1995, Willet et al. presented a food pyramid that reflected the Mediterranean dietary traditions, historically associated with good health. In the Mediterranean derived Pyramid, plant oils especially olive and canola were considered important and are localized near the base of the pyramid. However, consumption of saturated and *trans* fatty acids should be avoided with consumption less than 7% and 2% of energy, respectively. Life expectancy in countries that practiced a characteristically Mediterranean diet was among the highest in the world and rates of coronary heart disease (CHD), certain cancers and other diet-related chronic diseases were among the lowest (Willet et al., 1995).

If not the quantity, then the types of fat in diets vary. High-fat diets have benefits and risks for health and these effects are associated with the type and amount of fatty acids in the diet. The main nutrient-related to cardiovascular disease is *trans* fatty acid (Skeaff and Miller, 2009). A recent meta-analysis of a prospective cohort studies demonstrated that a 2% higher energy intake from *trans* fatty acid, as an isocaloric replacement for carbohydrate, was associated with increase in CHD risk. On the other hand, the replacement of partially hydrogenated vegetable oils (7.5% of energy) with alternative fats/oils showed in all randomized controlled trials and prospective observational studies a reduction in CHD risk (Mozaffarian and Clarke, 2009).

Also, the saturated fat intake increases LDL cholesterol and has been associated with CHD risk. The mechanism is the inhibition of LDL receptor activity and increasing apolipoprotein B (apoB)-containing lipoprotein production. However, the greater CHD risk with saturated fatty acid has been questioned, because their consumption also increases HDL cholesterol, and the total cholesterol/HDL cholesterol ratio is not altered (Siri-Tarino et al., 2010a).

Beyond the knowledge about the quality and quantity of fat in a diet, is important observe the molecular form, mainly in the case of fatty acids supplementation. Several studies have shown benefits in ω -3 PUFA addition, however, the amount of DHA and EPA and the ratio between ω:6/ω:3 and polyunsaturated/saturated fatty acid are necessary to estimate the time of cell membrane incorporation and mediators production alteration. (Yagoob et al., 2000; Rees et al., 2006).

In a study by McEneny et al. (2012) low-fat diet (20%) was showed being anti-atherogenic by protecting the subfractions VLDL, LDL and HDL against oxidation. Thus, increased fat intake may, by increasing the oxidation product within lipoprotein subfractions, increasing cardiovascular diseases. In an systematic review by Hooper et al. (2012) aimed assess the effect of reduction and/or modification of dietary fats on cardiovascular risk factors and outcomes like myocardial infarction, stroke and cancer diagnoses showed that reducing saturated fat by reducing and/or modifying dietary fat reduced the risk of cardiovascular events. They also showed that modified fat diets, where the proportion of saturated fat is replaced by unsaturated fats, without alteration on total fat intakes, had better effects on major cardiovascular risk factors than low-fat diets where the total fat intake is reduced with increase in carbohydrate intake. But in a study by Ebbeling et al. (2012), low-fat diet had unfavorable effects on most of the metabolic syndrome components studied: lower index of insulin sensitivity and lower levels of serum HDL cholesterol and higher levels of triglycerides and plasminogen activator inhibitor-1 (PAI-1) when compared to patients under other weight loss diets (low-glycemic index and very low-carbohydrate).

Low-fat diets have been associated with an increase in carbohydrate intake from plant-based foods what goes against the fact that a reduction in carbohydrate improves metabolic parameters related to heart disease and diabetes risks (Forsythe et al., 2008; Volek et al., 2009; Senef et al., 2011). The replacement of saturated fatty acids with carbohydrate can be harmful (Jakobsen et al., 2009; Kuipers et al., 2011; Senef et al., 2011). Among individuals who are insulin resistant, a low-fat/high-carbohydrate diet typically has adverse effect on lipid profiles. The consequence is a reduction on HDL cholesterol levels and increase in triglycerides levels, raising the risk for CHD. All types of fat compared with carbohydrate increases HDL cholesterol, excepting *trans* fatty acid (Baum et al., 2012).

The substitution of foods rich in saturated fatty acids with foods rich in monounsaturated fat has favorable outcomes on blood lipids, coagulant factors, improvement in insulin sensitivity and regulates glucose levels, reducing CHD risk (Allman-Farinelli et al., 2005; Gillingham et al., 2011). But this replacement of saturated fat by monounsaturated fat rather than by carbohydrate can induce an increase in fat consumption. Also, fat is less satiating than carbohydrate and protein, and a high fat/carbohydrate ratio in the diet promotes passive overconsumption, a positive energy balance and weight gain than low-fat diet with higher contents of carbohydrate and protein (Blundell and Stubbs, 1999). Dietary fat have been showed with weaker satiating effect than carbohydrate or protein in isoenergetic amounts (Rolls et al., 1994; Golay and Bobbioni, 1997), but with controversies (Poppitt et al., 1998). A reduction in dietary fat without restriction of total caloric intake can be more efficient in induce weight loss (Astrup et al., 2000; 2005).

When monounsaturated fat replace carbohydrates in the diet, triglycerides, VLDL cholesterol, high-sensitivity C-reactive protein and blood pressure decrease, while HDL-C and the major protein component of HDL Apolipoprotein A-I increase (Baum et al., 2012). Compared to monounsaturated fat, diets rich in carbohydrate may be associated with slightly higher blood pressure (Shah et al., 2007). In a meta-analysis with studies comparing high carbohydrate diets (49 to 60% of total energy) to high monounsaturated fat diets (22 to 33% of total energy) in patients with type 2 diabetes revealed that high MUFA diets improve lipoprotein profiles as well as glycemic control. Furthermore, there was no evidence that high monounsaturated fat diets induced weight gain in patients with diabetes mellitus when energy intake is controlled. The author suggested that a diet rich in monounsaturated fat can be advantageous for both patients with type 1 or type 2 diabetes who are trying to maintain or lose weight (Garg, 1998).

Previous studies in humans, reported no association between dietary fat intake and the risk of developing breast cancer (Graham et al., 1982; Goodwin and Boyd, 1987; Jones et al., 1987; Willett et al., 1987)). But more recently studies have been showing positive association between fat intake and risk of breast cancer (Howe et al., 1990; Prentice and Sheppard, 1990; Boyd et al., 1997; Wu et al., 1999). Plasma estradiol concentrations were significantly reduced in healthy postmenopausal women after 10–22 weeks of a low-fat diet (< 20% of daily energy intake from fat) intervention program (Prentice et al., 1990). Others studies also showed that a fat intake reduction (15-20%) reduces estradiol (Boyd and Lockwood, 1997; Wu et al., 1999; Rocks et al., 2004) and reduce breast cancer risk (Prentice and Sheppard, 1990). Plasma estradiol has been causally related to breast cancer risk in postmenopausal women (Dorgan et al., 1996; Hankinson et al., 1998). A 1-year follow-up diet intervention trial in a high-fiber, low-fat diet (21%) showed reduced serum bioavailable of estradiol concentration in women diagnosed with breast cancer (Rock et al., 2004). According to Boyd et al. (1997), a low-fat diet may reduce risk of breast cancer by reducing exposure to ovarian hormones that are a stimulus to cell division in the breast.

The diversity of colorectal cancer incidence rates around the world is attributed to differences in the diet (Mason 2002; Bingham and Riboli 2004). Epidemiologic studies suggest that intake of high-fat diet present in the Western diet and a high BMI are correlated with a high prevalence of colon cancer (Slattery et al., 1997; Doyle, 2007) and that low-fat products together with plant foods-based and diet low in calories may reduce colorectal cancer risk (Giovannucci et al., 1994; Flood et al., 2008; Miller et al., 2010). Also some observational studies showed that reduction on fat intake reduces risk of colorectal cancer but these effects are not conclusive (Carroll andKhoe, 1975; Prentice and Sheppard, 1990; Howe et al., 1992). A dietary modification trial showed no evidence that a low-fat dietary intervention reduces colorectal cancer in postmenopausal women (± 8 years of follow-up, diet with 20% fat) (Beresford et al., 2006). What is right is that these dietary factors are associated with elevated levels of insulin and insulin-like growth factors (IGFs). Elevated insulin production may predict CRC risk independently of BMI and IGF-1 level is positively associated with colorectal cancer risk (Giovannucci et al., 2000; Palmqvist et al., 2002).

Also, high-fat diets have been shown to be a risk factor for ulcerative colitis (Hunter, 1998; Geerling, 2000; Ma et al., 2007). The colon inflammation in rats with dextran sulfate sodium-induced colitis was significantly less severe in rats under a diet with a balance in the ω-6/ω -3 PUFA ratio (2:1, mixture of fish oil and soybean oil) than in rats under a diet with imbalance in the ω-6/ω-3 PUFA ratio (1:6). Several studies demonstrated the importance of modulating the ω-6/ω-3 ratio to obtain beneficial effects rather than simply reducing ω-6 PUFA levels (Camuesco et al., 2005). This imbalance in the ω-6/ω-3 ratio is observed in western diets (10:1) and may be related to increased production of pro-inflammatory cytokines and eicosanoids in autoimmune diseases (Calder, 2007). On the other hand, the same protocol using a HF diet enriched with ω-6 orω-3 fat acids, the high concentration of fat did not exacerbate de ulcerative colitis and additionally a good ω-6/ω-3 ratio was able to increase the anti-inflammatory cytokine IL-10 and IL-10/IL-4 ratio (Barros et al., 2010).

Regarding to metabolic syndrome, a low-fat (20% energy from fat) diet showed that postmenopausal women into this dietary modification significantly changed the components of the metabolic syndrome (waist circumference, serum triglycerides, blood pressure, HDL cholesterol and serum glucose) after 1 year of participation in the trial, but the effects of the dietary modification were non-statistically significant after 3 years (Neuhouser et al., 2012).

High-Fat and Low-Fat Diet Basic Research Evidences

Regarding the effects of high-fat diets in animal, several studies have shown that there is a positive relationship between the amount of fat in the diet and the incidence of obesity and metabolic syndrome (Bourgeois et al., 1983; Boozer et al., 1995; Takahashi et al., 1999; Ghibaudi et al., 2002; Woods et al., 2003; Yang et al., 2012). It is generally accepted that high-fat diets can be used to generate a rodent model of obesity (Oakes et al., 1997; Ahren et al., 1999; Lingohr et al., 2002; Buettner et al., 2007; Hariri and Thibault, 2010a). A high-fat diet increases plasma costicosterone levels and blunts its 24 hours variation, contributing to a state of hyperglycemia (Cano et al., 2008). There is a decrease in glucose uptake and stimulus for inappropriate glucose production, resulting in elevations in both circulating insulin and glucose characteristic of insulin resistance (Surwit, 1988). Likewise, many studies have demonstrated that high-fat diet affects insulin signaling in different tissues (Duplus et al., 2000; Vessby et al., 2003; Cerf, 2007) as well as affects adipokines involved in insulin sensitivity (Woods et al., 2003; 2004; Berk et al., 2005; Barnea et al., 2006; Bullen et al., 2007; Zhang et al., 2007; Boullu-Ciocca 2007; Bueno et al., 2008; Mullen et al., 2010; Oliveira et al., 2011).

There is a considerable variability in the results reported by diets with very different amount and type of fatty acids. Thus it is important to attempt to the experimental design and consider the proportion of certain fatty acids and the calorie density. Long-term ingestion (15 months) of high fat diet (42% of calories from fat) led to a significant weight gain when compared to a low-fat group consuming the same amount of calories (Osaci et al., 1984; 1987). Similarly, Storlien et al. (1986) have demonstrated that 2 months of high- fat diet led to an increase in white adipose tissue weight, but no change in body weight when compared with low-fat isocaloric diet with high carbohydrate content. In the same direction, the distinction between the effects of dietary composition and obesity was documented by Woods et al., (2003). In rats fed *ad libitum* with a diet containing high-fat (20%) or low-fat (4%) diet or the same high-fat diet matched to the energy intake of the low-fat rats, for 10 weeks, high-fat fed rats weighted 10% more than low-fat fed rats and had 50% more body fat. And more importantly, the rats fed with a high-fat diet matched to the energy intake of the low-fat fed rats had similar body weights but significantly more adipose tissue than low-fat diet fed rats. Thus, it seems that the fat mass content is always more pronounced in high-fat fed animals when compared to low-fat diet fed animals even when calories intake is matched.

Therefore, it is evident that high-fat diet has a direct effect on metabolic parameters, and not necessarily via obesity development (Storlien et al., 2000). Animals fed with a high-fat diet from weaning until 4 weeks of age had intrabdominal fat and metabolic abnormalities before an increase in the body weight (McDonald et al., 2011). Likewise, during fetal development maternal high-fat diet can adversely affect offspring's health, leading to programmed metabolic perturbations in adult age (Ferezou-Viala et al., 2007, Tamashiro et al., 2009, Sullivan et al., 2011).

However, not all types of fat predispose to obesity. The dietary fatty acid profile is an important variable in developing dietary obesity (Bougeois et al., 1983; Bell et al., 1997; Storlien et al., 2001; Akoum et al., 2010). Supporting this idea some animal studies have shown that saturated fatty acids are more obesogenic than PUFA, leading to greater accumulation of body fat and a higher body weight gain (Storlien et al. 1991, 1996; Hariri et al., 2010). PUFA are considered potential insulin sensitizers (Neschen et al., 2002; 2007; Taouis et al., 2002; Pighin et al., 2003) as well as an enhancer of lipid oxidation via PPAR-alpha (Duplus et al., 2000; Jump, 2002).

In an attemp to analyse the influence of the specific fat component, Buettner et al. (2006), compared high-fat diets based on coconut fat (saturated fatty acids); olive oil (MUFA); lard (similar quantities of saturated and MUFA) and fish oil (PUFA).

The high-fat lard and high-fat olive diets led to the most pronounced manifestations of obesity and insulin resistance. The animals in these groups gained more weight, had higher plasma glucose levels and showed less efficient insulin-induced glucose disposal than animals fed coconut fat, fish oil or standard rat chow. Although previous studies have already shown a negative effect from high fat diet olive oil (Del Moral et al., 1997; Storlien et al., 1991; Tsunoda et al., 1998).

It contradicts the positive impact of Mediterranean diet on health (Kris-Etherton, 1999) however, it must be considered that Mediterranean diet typically has a low-fat composition as noticed by authors. It is generally accepted that that high intake of saturated fat is associated with the development of the metabolic syndrome (Riccard et al., 2004). Further, even though in Buettner et al. (2006) study, coconut fat-fed animals did not showed clear signs of obesity and insulin resistance as demonstrated in the lard- or olive oil-fed rats, they had increased plasma triglyceride levels and a mild hepatic steatosis. This brings once more the importance of the quality and amount of fat consumed when considering health effects.

Conclusion

Inconsistencies on dietary fatty acid recommendation seem to be related to the difficulty of interpretation from scientific evidence due to methodological difference in the studies, differences between populations studied, accurate dietary reporting and compliance in human studies. The creation of fatty acids dietary guidelines is important to give an idea of the minimum and maximum amount to be consumed daily.

More studies about the long-term effects of these diets, the time into diets necessary to achieve results, their effects on risk factors for heart disease and other health problem as well the side effects are needed. Also, it is important to note that the type of fatty acid must be considered in order to point out the positive or negative health effects of dietary fat.

References

Ahren B; Gudbjartsson T; Al Amin AN; Martensson H; Myrsen-Axcrona U; Karlsson S; Mulder H; Sundler F (1999). Islet perturbations in rats fed a high-fat diet. *Pancreas* 18:75–83.

Akoum SE; Lamontagne V; Cloutier I; Tanguay JF (2011). Nature of fatty acids in high fat diets differentially delineates obesity-linked metabolic syndrome components in male and female C57BL/6J mice. *Diabetology andmetabolic syndrome* 3:34.

Allman-Farinelli MA, Gomes K, Favaloro EJ, Petocz P (2005). A diet rich in high-oleic-acid sunflower oil favorably alters low-density lipoprotein cholesterol, triglycerides, and factor VII coagulant activity. *J. Am. Diet Assoc.* 105(7):1071-1079.

Astrup A (2005). The role of dietary fat in obesity. *Semin. Vasc. Med.* 5(1): 40-47.

Astrup A, Astrup A, Buemann B, Flint A, Raben A (2002). Low-fat diets and energy balance: how does the evidence stand in 2002? *Proc. Nutr. Soc.* 61(2):299-309.

Astrup A, Grunwald GK, Melanson EL, Saris WH, Hill JO (2000). The role of low-fat diets in body weight control: a meta-analysis of ad libitum dietary intervention studies. *Int J Obes Relat Metab Disord* 24(12):1545-1552.

Astrup A, Toubro S, Raben A, Skov AR (1997). The role of low fats diets and fat substitutes in body weight management: what have we learned fromclinical studies? *J. Am. Dietetics Assoc.* 97(Suppl): 82S – 87S.

Barnea M; Shamay A; Stark AH; Madar Z (2006). A high-fat diet has a tissue-specific effect on adiponectin and related enzyme expression. *Obesity* 14:2145-2153.

Barros KV, Xavier RA, Abreu GG, Martinez CA, Ribero ML Gambero A, Carvalho PO, Nascimento CM, Silveira VL (2010). Soybean and fish oil mixture protects against DNA damage and decrease colonic inflammation in rats with dextran sulfate sodium (DSS). *Lipids Health Dis.* 68:8-14.

Baum SJ, Kris-Etherton PM, Willett WC, Lichtenstein AH, Rudel LL, Maki KC, Whelan J, Ramsden CE, Block RC (2012). Fatty acids in cardiovascular health and disease: A comprehensive update. *J. Clin. Lipidol.* 6(3):216-234.

Bell RR; Spencer MJ; Sherriff JL (1997). Voluntary exercise and monounsaturated canola oil reduce fat gain in mice fed diets high in fat. *J. Nutr.* 127:2006–2010.

Beresford SA, Johnson KC, Ritenbaugh C, Lasser NL, Snetselaar LG, Black HR, Anderson GL, et al. (2006). Low-fat dietary pattern and risk of colorectal cancer: the Women's Health Initiative Randomized Controlled Dietary Modification Trial. *JAMA* 295(6):643-654.

Berk ES; Kovera AJ; Boozer CN; Pi-Sunyer FX; Johnson JA; Albu JB (2005). Adiponectin levels during low- and high-fat eucaloric diets in lean and obese women. *Obes. Res.* 13:1566-1571.

Blake GJ, Otvos JD, Rifai N, Ridker PM (2002). Low density lipoprotein particle concentration and size as determined by nuclear magnetic resonance spectroscopy as predictors of cardiovascular disease in women. *Circulation* 106(15):1930-1937.

Blundell JE, Stubbs RJ (1999). High and low carbohydrate and fat intakes: limits imposed by appetite and palatability and their implications for energy balance. *Eur. J. Clin. Nutr.* 53(Suppl 1):148 -165.

Boozer CN; Schoenbach G; Atkinson RL (1995). Dietary fat and adiposity a dose response relationship in adult male rats fed isocalorically. *Am. J. Physiol. Endocrinol. Metab.* 268:546-550.

Boullu-Ciocca S; Achard V; Tassistro V; Dutour A; Grino M (2008). Postnatal Programming of Glucocorticoid Metabolism in Rats Modulates High-Fat Diet–Induced Regulation of Visceral Adipose Tissue Glucocorticoid Exposure and Sensitivity and Adiponectin and Proinflammatory Adipokines Gene Expression in Adulthood. *Diabetes* 57: 669 - 677.

Bourgeois F; Alexiu A; Lemonnier D (1983). Dietary induced obesity: effect of dietary fats on adipose tissue cellularity in mice. *Br. J. Nutr.* 49:17–26.

Boyd NF, Lockwood GA, Greenberg CV, Martin LJ, Tritchler DL (1997). Effects of a low-fat high-carbohydrate diet on plasma sex hormones in premenopausal women: results from a randomized controlled trial. Canadian Diet and Breast Cancer Prevention Study Group. *Br. J. Cancer* 76(1):127–135.

Bravata DM, Sanders L, Huang J, Krumholz HM, Olkin I, Gardner CD, Bravata DM (2003). Efficacy and safety of low-carbohydrate diets: a systematic review. *JAMA* 289(14):1837-1850.

Bray GA (2003). Low-carbohydrate diets and realities of weight loss. *JAMA* 289(14):1853-1855.

Bray GA, Popkin BM (1998). Dietary fat intake does affect obesity. *Am. J. Clin. Nutr.* 68: 1157-1173.

Brehm BJ, Seeley RJ, Daniels SR, D'Alessio DA (2003). A randomized trial comparing a very low carbohydrate diet and a calorie-restricted low fat diet on body weight and cardiovascular risk factors in healthy women. *J. Clin. Endocrinol. Metab.* 88:1617–1623.

Brinkworth GD, Noakes M, Buckley JD, Keogh JB, Clifton PM (2009). Long-term effects of a very-low-carbohydrate weight loss diet compared with an isocaloric low-fat diet after 12 months. *Am. J. Clin. Nutr.* 90(1):23-32.

Bueno AA, Oyama LM, de Oliveira C, Pisani LP, Ribeiro EB, Silveira VL, Oller do Nascimento CM (2008). Effects of different fatty acids and dietary lipids on adiponectin gene expression in 3T3-L1 cells and C57BL/6J mice adipose tissue. *Pflugers Arch.* 455:701-709.

Buettner R, Parhofer KG, Woenckhaus M, Wrede CE, Kunz-Schughart LA, Schölmerich J, Bollheimer LC (2006). Defining high-fat-diet rat models: metabolic and molecular effects of different fat types. *J. Mol. Endocrinol.* 36:485-501.

Bullen JWJr, Bluher S, Kelesidis T, Mantzoros CS (2007). Regulation of adiponectin and its receptors in response to development of diet-induced obesity in mice. *Am. J. Physiol. Endocrinol. Metab.* 292:1079-1086.

Calder PC (1996). Effects of fatty acids and dietary lipids on cell of the immune system. *Proc. Nutr. Soc.* 55:127-150.

Calder PC (2007). Immunomodulation by omega-3 fatty acids. *Prostaglandins Leukot. Essent. Fatty Acids* 77:327-335.

Calder PC (2012). Long-chain fatty acids and inflammation. *Proc. Nutr. Soc.* 71(2):284-289.

Camuesco D, Gálvez J, Nieto A, Comalada M, Rodriguez-Cabezas ME, Concha A, Xaus J, Zarzuelo A (2005). Dietary olive oil supplemented with fish oil, rich in EPA and DHA (n-3) polyunsaturated fatty acids, attenuates colonic inflammation in rats with DSS-induced colitis. *J. Nutr.* 135:687-694.

Cano P, Jimenez-Ortega V, Larrad A, Toso CFR, Cadinali DP, Esquifino AI (2008). Effect of a high-fat diet on 24h pattern of circulating levels of prolactin, luteinizing hormone, testosterone, corticosterone, thyroid-stimulating hormone and glucose, and pineal melatonin content in rats. *Endocrine* 33:118-125.

Carroll KK, Khor HT (1975). Dietary fat in relation to tumorigenesis. *Prog. Biochem. Pharmacol.* 10:308-353.

Cerf ME (2007). High fat diet modulation of glucose sensing in the beta-cell. *Med. Sci. Monit.* 13: 12-17.

Cordain L, Eaton SB, Sebastian A, Mann N, Lindeberg S, Watkins BA, O'Keefe JH, Brand-Miller J (2005). Origins and evolution of the Western diet: health implications for the 21st century. *Am. J. Clin. Nutr.* 81:341–354.

Crowe TC (2005). Safety of low-carbohydrate diets. *Obes Rev* 6(3):235-245.

Crujeiras AB, Goyenechea E, Abete I, Lage M, Carreira MC, Martínez JA, Casanueva FF (2010). Weight regain after a diet-induced loss is predicted by higher baseline leptin and lower ghrelin plasma levels. *J. Clin. Endocrinol. Metab.* 95(11):5037-5044

Dayton S, Pearce ML, Hashimoto S, Cixon WJ, Tomlyasu U (1969). A controlled trial of a diet high in unsaturated fat for preventing complications of atherosclerosis. *Circulation* 60(suppl 2) 111-163.

Del Moral ML, Esteban FJ, Torres MI, Camacho MV, Hernandez R, Jimenez A, Aranega A, Pedrosa JA, Peinado MA (1997). High-fat sunflower and olive oil diets affect serum lipid levels in steatotic rat liver differently. *Journal of Nutritional Science and Vitaminology* 43:155–160.

Dorgan JF, Longcope C, Stephenson HE Jr, Falk RT, Miller R, Franz C, Kahle L, Campbell WS, Tangrea JA, Schatzkin A (1996). Relation of prediagnostic serum estrogen and androgen levels to breast cancer risk. *Cancer Epidemiol. Biomarkers Prev.* 5:533-539.

Doyle VC (2007). Nutrition and colorectal cancer risk: a literature review. *Gastroenterol Nurs.* 30(3):178-182.

Duplus E, Glorian M, Forest C (2000). Fatty acid regulation of gene transcription. *J. Biol. Chem.* 275:30749 –30752.

Ebbeling CB, Swain JF, Feldman HA, Wong WW, Hachey DL, Garcia-Lago E, Ludwig DS (2012). Effects of dietary composition on energy expenditure during weight-loss maintenance. *JAMA* 307(24):2627-2634.

Erez G, Tirosh A, Rudich A, Meiner V, Schwarzfuchs D, Sharon N, Shpitzen S, Blüher M, Stumvoll M, Thiery J, Fiedler GM, Friedlander Y, Leiterstdorf E, Shai I (2011). Phenotypic and genetic variation in leptin as determinants of weight regain. *Int. J. Obes. (Lond)* 35(6):785-792

Ferezou-Viala J, Roy AF, Serougne C, Gripois D, Parquet M, Bailleux V, Gertler A, Delplanque B, Djiane J, Riotto M, Taouis M (2007). Long-term consequences of maternal high-fat feeding on hypothalamic leptin sensitivity and diet-induced obesity in the offspring. *Am. J. physiol. Regul. Integr. Comp. Physiol.* 293:1056-1062.

Fleming RM (2002). The effect of high-, moderate-, and low-fat diets on weight loss and cardiovascular disease risk factors. *Prev. Cardiol.* (3):110-118.

Flood A, Rastogi T, Wirfält E, Mitrou PN, Reedy J, Subar AF, Kipnis V, Mouw T, Hollenbeck AR, Leitzmann M, Schatzkin A (2008). Dietary patterns as identified by factor analysis and colorectal cancer among middle-aged Americans. *Am. J. Clin. Nutr.* 88(1):176-184.

Forsythe CE, Phinney SD, Fernandez ML, Quann EE, Wood RJ, Bibus DM, Kraemer WJ, Feinman RD, Volek JS (2008). Comparison of low fat and low carbohydrate diets on circulating fatty acid composition and markers of inflammation. *Lipids* 43(1):65-77.

Foster GD, Wyatt HR, Hill JO, McGuckin BG, Brill C, Mohammed BS, Szapary PO, Rader DJ, Edman JS, Klein S (2003). A randomized trial of a low-carbohydrate diet for obesity. *N. Engl. J. Med.* 348(21):2082-2090.

Garg A (1998). High-monounsaturated-fat diets for patients with diabetes mellitus: a meta-analysis. *Am. J. Clin. Nutr.* 67(3 Suppl):577-582.

Geerling BJ, Dagnelie PC, Badart-Smook A, Russel MG, Stockbrugger RW, Brummer RJ (2000). Diet as a risk factor for the development of ulcerative colitis. *Am. J. Gastroenterol.*, 95:1008–1013

Ghibaudi L, Cook J, Farley C, Van Heek M, Hwa JJ (2002). Fat intake affects adiposity, comorbidity factors, and energy metabolism of Sprague–Dawley rats. *Obes. Res.* 10:956–963.

Gillingham LG, Harris-Janz S, Jones PJ (2011). Dietary monounsaturated fatty acids are protective against metabolic syndrome and cardiovascular disease risk factors. *Lipids* 46(3):209-228.

Giovannucci E, Pollak MN, Platz EA, Willett WC, Stampfer MJ, Majeed N, Colditz GA, Speizer FE, Hankinson SE (2000). A prospective study of plasma insulin-like growth factor-1 and binding protein-3 and risk of colorectal neoplasia in women. *Cancer Epidemiol. Biomarkers Prevn.* (4):345-349.

Giovannucci E, Willett WC (1994). Dietary factors and risk of colon cancer. *Ann. Med.* 26(6):443-52.

Golay A, Bobbioni E (1997). The role of dietary fat in obesity. *Int. J. Obes. Relat. Metab. Disord.* 21(3):2-11.

Goodwin PJ, Boyd NF (1987). Critical appraisal of the evidence that dietary fat intake is related to breast cancer risk in humans. *J. Nati. Cancer Inst.* 79:473-485.

Graham S, Marshall J, Mettlin C, Rzepka T, Nemoto T, Byers T (1982). Diet in the epidemiology of breast cancer. *Am. J. Epidemiol.* 116: 68-75.

Hankinson SE, Willett WC, Manson JE, Colditz GA, Hunter DJ, Spiegelman D, Barbieri RL, Speizer FE (1998). Plasma sex steroid hormone levels and risk of breast cancer in postmenopausal women. *J. Natl. Cancer Inst.* 90(17):1292-1299.

Hariri H, Gougeon R, Thibault L (2010b). A highly saturated fat-rich diet is more obesogenic than diets with lower saturated fat content. *Nutrition research* 30:632-643.

Hariri N, Thibault L (2010a). High-fat diet-induced obesity in animal models. *Nutr. Res. Rev.* 23: 270-299.

Hite AH, Berkowitz VG, Berkowitz K (2011). Low-carbohydrate diet review: shifting the paradigm. *Nut. Clin. Pract.* 26:300-308.

Howard BV, Van Horn L, Hsia J, Manson JE, Stefanick ML, Wassertheil-Smoller S, Kuller LH et al. (2006). Low-fat dietary pattern and risk of cardiovascular disease: the Women's Health Initiative Randomized Controlled Dietary Modification Trial. *JAMA* 295(6):655-666.

Howe GR, Benito E, Castelleto R, Cornée J, Estève J, Gallagher RP, Iscovich JM, Deng-ao J, Kaaks R, Kune GA, et al. (1992). Dietary intake of fiber and decreased risk of cancers of the colon and rectum: evidence from the combined analysis of 13 case-control studies. *J. Natl. Cancer Inst.* 84(24):1887-1896.

Howe GR, Hirohata T, Hislop TG, Iscovich JM, Yuan JM, Katsouyanni K, Lubin F, Marubini E, Modan B, Rohan T, et al (1990). Dietary factors and risk of breast cancer: combined analysis of 12 case-control studies. *J. Natl. Cancer Inst.* 82(7):561-569.

Hu FB, Manson JE, Stampfer MJ, Colditz G, Liu S, Solomon CG, Willett WC (2001). Diet, lifestyle, and the risk of type 2 diabetes mellitus in women. *N. Engl. J. Med.* 345(11):790-797.

Hunter JO (1998). Nutritional factors in inflammatory bowel disease. *Eur. J. gastrol Hepatol* 10:235–237.

Jakobsen MU, O'Reilly EJ, Heitmann BL, Pereira MA, Bälter K, Fraser GE, Goldbourt U, Hallmans G, Knekt P, Liu S, Pietinen P, Spiegelman D, Stevens J, Virtamo J, Willett WC, Ascherio A (2009). Major types of dietary fat and risk of coronary heart disease: a pooled analysis of 11 cohort studies. *Am. J. Clin. Nutr.* 89(5):1425-1432.

Jones DY, Schatzkin A, Green SB, Block G, Brinton LA, Ziegler RG, Hoover R, Taylor PR (1987). Dietary fat and breast cancer in the National Health and Nutrition Examination Survey I Epidemiologie Followup Study. *J. Nati. Cancer Inst.* 79:465-471.

Jump, DB (2002). Dietary polyunsaturated fatty acids and regulation of gene transcription. *Curr. Opin. Lipidol.* 13:155-164.

Kris-Etherton PM (1990). Monounsaturated fatty acids and risk of cardiovascular disease. *Circulation* 100:1253-1258.

Kris-Etherton PM, Harris WS, Appel LJ (2002). American Heart Association Nutrition Committee. Fish consumption, fish oil, omega-3 fatty acids, and cardiovascular disease. *Circulation* 106(21):2747-2757.

Kuipers RS, de Graaf DJ, Luxwolda MF, Muskiet MH, Dijck-Brouwer DA, Muskiet FA (2011). Saturated fat, carbohydrates and cardiovascular disease. *Neth. J. Med.* 69(9):372-378.

Leibel RL, Rosenbaum M, Hirsch J (1995). Changes in energy expenditure resulting from altered body weight. *N. Engl. J. Med.* 332(10):621-628.

Lingohr MK, Buettner R, Rhodes CJ (2002). Pancreatic beta-cell growth and survival – a role in obesity-linked type 2 diabetes? *Trends in Molecular Medicine* 8:375–384.

Long NC, Morimoto A, Nakamori T, Yamashiro O and Murakami N (1991). Intraperitoneal injections of prostaglandin E2 attenuate hyperthermia induced by restraint or interleukin-1 in rats. *J. Physiol.* 444, 363-373.

Ma X, Torbenson M, Hamad ARA, Soloski MJ, Li Z (2007). High-fat diet modulates non-CD1d-restricted natural killer T cells and regulatory T cells in mouse colon and exacerbates experimental colitis. *Clinical and Experimental Immunology* 151:130-138.

Mason JB (2002). Diet, folate, and colon cancer. *Curr. Opin. Gastroenterol* 18(2):229-234.

McDonald SD, Pesarchuk E, Don-Wauchope A, Zimaity HE, Holloway AC (2011). Adverse metabolic effects of a hypercaloric, high-fat diet in rodents precede observable changes in body weight. *Nutrition Research* 31:707-714.

McEneny J, McPherson P, Spence M, Bradley U, Blair S, McKinley M, Young I, Hunter S (2012). Does a diet high or low in fat influence the oxidation potential of VLDL, LDL and HDL subfractions? *Nutr. Metab. Cardiovasc. Dis.* [Epub ahead of print] PubMed PMID: 22405535.

McManus K, Antinoro L, Sacks F (2001). A randomized controlled trial of a moderate-fat, low-energy diet compared with a low fat, low-energy diet for weight loss in overweight adults. *Int. J. Obes. Relat. Metab. Disord.* 25(10):1503-1511.

Miller PE, Lazarus P, Lesko SM, Muscat JE, Harper G, Cross AJ, Sinha R, Ryczak K, Escobar G, Mauger DT, Hartman TJ (2010). Diet index-based and empirically derived dietary patterns are associated with colorectal cancer risk. *J. Nutr.* 140(7):1267-1273.

Moussavi N, Gavino V, Receveur O (2007). Could the quality of dietary fat, and not just its quantity, be related to risk of obesity. *Obesity (Silver Spring)* 16:7-15.

Mozaffarian D, Clarke R (2009). Quantitative effects on cardiovascular risk factors and coronary heart disease risk of replacing partially hydrogenated vegetable oils with other fats and oils. *Eur. J. Clin. Nutr.* 63(2):22-33.

Mullen KL, Tishinsky JM, Robinson LE, Dyck DJ (2010). Skeletal muscle inflammation is not responsible for the rapid impairment in adiponectin response with high-fat feeding in rats. *Am. J. Physiol. Regul. Integr. Comp. Physiol.* 299:500-508.

Neschen S, Moore I, Regittnig W, Yu CL, Wang Y, Pypaert M, Petersen KF, Shulman GI (2002). Contrasting effects of fish oil and safflower oil on hepatic peroxisomal and tissue lipid content. *Am. J. Physiol. Endocrinol. Metab.* 282:395-401.

Neschen S, Morino K, Dong J, Wang-Fischer Y, Cline GW, Romanelli AJ, Rossbacher JC, Moore IK, Regittnig W, Munoz DS, Kim JH, Shulman GI (2007). N-3 Fatty Acids Preserve Insulin Sensitivity in vivo in a Peroxisome Proliferator-Activated Receptor-Dependent Manner. *Diabetes* 56:1034-1041.

Ness-Abramof R, Apovian CM (2006). Diet modification for treatment and prevention of obesity. *Endocrine* 29(1):5-9.

Neuhouser ML, Howard B, Lu J, Tinker LF, Van Horn L, Caan B, Rohan T, Stefanick ML, Thomson CA (2012). A low-fat dietary pattern and risk of metabolic syndrome in postmenopausal women: The Women's Health Initiative. *Metabolism.* [Epub ahead of print] PubMed PMID: 22633601.

Oakes ND, Cooney GJ, Camilleri S, Chisholm DJ, Kraegen EW (1997). Mechanisms of liver and muscle insulin resistance induced by chronic high-fat feeding. *Diabetes* 46:1768–1774.

Oliveira C, Mattos ABM, Biz C, Oyama LM, Ribeiro EB, Nascimento CM (2011). High-fat diet and glucocorticoid treatment cause hyperglycemia associated with adiponectin receptor alterations. *Lipids health and Disease*. 10:11.

Oscai LB, Brown MM, Miller WC (1984). Effect of dietary fat on food intake, growth and body composition in rats. *Growth* 48:415–424.

Oscai LB, Miller WC, Arnall DA (1987). Effects of dietary sugar and of dietary fat on food intake and body fat content in rats. *Growth* 51: 64–73.

Palmqvist R, Hallmans G, Rinaldi S, Biessy C, Stenling R, Riboli E, Kaaks R (2002). Plasma insulin-like growth factor 1, insulin-like growth factor binding protein 3, and risk of colorectal cancer: a prospective study in northern Sweden. *Gut* 50(5): 642–646.

Pighin D, Karabatas L, Rossi A, Chicco A, Basabe JC, Lombardo YB (2003). Fish oil affects pancreatic fat storage, pyruvate dehydrogenase complex activity, and insulin secretion in rats fed a sucrose-rich diet. *J. Nutr.* 133:4095-4101.

Pirozzo S, Summerbell C, Cameron C, Glasziou P (2002). Advice on low-fat diets for obesity. *Cochrane Database Syst. Rev.* (2):CD003640.

Poppitt SD, McCormack D, Buffenstein R (1998). Short-term effects of macronutrient preloads on appetite and energy intake in lean women. *Physiol Behav* 64(3):279–285.

Prentice RL, Sheppard L (1990). Dietary fat and cancer: consistency of the epidemiologic data, and disease prevention that may follow from a practical reduction in fat consumption. *Cancer Causes Control*, 1:81–97.

Rees D, Miles EA, Banerjee T, Wells SJ, Roynette CE, Wahle KW, Calder PC (2006). Dose-related effects of eicosapentaenoic acid on innate immune function in healthy humans: a comparison of young and older men. *Am. J. Clin. Nutr.* 83;331-342.

Riccardi G, Giacco R, Rivellese AA (2004). Dietary fat, insulin sensitivity and the metabolic syndrome. *Clin. Nutr.* 23:447-456.

Rock CL, Flatt SW, Thomson CA, Stefanick ML, Newman VA, Jones LA, Natarajan L, Ritenbaugh C, Hollenbach KA, Pierce JP, Chang RJ (2004). Effects of a high-fiber, low-fat diet intervention on serum concentrations of reproductive steroid hormones in women with a history of breast cancer. *J. Clin. Oncol.* 12:2379–2387.

Rolls BJ, Kim-Harris S, Fischman MW, Foltin RW, Moran TH, Stoner SA (1994). Satiety after preloads with different amounts of fat and carbohydrate: implications for obesity. *Am. J. Clin. Nutr.* 60(4):476–487.

Samaha FF, Iqbal N, Seshadri P, Chicano KL, Daily DA, McGrory J, Williams T, Williams M, Gracely EJ, Stern L (2003). A low-carbohydrate as compared with a low-fat diet in severe obesity. *N. Engl. J. Med.* 348(21):2074-2081.

Seneff S, Wainwright G, Mascitelli L (2011). Is the metabolic syndrome caused by a high fructose, and relatively low fat, low cholesterol diet? *Arch Med Sci* 7(1):8-20.

Shah M, Adams-Huet B, Garg A (2007). Effect of high-carbohydrate or high-cis-monounsaturated fat diets on blood pressure: a meta-analysis of intervention trials. *Am. J. Clin. Nutr.* 85(5):1251-1256.

Siri-Tarino PW, Sun Q, Hu FB, Krauss RM (2010a). Saturated fat, carbohydrate, and cardiovascular disease. *Am. J. Clin. Nutr.* 91:502–509.

Siri-Tarino PW, Sun Q, Hu FB, Krauss RM (2010b). Saturated fatty acids and risk of coronary heart disease: modulation by replacement nutrients. *Curr. Atheroscler. Rep.* 12(6):384-390.

Skeaff CM, Miller J (2009). Dietary fat and coronary heart disease: summary of evidence from prospective cohort and randomised controlled trials. *Ann. Nutr. Metab.* 55(1-3):173-201.

Slattery ML, Potter JD, Duncan DM, Berry TD (1997). Dietary fats and colon cancer: assessment of risk associated with specific fatty acids. *Int. J. Cancer* 73:670–677.

Smit LA, Mozaffarian D, Willett W (2009). Review of fat and fatty acid requirements and criteria for developing dietary guidelines. *Ann. Nutr. Metab.* 55: 44–55.

Stern, N., Iqbal, N., Seshadri, P., et al. (2004). *Ann. Intern. Med.* 140, 778–785.

Storlien LH, Baur LA, Kriketos AD, Pan DA, Cooney GJ, Jenkins AB, Calvert GD, Campbell LV (1996). Dietary fats and insulin action. *Diabetologia* 39:621–631.

Storlien LH, Higgins JA, Thomas TC, Brown MA, Wang HQ, Huang XF, Else PL (2000). Diet composition and insulin action in animal models. *Br. J. Nutr.* 83:85–90.

Storlien LH, Huang XF, Lin S, Xin X, Wang HQ, Else PL (2001). Dietary fat subtypes and obesity. *World Rev. Nutr. Diet* 88:148–154.

Storlien LH, James DE, Burleigh KM, Chisholm DJ, Kraegen EW (1986). Fat feeding causes widespread in vivo insulin resistance, decreased energy expenditure, and obesity in rats. *Am. J. Physiol.* 251: 576–583.

Storlien LH, Jenkins AB, Chisholm DJ, Pascoe WS, Khouri S, Kraegen EW (1991). Influence of dietary fat composition on development of insulin resistance in rats. Relationship to muscle triglyceride and omega-3 fatty acids in muscle phospholipid. *Diabetes* 40:280–289.

Sullivan EL, Smith MS, Grove KL (2011). Perinatal exposure to high-fat diet programs energy balance, metabolism and behavior in adulthood. *Neuroendocrinology* 93:1-8.

Sumithran P, Prendergast LA, Delbridge E, Purcell K, Shulkes A, Kriketos A, Proietto J (2011). Long-term persistence of hormonal adaptations to weight loss. *N. Engl. J. Med.* 365(17):1597-1604.

Surwit RS, Kuhn CM, Cochrane C, McCubbin JA, Feinglos MN (1988). Diet-induced type II diabetes in C57BL/6J mice. *Diabetes* 37:1163-1167.

Takahashi M, Ikemoto S, Ezaki O (1999). Effect of the fat/carbohydrate ratio in the diet on obesity and oral glucose tolerance in C57BL/6J mice. *J. Nutr. Sci. Vitaminol.* 45:583–593.

Tamashiro KLK, terrillion CE, Hyun J, Koenig JI, Moran TH (2009). Prenatal stress or high-fat diet increases susceptibility to diet-induced obesity in rat offspring. *Diabetes* 58:1116-1125.

Taouis M, Dagou C, Ster C, Durand G, Pinault M, Delarue J (2002). N-3 Polynsaturated fatty acids prevent the defect of insuin receptor signaling muscle *Am. J. Physiol. Endocrinol. Metab.* 282:611-671.

Tsunoda N, Ikemoto S, Takahashi M, Maruyama K, Watanabe H, Goto N, Ezaki O (1998). High-monounsaturated fat diet-induced obesity and diabetes in C57BL/6J mice. *Metabolism* 47:724–730.

U.S. Department of Agriculture (1992). The food guide pyramid: a guide to daily food choices. Washington (DC): Center for Nutrition Policy and Promotion. Home and Garden Bulletin, nº 252.

Vessby B (2003). dietary fat, fatty acid composition in plasma and the metabolis syndrome. *Curr. Opin. Lipidol.* 14:15-19.

Volek J, Sharman M, Gómez A, Judelson D, Rubin M, Watson G, Sokmen B, Silvestre R, French D, Kraemer W (2004). Comparison of energy-restricted very low-carbohydrate and low-fat diets on weight loss and body composition in overweight men and women. *Nutr. Metab. (Lond)* 1(1):13.

Volek JS, Phinney SD, Forsythe CE, Quann EE, Wood RJ, Puglisi MJ, Kraemer WJ, Bibus DM, Fernandez ML, Feinman RD (2009). Carbohydrate restriction has a more favorable impact on the metabolic syndrome than a low fat diet. *Lipids* 44(4):297-309.

White PB, Ziegler KM, Swartz-Basile DA, Wang SS, Lillemoe KD, Pitt HA, Zyromski NJ (2012). Obesity, but not high-fat diet, promotes murine pancreatic cancer growth. *J Gastrointest Surg*. [Epub ahead of print] *Pub. Med. PMID*:22688418.

Willett WC, Sacks F, Trichopoulou A, Drescher G, Ferro-Luzzi A, Helsing E, Trichopoulos D (1995). Mediterranean diet pyramid: a cultural model for healthy eating. *Am. J .Clin. Nutr.* 61(6 Suppl):1402-1406.

Willett WC, Stampfer MJ, Colditz GA, Rosner BA, Hennekens CH, Speizer FE (1987). Dietary fat and the risk of breast cancer. *N. Engl. J. Med.* 316: 22-28.

Wing RR, Hill JO (2001). Successful weight loss maintenance. *Annu. Rev. Nutr.* 21:323–341.

Woods SC, alessio ADA, Tso P, Rushing PA, Clegg DJ, Benoit SC, Gotoh K, Liu M, Seeley RJ (2004). Consuption of a high-fat diet alters the homeostatic regulation of energy balance. *Physiology and Behavior* 83:573-578.

Woods SC, Seeley RJ, Rushing PA, D'Alessio D, Tso P (2003). A controlled high-fat diet induces an obese syndrome in rats. *Journal of Nutrition* 133:1081–1087.

Wu AH, Pike MC, Stram DO (1999). Meta-analysis: dietary fat intake, serum estrogen levels, and the risk of breast cancer. *J. Natl. Cancer Inst.* 91:529–534.

Yagoob P, Pala HS, Cortina-Borja M, Newaholme EA, Calder PC (2000). Encapsulated fish oil enriched in alpha-tocopherol alters plasma phospholipids and mononuclear cells fatty acid composition but not mononuclear cells function. *Eur. J. Clin. Invest.* 30(3):260-274.

Yancy WS, Olsen MK, Guyton JR, Bakst RP, Westman EC (2004). A low-carbohydrate, ketogenic diet versus a low-fat diet to treat obesity and hyperlipidemia: a randomized, controlled trial. *Ann. Intern. Med.* 140(10):769-777.

Yang ZH, Miyahara H, Takeo J, Katayama M (2012). Diet high in fat and sucrose induces rapid onset of obesity-related metabolic syndrome partly through rapid response of genes involved in lipogenesis, insulin signalling and inflammation in mice. *Diabetol. Metab. Syndr.* 4:32.

Zhang H, Chen X, Aravindakshan J, Ram Sairam M (2007). Changes in Adiponectin and Inflammatory Genes in Response to Hormonal Imbalances in Female Mice and Exacerbation of Depot Selective Visceral Adiposity by High-Fat Diet: Implications for Insulin Resistance. *Endocrinology* 148:5667-5679.

In: Low and High-Fat Diets: Myths vs. Reality
Editors: J. E. Ferreira and N. Muniz
ISBN: 978-1-62257-797-2

Chapter IV

Dietary Fat and Its Impact on Health: Analysis of Basic, Clinical and Epidemiological Evidence

Juan Guillermo Gormaz[1] and Marcia Erazo[2]
[1]Molecular and Clinical Pharmacology Program, Institute of Biomedical Sciences, Faculty of Medicine, University of Chile, Santiago, Chile
[2]Department of Nutrition and School of Public Health, Faculty of Medicine, University of Chile, Santiago, Chile

Abstract

Lipids are essential nutrients for life development and maintenance. However, due to the current worldwide epidemiological context, adverse health effects have been attributed to high-fat diets, without consider dietary lipid composition and total calorie intake. Epidemiological and clinical studies have shown strong association between dietary fat intake and cardiovascular disease and various types of cancer.

High- and low-fat diets, do not necessarily equate to high- or low-calorie diets. When analyzing the health effects of high or low fat diets with an excess of calories, it should be noted that whatever the effect attributable to dietary lipids, there are negative effects of a positive energy imbalance. Therefore, it is incorrect to refer to dietary fat's effects in terms of "high and low fat" diets. It is necessary to consider intrinsic food variables, as well as extrinsic dietary conditions, such as physiological status and environmental and genetic factors.

In post-epidemiological-transition populations, the health effects of the proportion, amount and type of dietary fat cannot be isolated. Interaction with other energetic nutrients, proteins and carbohydrates can significantly modulate the metabolism of lipids according to their proportions and origins in diet. Under certain conditions, all dietary lipid components can be harmful, favoring the development and progression of various diseases. However while the intake of some lipids is considered unhealthy in most cases, other lipids will promote diseases only under very specific circumstances. In the development of non-communicable chronic diseases, deterioration of tissue functionality derived from lipotoxicity is associated with several causes including oxidative stress, inflammation, cell death and uncontrolled proliferation. Lipotoxicity is mainly mediated by two major groups of fats, cholesterol derivatives and saturated free fatty acids. Low-fat diets with high-calorie content could have harmful effects due to an excess of circulating lipids derived from an endogenous lipogenesis derived from other energy nutrients, especially carbohydrates. The most important benefits of high-fat diets at population level are associated with marine omega-3 LCPUFA.

In conclusion the proportion of dietary fat is not the only variable to be considered when analyzing the lipid impact on health. The major type of fat in the diet, the proportions of different types of lipids and fatty acids families, the interaction with other nutrients and total calories consumed also primarily determines the effects that a high- or low-fat diet will have on health.

1. Introduction

Lipids, like all other nutrients, are essential for life development and maintenance. They are useful for fulfilling various physiological processes, including energy metabolism and immune system modulation, among others (Kaul, 2003; Gormaz et al., 2010; Tvrzicka et al., 2011; Molendi Coste et al., 2011; Hofmann, 2009). Lipids can be classified into two categories: essential and nonessential. The first group can only be derived from foods and the second, or non-essentials, can be synthesized by the organism. (Valenzuela et al., 2012).

Today science recognizes that it is incorrect to refer to dietary fat's effects in terms of "high and low fat", in the sense of the total proportion of these nutrients in food intake (Junker et al., 2001; Erkkilä et al., 2008; Stanley et al., 2012). Therefore, to evaluate the risks and benefits of dietary lipids, it is necessary to consider intrinsic food variables, as well as extrinsic dietary conditions, such as physiological status and environmental and genetic factors. This chapter will focus on analyzing the variables of greatest influence of the effects of dietary fat on human health, including requirements, lipid composition, intake levels, energy balance and interaction with other nutrients. In addition, it will address the relationship between dietary fat and toxic or beneficial effects of lipids, including the historical and epidemiological contexts that have established many myths associated with the consumption of these nutrients.

2. Biological Functions of Lipids

Dietary lipids, to a greater or lesser extent, must be considered nutrients essential to life, regardless of the current worldwide epidemiological context, which has attributed adverse health effects to high-fat diets, independent of their lipid composition and energy balance. Dietary lipids can be grouped into three main categories; fatty acids, sterols and terpenoids, which are widely associated with the effects of fats on human health.

Dietary fatty acids can be categorized into four major subgroups according to their different physiological roles apart from energy generation and storage: 1) trans (TFA), 2) saturated (SFA), 3) monounsaturated (MUFA) and polyunsaturated (PUFA) and 4) long chain polyunsaturated fatty acids (LCPUFA). The role of dietary TFA acids, other than energy production, remains unknown (Thompson et al., 2011). Saturated fatty acids possess many biological functions, including structural roles in biological membranes, waxes and sphingolipids (Tvrzicka et al., 2011). The MUFA and PUFA are also components of cell membranes. PUFA also can serve as precursors for LCPUFA (Tvrzicka et al., 2011). LCPUFA are divided into two major families: Omega-3 and Omega-6. Both families are very important components of cell membranes and are primarily responsible for the functionality of these structures which includes molecules transportation, signal transduction and conduction of nerve impulses among others (Valentine & Valentine, 2004). They also modulate energy metabolism, inflammatory responses, vascular physiology, and antioxidant-response regulation (Dyerberg & Bang, 1979; Gormaz et al., 2010; Tvrzicka et al., 2011; Rodrigo, 2012; González-Mañán et al., 2012).

The two LCPUFA are: 1) pre-formed LCPUFA that comes from diet and 2) endogenous LCPUFA which is derived from biosynthesis. The latter process depends on the availability of vegetal PUFA, essential components that cannot be biosynthesized by the human body (Gormaz et al., 2010). The major source of omega-6 LCPUFA comes from animal derived products, and omega-3 LCPUFA originate in some seafood as well as some fish oils. Western populations tend to have low omega-3 LCPUFA dietary intakes, and so, for them, the major source of these lipids is endogenous biosynthesis. However, this process is inefficient and limited in the human body, especially in western populations. In optimal conditions, it is barely enough to meet the minimum requirements. For example, biosynthesis of these lipids is insufficient during pregnancy, lactation and early life (Cunnane, 2003; González-Mañán et al., 2012) or in the presence of liver and metabolic disorders (Gormaz et al., 2010).

Dietary sterols can be divided into animal and plant sterols. Plant sterols have no known physiological role and their only effect is to inhibit intestinal cholesterol absorption by competition (Rocha et al., 2011). Animal sterols are derived from cholesterol, which has a structural function in biological membranes. Animal sterols include steroidal hormones and bile salts, which are involved in dietary fat absorption and the excretion of certain substances (Kaul, 2003; Hofmann, 2009).

Terpenoids are a large family of compounds derived from isoprenoid units of different length. Coexisting in this group are carotenoid pigments, tocopherols and other substances with essential roles, or indirect functions as precursors to other micronutrients. These lipids have no direct involvement in energy metabolism, but imbalances in dietary intake of terpenoids, especially synthetic terpenoids, can severely affect health-disease equilibrium. (Atkinson et al., 2008; Patrick, 2000).

3. Requirements and Energy Balance

Intake recommendations for each class of lipids and most nutrients vary according to developmental stage, physiological and pathological status, interaction with other nutrients, sex, lifestyle and many other genetic and environmental variables (Bidlack, 1996; Russell, 2007; Tsiaousi et al., 2008, Genton et al., 2010). This determines, in a complex manner, the overall effects of lipids on health-disease balances in humans and other animal species (Bidlack, 1996; Erkkila et al., 2008; Clayton et al., 2008).

It should be noted that only the determination of the recommended daily intake of each family of lipids, for each stage of human life, under optimum physiological, genetic and environmental conditions, is a challenge that is still far from resolved. The general consensus is that the current reference ranges are not well established (Cunnane, 2003).

The determination of the recommended intakes under suboptimal conditions and even in pathological stages has been recently discussed, and is increasingly becoming more relevant in current clinical practice (Tsiaousi et al., 2008).

Regardless of the status of requirements to consider, the recommendation of intake for the different groups of lipids and other nutrients will move in complex multi-dimensional intervals of variable amplitude, whose lower bounds (potential deficiencies) and upper bounds (toxicity) are dependent on multiple biological variables (Mercer, 1992), including all conditions mentioned above.

For non-essential lipids under physiological conditions, when energy requirements and supply of other nutrients are covered (that allow adequate endogenous lipogenesis without affecting other biological processes), the lowest value of the interval is zero (Cunnane, 2003).

Essential lipids (omega-3 and omega-6 families) have a lower bound greater than zero. It is difficult to determine accurately the lower limit given: 1) the complex interaction between essential PUFA precursors and the LCPUFA bioactive products, 2) the competition between the two families for the same metabolic pathways and 3) the interdependence between the two omega families for the maintenance of physiological homeostasis (Gormaz et al., 2010; Molendi-Coste et al., 2011).

The upper level has a relatively wide range of safety, where no important biological effects arising from the increase in these nutrients will occur. Exceeding this range, non-essential and essential lipids will have different effects.

Non-essential lipids will have negative impact. Essential lipids, especially the omega-3 LCPUFA, begin to exert more positive effects. Those effects are associated with the prevention of chronic non-communicable diseases (NCD), particularly cardiovascular desesases (Roth & Harris, 2010) and are proportional to the ingested dose up to an upper limit, prior to toxicity, mainly related to oxidative stress (Di Nunzio et al., 2011).

This limit also will depend on many other variables such as the interaction with omega-6 fatty acids and other nutrients (Cunnane, 2003; Gómez Candela et al., 2011).

Chronic effects on health, positive and negative, associated with consumption of dietary fat under ideal conditions, i.e., "young healthy adults with optimal genetic and environmental conditions", is primarily based on four interrelated key variables: 1) total fat intake, 2) total caloric intake, 3) the proportion of each group of lipids in total fat and 4) the interaction with other dietary nutrients. When all other nutrients are balanced, excessive fat intake, despite maintaining an optimal composition of lipids, can determine an excessive calorie intake with the subsequent development of obesity (Bessesen et al., 2008).

A low dietary fat intake will be associated with deficiencies only if there is a total energy deficit or if the diet does not cover the minimum requirement of essential lipids (Cunnane, 2003). In addition, under ideal conditions both an excess of total fat intake and a significant reduction of dietary lipids may affect the physiology when a diet has imbalances between the different groups of lipids (Molendi Coste et al., 2011; Gómez Candela et al., 2011). In real conditions, changes in total fat intake accompany changes in the intake of other nutrients and likewise changes in the proportions of different groups of fat.

High- and low-fat diets, do not necessarily equate to high- or low-calorie diets. Thus, a normocaloric diet can be high or low in fat, compensating for the lipid changes with variations in other macronutrients (Gay et al., 1977). Therefore, when analyzing the health effects of high or low fat diets with an excess of calories, it should be noted that whatever the effect attributable to dietary lipids, the negative effects of a positive energy imbalance can: 1) attenuate or mask the potential benefits of healthy fats and 2) potentiate the harmful effects of unhealthy fats. However, most of high-fat diets are also hypercaloric and the consumption of diets with both properties is highly prevalent in regions that already experience the epidemiological transition (which have high obesity and NCD rates). Therefore it is difficult to study the effects of both properties separately, especially at population level (Odermatt, 2012).

Finally, it is necessary to consider that many of the harmful effects of low-fat diets with high-calorie content may be attributable to an excess of circulating lipids derived from an endogenous lipogenesis coupled with the oxidation of other energy nutrients, especially carbohydrates (Hellerstein, 2002), as shown below. In addition, genetic conditions, such as familial dyslipidemia, may account for an excess of circulating lipids that are harmful to the body (Vuorio et al., 1997), even with normocaloric low fat diet consumption.

4. History of the Relationship between Dietary Fat and Balance Disorders of Health and Disease

From the origins of medicine, several centuries before Christ, it was suggested that there was some degree of association between obesity and an increased prevalence of several chronic pathologies, especially diabetes and cardiovascular diseases, hinting that the cause of this relationship would be lifestyle, including dietary fat and overfeeding (Haslam, 2007).

Given the complexity of the biochemistry and molecular link between obesity and type 2 diabetes mellitus, it was not until the late 20th century that scientists began to understand how dietary lipid inadequacies stimulate the development and progression of insulin resistance (Kusunoki et al., 1995), depending on lipotoxicity mechanisms linked to inflammation and oxidative stress (Houstis et al., 2006). The same happened in the association with cancer, where the complexity of the link with dietary fat is even greater (Stemmer et al., 2012). It has been much easier to identify the relationship between dietary fats and pathologies associated with lipid accumulation, as in the instance of nonalcoholic fatty liver disease (Gormaz & Rodrigo, 2009). Finally, the possible link between lipid abnormalities and neurodegenerative diseases is still being investigated, with current research existing solely at the molecular level (Fantini & Yahi, 2010). In these diseases a strong clinical and epidemiological evidence to show any relationship between the etiology and the fat composition of the diet are still unknown (Solfrizzi et al., 2011).

From a cardiovascular standpoint, only since the early 20th century the biomedical sciences could begin to determine how over-consumption of calories, mainly related with dietary fat, is associated with a series of biochemical alterations in the affected tissues, including blood. These alterations were correlated to the development of atherosclerosis, forging the concept of dyslipidemia, which in that time was primarily associated with total cholesterol levels (Adler, 1914).

After World War II several studies were conducted to determine the etiology of chronic cardiovascular diseases, in response to the special interest in the effect of dietary fats on dyslipidemias (Gofman et al., 1950). A strong association was found which led to an intensive search aimed at determining which families within the fats were mostly involved in nutritional-origin blood lipid profile changes, as well as distinguishing important differences in the level of unsaturation of fatty acids (Anderson et al., 1957). From that time and for the next 20 years a large number of studies that associated certain specific lipid components with atheroma development and subsequent cardiovascular mortality were published (McGandy et al., 1967; Keys, 1968). Also, cases such as the monounsaturated erucic acid (20:1 n-9), originally syndicated as a major atherogenic component of certain oils for human consumption, arose from this period. This theory was later discarded, according to evidence from other studies (Becker & Bruce, 1985). However, this controversy was key in proving that rats and mice, in many cases, do not provide good models for studying lipid metabolism in humans (Esteve et al., 2005).

In the early 70's, most of the evidence gathered showed that high fat diets were deleterious to health. However, parallel studies demonstrated that some Eskimo populations with high fat consumption had a low prevalence of cardiovascular disease (Dyerberg et al., 1975), an association that was not observed in urbanized Eskimos, questioning an old myth. It was originally speculated that, given the known association between fat and energy metabolism (Stewart et al., 1931) the level of physical activity and the continuous exposure to low temperatures, would allow the Eskimo population to offset the effects of a high fat diet. But this could no longer explain the low prevalence of cardiovascular disease. The Eskimo native diet have had high levels of omega-3 LCPUFA, EPA (20:5 n-3) and DHA (22:6 n-3), and low levels of omega-6 LCPUFA; AA (20:4 n-6) and DGLA (20:3 n-6), a condition which proved to be protective against cardiovascular disease. Omega-6 LCPUFA and its vegetal precursor, linoleic acid (18:2 n-6) (major component of vegetable oils such as soybean oil, sunflower oil and corn oil), may indirectly promote a pro-thrombotic state through the pathway of the prostaglandins (Pellufo et al., 1963; Anggård & Samuelsson, 1965; Weeks et al., 1969). The simultaneous discovery of the ability of EPA to modulate the pathway of prostaglandins, (Luckner & Renz, 1975), began to dispel doubts.

In the early 80's, there was substantial evidence to support the theory that high intake of marine omega-3; EPA and DHA (but not of omega-3 from vegetable origin, derived from Chia oil and Linseed oil among other sources) was primarily responsible for the low prevalence of cardiovascular disease in native Eskimo populations (Dyerberg & Bang, 1979). During this time, from the standpoint of public health, scientists began to be realize that determining the lipid composition of dietary fat is just as important as establishing the amount of total fat consumed by a population (Rifkind, 1984). Unfortunately, at present, the effects of high fat diets tend to be analyzed as a whole, without mentioning other important variables to public health, such as the presence of different types of lipids in the diet (Stanley et al., 2012).

5. Mechanisms of Lipotoxicity in the Development of Non-communicable Chronic Diseases

Lipotoxicity is defined as a condition that accounts for the pathologic modifications in non-adipose tissues, such as muscle, pancreas and liver tissues, due to the toxic effects of an alteration in lipid homeostasis (Chavez & Summers, 2010; Wanders et al., 2010; Khan et al., 2010). Deterioration of tissue functionality derived from lipotoxicity is associated with several causes including oxidative stress, inflammation, cell death and uncontrolled proliferation (Gormaz & Rodrigo, 2009; Chavez & Summers, 2010; Wanders et al 2010; Stemmer et al 2012). Regarding the type of fat, it is also necessary to distinguish between the different lipid groups because the intensity of lipotoxic effect and mechanisms of action of each of these lipids are different. In addition, the energy intake derived from other nutrients, particularly digestible carbohydrates, can induce indirect lipotoxic effects, since the surplus of these substances is converted into lipids (Hellerstein, 2002).

5.1. Lipotoxicity Directly Associated with Lipid Nutrients

Lipotoxicity is mainly mediated by two major groups of fats, cholesterol derivatives and free fatty acids (Han et al, 2012). However, under certain conditions, other lipids such as ceramides (a structural component of sphingolipids) and some isoprenoids derivates, could seriously affect cell functionality (Patrick, 2000; Summers, 2006).

Paradoxically, the terminal effects of lipotoxicity in tissues are related to two opposite conditions: cell death (Nolan & Larter, 2009) and uncontrolled proliferation (Stemmer et al., 2012), both of which possess a strong immune component. The origin of this immune component lies in the relationship between alterations of intracellular lipid metabolism and the induction of pro-inflammatory states. The progression of these states interferes with immunological modulation of the entire tissue and could even cause inflammatory alterations at the systemic level (Gormaz & Rodrigo, 2009). The mechanisms that determine the terminal effects of lipotoxicity in the different tissues are extraordinarily complex, currently poorly understood and still under intense study.

Cholesterol and its derivatives were first associated with the development of vascular atheroma. This complex phenomenon is related to an alteration in plasmatic lipid transport and the subsequent abnormal activation of innate immune system in blood vessel endothelium, with heavy participation of oxidative stress and inflammation (Molina & Rodrigo, 2009). In fact, for decades the lipotoxicity of sterols has been recognized as a major pathophysiological origin of atherosclerosis at the epidemiological level (Rifkind, 1984). Lipotoxicity is associated with both cholesterol and some of its oxidized derivatives, mainly of oxysterols of endogenous (Brown & Jessup, 2009) and dietary origin (Wielkoszynski et al., 2006).

In vascular tissue, it has been proven that the sterol accumulation in immune cells is an essential early stage in the development of pathological changes in the endothelium (Molina & Rodrigo, 2009). For example, in the vascular endothelium, the accumulation of cholesterol and oxysterols in macrophages, leads to the transformation of these leukocytes into primary foam cells. This phenomenon promoting a cascade of chronic inflammatory events strongly associated with the hardening and clogging of the arteries (Vainio & Ikonen, 2003). Atherosclerosis is highly associated with total cholesterol circulating levels, especially the low density lipoprotein cholesterol-cholesterol (LDL-cholesterol) fraction, and the degree of oxidation of these lipoprotein, but also with cholesterol carrier molecules, responsible for the efflux of sterols from the inside to the outside of the cells (Yvan-Charvet et al., 2010). However, the effect of intracellular cholesterol excess in immune cells remains unclear. There is no conclusive information about molecular mechanisms that trigger the activation of foam cells, with the subsequent expression of pro-inflammatory responses including cellular infiltration, proliferation and oxidative stress. It has been reported that a decrease in macrophage cell membranes fluidity (associated with increases in intracellular cholesterol content), induces hypersensitivity of some immunological receptors, favoring the activation of these cells (Yvan et al., 2010). It has also been postulated that some classical mechanisms of the immune response, associated with cellular surface receptors, could be being activated by excess cholesterol and oxysterols through different pathways. These mechanisms induce an expression of intracellular inflammatory mediators linked to the activation of macrophages (Seneviratne et al., 2012).

More recently, research derived from cellular studies of neurodegenerative diseases has proposed a novel model of lipotoxicity linked to cholesterol. In this model it was suggest that a high concentration of cholesterol in the cell membranes interacts with sphingolipids, influencing the pathological changes in protein conformation related to the formation of amyloid bodies (Fantini et al., 2010). When these conformational changes exceed a certain threshold, it may become important in inducing inflammation, through dependent and independent oxidative stress pathways (Gormaz & Rodrigo, 2009; Sardi et al., 2011). This form of cholesterol lipotoxicity, may also participate, to some degree, in the induction of inflammation in the foam cells, although at present little is known about that.

Unlike the toxic effects of animal sterols, mainly associated with cardiovascular disease and cholelithiasis, the free fatty acids (FFA)-induced lipotoxicity, is a more widespread process, with supporting evidence of their involvement in multiple pathophysiological models. In addition to cardiovascular diseases (Pilz & März, 2008) and nonalcoholic fatty liver disease (Gormaz & Rodrigo, 2009), these lipotoxic agents have been associated with insulin resistance and type 2 diabetes mellitus (Chavez & Summers, 2009; Thompson et al., 2011), chronic kidney disease (Nosadini & Tonolo, 2011), obesity (Bessesen et al., 2008) and neurodegenerative diseases (Ramesh et al., 2010). The fatty acid-induced lipotoxicity affects cell viability mainly through direct and indirect association with oxidative stress, but also by parallel mechanisms, that favor cellular alterations (Chavez & Summers, 2010; Wanders et al., 2010).

One of the most studied mechanisms of lipotoxicity associated with fatty acids, with an independent oxidative stress origin, is the ability of an excess of saturated and trans FFA to conform calcium salts aggregates in the endoplasmic reticulum (ER) (Gormaz & Rodrigo, 2009). This process alone could generate the disruption of this organelle if a rapid and massive accumulation of saturated and trans FFA occurs. However, slight increases of these intermediaries for extended periods of time can damage the cell since they affect protein metabolism, inhibiting the cellular capacity to properly "fold" proteins (Puri et al., 2008). The accumulation of misfolded proteins in the ER not only favors the direct disruption of this organelle. This phenomenon could also induce futile protein repair cycles that increase cellular energy expenditure, causing a decreasing of cellular reducing equivalents with antioxidants functions such as reduced glutathione (GSH), and simultaneously promotes the enzymatic generation of oxidative stress (Malhotra & Kaufman, 2007). Abnormal protein folding in ER originates in a membranous process whose first pathological manifestation is the ER membranes fluidity decrease. This effect is also attributable to an excess of cholesterol. Therefore, we could be facing a similar pathologic mechanism among neurodegenerative diseases and other NCD. Moreover, disruption of the endoplasmic reticulum, independent of the pathway, triggers a permeability of calcium into the cytoplasm, a condition associated with oxidative stress, apoptosis and inflammation (Bogeski et al.,

2011). The monounsaturated and polyunsaturated free fatty acids have a much lower affinity for calcium and in general are more efficiently metabolized by the human body (Li et al, 2009; Nolan & Larte, 2009; Trauner et al., 2010; Cho et al., 2012).

Other cytotoxic pathways associated with fatty acids lipotoxicity are related to a direct and indirect induction of oxidative stress. Indirectly, a pathological increase of FFA can induce oxidative stress by: 1) triggering a structural and functional alteration of mitochondria, 2) activating the cytochrome P450 monoxygenases system and 3) inducing the synthesis of ceramides (Gormaz & Rodrigo, 2009). Direct FFA lipotoxicity induction is associated with the ability of free LCPUFA and PUFA to induce and propagate lipid peroxidation (Di Nunzio et al., 2011). These mediators are more prone to oxidation than the esterified fatty acids forms located in phospholipids or fat vacuoles, because the latter are part of biological membranes and lipid vacuoles. The latter structures have a great antioxidant protection depending on multiple mechanisms (Atkinson et al., 2008; Cederbaum, 2009). Indirect lipotoxic effects of LCPUFA are related to imbalances in the omega-3:omega-6 ratio (Gómez Candela et al., 2011), that has been suggested to be 1:1 (Molendi-Coste et al., 2011). A non-balanced increase in the omega-6 family can be pro-inflammatory (Khan et al., 2010; Gómez Candela et al., 2011) while an imbalance towards the omega-3 LCPUFA family, though much less likely in post-epidemiological transition populations, may affect coagulation (Dyerberg & Bang., 1979).

5.2. Indirect Lipotoxicity Induced by Intake of Non-lipidic Energetic Nutrients

In post-epidemiological-transition populations, the health effects of the proportion, amount and type of dietary fat cannot be isolated. Interaction with other energetic nutrients, proteins and carbohydrates can significantly modulate the metabolism of lipids according to their proportions and origins in diet. The study of the interaction of dietary fat intake with total protein and different protein sources has recently started to become relevant, suggesting that the protein source may influence the development and progression of lipotoxicity (Tovar & Torres, 2009) However, more studies, are needed to establish an association. Conversely, the study of interactions between dietary fat and the level of digestible carbohydrate in diet has been of special interest for a long time. (McGandy et al., 1967).

At population level, a low dietary intake of non-healthy fats, coupled with a high level of digestible carbohydrates, may be more harmful than the reverse combination, especially in individuals with genetic tendency towards insulin resistance (Bloch, 2005; Neuschwander-Tetri, 2010; Kuipers et al., 2011). The mechanism would be associated with the body's ability to store excess consumed carbohydrates in the form of fat, mainly SFA, whose harmful effects are indistinguishable from the same compounds of dietary origin (Hellerstein, 2002). Conversely, the human body is incapable of transforming the various components of fats (except glycerol) into carbohydrates, making it difficult for a high-fat and low-digestible carbohydrate diet to be a source of high glucose plasma levels. Since physiological levels of glucose are essential to life, in the high-fat, carbohydrate free Eskimos diet, this nutrient comes from dietary protein (Schaefer, 1968).

Dietary carbohydrate excess favors its anaerobic metabolism in the liver, generating large amounts of the metabolic intermediate acetyl-CoA, a substrate that is removed coupled with saturated lipid biosynthesis in a process that biochemically inhibits mitochondrial oxidation of fatty acids (Neuschwander-Tetri, 2010). This metabolic condition favors the presence of saturated FFA in the body with the subsequent pathological effects (Trauner et al., 2010; Kuipers et al., 2011). The deleterious effects of low-fat diets, with high digestible carbohydrate content, can also be a risk factor for individuals with familial dyslipidemia antecedents (Bloch, 2005). Conversely, given the natural tendency of the human body to obtain energy first from carbohydrates and later from fats, high-fat but low-carbohydrate diets will promote the energetic metabolism of the latter, and the subsequent oxidation of a fraction of the fats in order to cover the maintenance requirements (Cahill, 2006). This condition inhibits the lipogenesis, driving acetyl-CoA (derived from the degradation of nutrients) to cellular respiration and not to fatty acids biosynthesis, in order to prevent futile cycles of degradation and de-novo synthesis of fatty acids. Thus, in these diets, the dietary fatty acids that exceed the requirements are a mixture of SFA, MUFAs and PUFAs with a less lipotoxic effect than SFA alone (Trauner et al., 2010). In addition, MUFA and PUFA can protect against the SFA-induced lipotoxicity (Nolan & Larter, 2009; Cho et al; 2012).

A high-fat and low-carbohydrate diet could be associated with a low intake of cholesterol, SFA and pro-inflammatory omega-6 fatty acids, as in a diet whose lipid fraction comes mostly from certain vegetable oils (mainly olive and avocado). These diets could be healthier from the perspective of the familial dyslipidemia, than diets high in carbohydrates and low in fat, as previously discussed.

6. Clinical Effects of Lipids in Dietary Fat

Under certain conditions, all dietary lipid components can be harmful, favoring the development and progression of various diseases. However, as we discussed above, while the intake of some lipids is considered unhealthy in most cases, other lipids will promote diseases only under very specific circumstances, having a neutral and/or beneficial effect in most cases.

Among those lipids whose consumption should be limited in different degrees in post-epidemiological transition populations, would be TFA, SFA, animal sterols, and possibly the omega-6 family. In parallel, the local existence of genetic factors in some populations and individuals can significantly modulate the beneficial and harmful effects associated to the consumption of certain types of fats. That is the case of the population of North Karelia, who presented high cardiovascular risks due to a high familial-dyslipidemias prevalence (Vuorio et al., 1997).

Significant amounts of dietary TFA are of industrial origin, corresponding mostly to molecules that are not found in nature (Thompson et al., 2011), and unknown to the human physiology, resulting in the absence of specific metabolic pathways. Natural TFA comes only from ruminant products, foods that only have small amounts of specific isomers of microbial origin, whose intake in these quantities would not be associated with harmful effects (Thompson et al., 2011). SFA and cholesterol are not essential nutrients, and are efficiently biosynthesized by the human body, and given their potential lipotoxic effects, their intake should be reduced (Nolan & Larte., 2009; Yvan-Charvet et al., 2010). Omega-6 LCPUFA are essential to physiology. However in spite of their beneficial health effects, a high intake of these fatty acids and their PUFA precursors, not compensated with an equivalent consumption of omega-3, may promote pro-inflammatory conditions (Khan et al., 2010; Molendi Coste et al., 2011; Gómez Candela et al., 2011), very favorable for the development and progression of NCD. Given the large amounts of omega-6 fatty acids and small amounts of omega-3 LCPUFA currently present in most diets of the post-epidemiological transition countries, it is preferable to limit, as far as possible, the omega-6 intake.

The potential effects of MUFA and PUFA on health may be positive or negative, depending on a set of variables such as level of intake, the fat matrix in which they were ingested, the level of oxidation, and the pathophysiological status of the consumer. From this perspective, any excess of fat can contribute to obesity, although the consumption of LCPUFA, especially omega-3 of marine origin, have the ability to induce the β-oxidation of fatty acids, partially offsetting the promoting effect of obesity, that has an over-intake of total lipids (Gormaz et al., 2010). However, these lipids, and other PUFA in lesser extent, could aggravate a condition of severe oxidative stress (Di Nunzio et al., 2011), for example, in patients with steatohepatitis (Gormaz and Rodrigo, 2009).

The MUFA and PUFA are better metabolic substrates for the human body than TFA and SFA. Therefore unsaturated FFA have a smaller half-life than saturated FFA which substantially reduces their potential lipotoxic effects in pathologies related with lipid-accumulation (Li et al 2009; Trauner et al., 2010; Cho et al., 2012), and further provides a protective effect against induced lipotoxicity by SFA (Nolan & Larter, 2009; Cho et al., 2012). Moreover, both MUFA and PUFA have a lower affinity for calcium than SFA (see above) and are consequently less toxic. On the other hand, the high intake of MUFA, in the absence of appreciable amounts of other fatty acids, usually derivates from dietary regimes with significant contributions of vegetable oils such as olive or avocado oil which are both rich in bioactive compounds and have antioxidant and anti-inflammatory properties. (Pérez-Martínez et al., 2011).

The most important benefits of high-fat diets at population level are associated with marine omega-3 LCPUFA, whose intake in large quantities has been considered the main determinant of a low prevalence of cardiovascular disease in Eskimo populations (Dyerberg & Bang, 1979). When these populations are subjected to western diets, low in omega-3 LCPUFA with a greater presence of other fats as well as high amounts of carbohydrates, the Eskimos start to show early metabolic alterations, including insulin resistance, a characteristic trait of developed countries, (Schaefer, 1968). At the epidemiological level, it has been demonstrated that Western populations with higher intakes of omega-3 LCPUFA have lower cardiovascular risk (primary and secondary), than populations with low intake of these lipids (Roth & Harris, 2010). At the biochemical level, clinical effects of omega-3 LCPUFA are usually associated with several mechanisms, including stabilization of biological cell membranes, inhibition of platelet aggregation, anti-inflammatory properties, improving antioxidant capacity and the optimization of energetic metabolism, among others (Bang & Dyerberg, 1979; Valentine & Valentine, 2004; Gormaz et al., 2010; Tvrzicka et al., 2011; Rodrigo, 2012).

Possible benefits of consumption of omega-3 LCPUFA in the prevention of NCD, other than cardiovascular disease and fatty liver disease (Parker et al., 2012), have yet to be demonstrated from the epidemiological perspective, requiring new and more robust studies, to establish a more solid association (Fassett et al., 2010; Wu et al., 2012; Ortega et al., 2012; Gerber et al., 2012).

Finally, it is important to consider that the benefits of a high omega-3 LCPUFA diet may be completely masked by high concentrations of environmental pollutants, especially mercury in seafood (Guallar et al., 2002). However, it has been shown that this masking is only relevant in cases of high mercury exposure, because the positive effects on the cardiovascular system with a high consumption of seafood, rich in DHA and low in mercury, far outweigh the negative effects (Roth & Harris, 2010). From this perspective, it is important to increase the consumption of seafood, rich in omega-3 LCPUFA and low in mercury and other pollutants, such as fatty fish, pelagic and farmed, from the southern Pacific Ocean and the east coast of the North Pacific Ocean, primarily salmonids, mackerel, herring, sardines and whitefish.

7. Epidemiological and Clinical Evidence of the Role of Dietary Fat on the Increased Risk of Non-Communicable Diseases

There have been many epidemiological and clinical studies aimed to determine the association between consumption of dietary fat and various types of chronic non-communicable diseases. As observational epidemiologic studies are subject to bias, especially memory, selection and confusion, besides existing scientific literature that presents diverse conflicting information, it was decided to include in this chapter, only meta-analysis of prospective cohort studies and randomized controlled clinical trials, for being the most robust designs when establishing causal inference. Associations with cardiovascular disease and cancer are the only ones that present strong evidence.

7.1. Meta-analysis of Studies on Cardiovascular Disease

Schwingshackl et al. in 2011, published a meta-analysis that studied the effect of monounsaturated fatty acids on cardiovascular risk factors (Schwingshackl et al., 2011). In that publication, the authors note that the pooled estimates of the effects of a diet high in monounsaturated fatty acids vs. a diet low in MUFA on the weight of individuals was -0.82 kg (95% CI -1.87 to 0.22). However, post hoc analysis showed that body weight reduction was significantly more pronounced after a diet rich in monounsaturated fatty acids when compared with a low fat diet [average decrease: -1.71 kg (95%: -3.41 to -0.02), P = 0.05]. It was also observed an average decrease of -1.94 kg (95% CI -3.72 to 0.17) fat mass, which was statistically significant (p = 0.03), compared with diets high in MUFA. No effects on waist circumference when comparing both types of diets were observed. When they analyzed the effect of diets on serum lipids, no significant differences between the high content of monounsaturated fatty acids with low MUFA: total cholesterol were observed [average decrease: -1.33 mg / dl (95% CI: - 4.45 to 1.78), p = 0.40], LDL [MD: -0.85 mg / dl (95% CI -4.86 to 3.17), p = 0.68], HDL cholesterol [DP: 0.95 mg / dl (95% CI -0.88 to 2.79), p = 0.31] and TG [DP: -6.30 mg / dl (95% - 14.24 to 1.64), p = 0.12].The pressure effects were significantly lower for individuals who consumed diets high in MUFA [MD: -1.15 mm Hg

(95% CI -1.96 to -0.34), p = 0.005]. There was no statistically significant effect on C - reactive protein.

In 2011, Nordmann et al. published a study comparing the effect of the Mediterranean diet and low fat diets on the modification of cardiovascular risk factors (Nordmann et al., 2011). The investigators founded that individuals consuming Mediterranean diet for two years, had higher average changes in body weight (-2.2 kg; 95% CI:- 3.9 to- 0.6), body mass index (-0.6 kg/m^2; 95% CI: - 1 to -0.1), systolic blood pressure (-1.7 mm Hg; 95% CI: -3.3 to -0.05), diastolic blood pressure (-1.5 mm Hg; 95% CI: -2.1 to -0.8), fasting plasma glucose (-3.8 mg/dL, 95% CI: -7 to -0.6), total cholesterol (-7.4 mg/dL; 95% CI: -10.3 to -4.4), and high-sensitivity C-reactive protein (- 1.0 mg/L; 95% CI: -1.5 to -0.5). Nevertheless, is important to take into account that some methodological bias was included in these studies. For instance, participants in Mediterranean groups received individual programs, motivational interviews, educational sessions, and increased their physical activity, that could help to explain the changes observed.

Another meta-analysis conducted by Ralston et.al, demonstrated that the consumption of low-fat dairy food, is a protective factor of elevated blood pressure (RR: 0.84; 95% CI: 0.74 to 0.95) (Ralston et al., 2012).

Although in previous studies, the association with different diets is well documented, the relationship between saturated fat intake and cardiovascular disease is still uncertain. Siri-Tarino et al. published in 2010 an article that included 21 cohort studies, following around 348,000 individuals, during 5-23 years (Siri-Tarino et al., 2010). After the estimation of polled relative risks, the authors concluded that the evidence does not support the hypothesis that the consumption of saturated fat is associated with an increased risk of coronary heart disease (pooled RR: 1.07; 95% CI: 0.96 to 1.19; P = 0.22), stroke (PRR: 0.81; 95% CI: 0.62 to 1.05; P = 0.11) and cardiovascular disease (1.00; 95% CI: 0.89 to 1.11; P = 0.95). The results did not vary when controlled for age, sex, and study quality. The authors discuss about dietary methods used to assess fat intake, and declare that 24H questionnaires are prone to produce measurement errors, and Food Frequency Questionnaires reflects better the consumption of an individual, and are currently being used in large epidemiological studies. They also state that results suggest publication bias. Studies where significant associations are demonstrated tend to be accepted for publication, instead of studies without association. As studies with null associations are not published and not included in this meta-analysis, is possible that the pooled RR estimation could be even closer than null hypothesis.

These conclusions were previously presented by Skeaff and Miller in 2009 (Skeaff & Miller, 2009), in a meta-analysis of cohort studies of total fat and coronary heart disease (CHD). Investigators demonstrated that the intake of total fat is not associated with CHD mortality and event (PRR mortality: 0.94 (95% CI 0.74–1.18, p = 0.583); PRR event: 0.93, 95% CI 0.84–1.03, p = 0.177). Even, when a 5% increase in total fat and total energy intake was used for the analyses, no significant association was observed. Saturated fatty acids, are neither associated with CHD mortality (PRR: 1.14 (95% CI 0.82–1.60, p = 0.431) and events (PRR: 0.93, 95% CI: 0.83–1.05, p = 0.269), furthermore, null association remained stable with a 5% increase in saturated fatty acid intake. Nevertheless, trans fatty acid consumption is strongly associated with CHD mortality (PRR: 1.32; 95% CI 1.08–1.61, p=0.006) and event (PRR: (RR 1.25, 95% CI 1.07–1.46, p = 0.007).

Another type of analysis has been focused on the effects of low-carbohydrates and low-fat diets. Nordman et al. analyzed in 2006 five clinical trials comparing the effects of these two types of diets without energy restriction (Nordman et al., 2006). Individuals assigned to low-fat diets, showed a remarked decrease in total cholesterol (Mean difference: - (8.9 mg/dL [0.23 mmol/L]; 95% CI, 3.1-14.3 mg/dL [0.08-0.37 mmol/L]) and low-density lipoprotein cholesterol values (Mean difference: -5.4 mg/dL [0.14 mmol/L]; 95% CI, 1.2-10.1) mg/dL [0.03-0.26 mmol/L]). On the other hand, patients with low-carbohydrate diets exhibit more weight loss at month 6 (–3.3 kg; 95% CI: −5.3 to −1.4 kg), difference that no longer persisted after 12 months, same for high-density lipoprotein cholesterol. No difference for blood pressure was observed.

7.2. Meta-analysis of Studies in Cancer

7.2.1. Breast Cancer

Few cohort studies have provided data of fat consumption and breast cancer. In a recent meta-analysis including different epidemiological studies, concluded that cohort studies show a significant (but weak) association between polyunsaturated fatty acids and breast cancer (PRR: 1.091, 95% CI: 1.001 to 1.184), especially in post-menopausal women (total fat PRR: 1.042, 95%CI: 1.013 to 1.073) and PUFA intake (PRR: 1.22, 95% CI: 1.08 to 1.381), nevertheless, in pre-menopausal women total fat and PUFA seems to prevent breast cancer (PRR total fat: (0.973, 95% CI: 0.935; 1.013; and PUFA PRR: 0.943, 95% CI: 0.808 to 1.100) (Turner, 2011). The author states that high fat consumption is associated with higher levels of estradiol that has been pointed out as increasing the risk of breast cancer through different mechanisms. Perhaps the most important reflection that the researcher discusses is the importance of the change in the ratio of poly-unsaturated n-3 to n-6. Nowadays, the ratio of n-6: n-3 PUFAs ranges from < 20–30:1, the traditional range is 1–2:1, contributing with an increase in breast cancer incidence.

7.2.2. Prostate Cancer

A meta-analysis published in 2004 that included 37 prospective cohort studies and 4 clinical trials, evaluated the association between diet and prostate cancer and concluded that the evidence is inconclusive in demonstrating the association between meat, dairy products, fat consumption and prostate cancer. Authors discuss that these inconsistences may be due to methodological issues such as bias, sample size and dietary evaluation (Dagnelie et al., 2004).

7.2.3. Ovarian Cancer

In 2001, a meta-analysis including 8 observational studies was published (Hunchareck et al., 2001). In the article, the authors concluded that a high fat diet is associated with an increase in the risk of having ovarian cancer (Pooled RR: 1.24; 95% CI = 1.07–1.43). At the same time, diet with high saturated fat content is also significant, increasing the risk of developing ovarian cancer in a 20% of the women (PRR: 1.20; 95% CI = 1.04–1.39), being those who eat a diet rich in animal fat, the ones that have the highest risks (PRR: 1.70; 95% CI = 1.43–2.03).

Conclusion and Suggestions

In conclusion, there is now clear scientific evidence, at various levels, which shows that the proportion of dietary fat is not the only variable to be considered when analyzing the lipid impact on health. The major type of fat in the diet, the proportions of different types of lipids and fatty acids families, the interaction with other nutrients and total calories consumed also primarily determines the effects that a high- or low-fat diet will have on health. Finally the interaction between food, genetic factors and environmental conditions chiefly associated with lifestyle, ultimately modulates the effects of nutrition on health at population level.

In this scenario, the nutritional management of the fat portion of the diet at the individual level is a complex issue. At population level, the issue is even more complex, requiring large-scale studies to establish recommendations and set policy. These studies should consider not only clinical factors, but should also include analysis of the costs associated with the prevalence of chronic non-communicable diseases (including obesity), considering the diet-attributable fraction, especially weighing the effect of fat, carbohydrate digestibility and level of daily calorie intake. The ultimate goal should therefore be to set up, at individual and population levels, the acquisition of healthy lifestyles. At the level of dietary management of fats, consider the following suggestions: 1) substantially raise the intake of healthy fats such as omega-3 LCPUFAs EPA and DHA while simultaneously decreasing other less healthy polyunsaturated lipids and 2) Replace the maximum dietary animal sterols, TFA and SFA with plant sterols and monounsaturated fatty acids, preferring fats sources rich in bioactive components, for example vegetable oils including, but not limited to, olive or avocado oil (Figure 1).

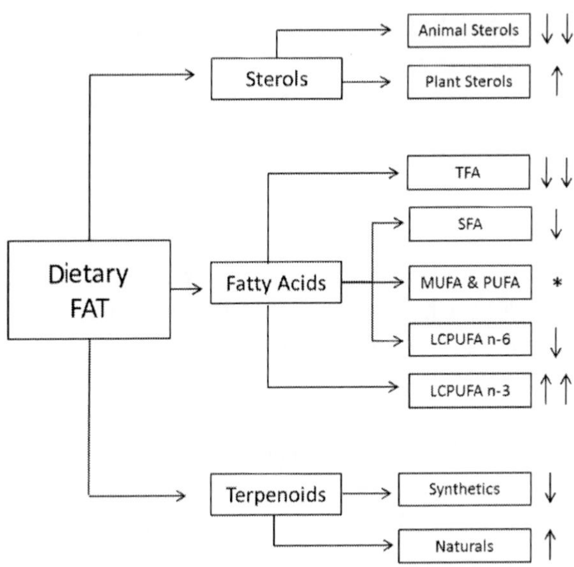

Figure 1. Preliminary recommendation of nutritional intervention aimed at changing the major lipid components of the diet based on current evidence. * Modular dose preferably through vegetable oils rich in monounsaturated and bioactive compounds and moderate vegetable n-6 PUFA (olive and avocado among others), always considering not exceed the total intake of calories in the diet. Abbreviations: TFA, trasn fatty acids, SFA, saturated fatty acids, MUFA, monounsaturated fatty acids, PUFA, polyunsaturated fatty acids, LCPUFA, long chain polyunsaturated fatty acids, n-3, omega-3, n-6, omega-6.

References

Adler I. Studies in experimental atherosclerosis: a preliminary report. *J Exp Med.* 1914;20:93-107.

Anderson JT, Keys A, Grande F. The effects of different food fats on serum cholesterol concentration in man. *J Nutr.* 1957;62:421-424.

Anggård E, Samuelsson B. Biosynthesis of prostaglandins from arachidonic acid in guinea pig lung. Prostaglandins and related factors. 38. *J Biol Chem.* 1965;240:3518-3521.

Atkinson J, Epand RF, Epand RM. Tocopherols and tocotrienols in membranes: a critical review. *Free Radic Biol Med.* 2008;44:739-764.

Becker W, Bruce A. Autoradiographic studies with fatty acids and some other lipids: a review. *Prog. Lipid Res.* 1985;24:325–346.

Bessesen DH, Bull S, Cornier MA. Trafficking of dietary fat and resistance to obesity. *Physiol Behav.* 2008;94:681-688.

Bidlack WR. Interrelationships of food, nutrition, diet and health: the National Association of State Universities and Land Grant Colleges White Paper. *J Am Coll Nutr.* 1996;15:422-433.

Bloch AS. Low carbohydrate diets, pro: time to rethink our current strategies. *Nutr Clin Pract.* 2005;20:3-12.

Bogeski I, Kappl R, Kummerow C, Gulaboski R, Hoth M, Niemeyer BA. Redox regulation of calcium ion channels: chemical and physiological aspects. *Cell Calcium.* 2011;50:407-423.

Brown AJ, Jessup W. Oxysterols: Sources, cellular storage and metabolism, and new insights into their roles in cholesterol homeostasis. *Mol Aspects Med.* 2009;30:111-122.

Cahill GF Jr.Fuel metabolism in starvation. *Annu Rev Nutr.* 2006;26:1-22.

Cederbaum A. Nrf2 and antioxidant defense against CYP2E1 toxicity. *Expert Opin Drug Metab Toxicol.* 2009;5:1223-1244.

Charlton KM, Corner AH, Davey K, et al. Cardiac lesions in rats fed rapeseed oils. *Can. J. Comp. Med.* 1975;39:261–269.

Chavez JA, Summers SA. Lipid oversupply, selective insulin resistance, and lipotoxicity: molecular mechanisms. *Biochim Biophys Acta.* 2010;1801:252-265.

Cho YS, Kim CH, Kim KY, Cheon HG. Protective effects of arachidonic acid against palmitic acid-mediated lipotoxicity in HIT-T15 cells. *Mol Cell Biochem.* 2012 May;364(1-2):19-28.

Clayton EH, Hanstock TL, Watson JF. Estimated intakes of meat and fish by children and adolescents in Australia and comparison with recommendations. *Br J Nutr.* 2009;101:1731-1735.

Cunnane SC. Problems with essential fatty acids: time for a new paradigm? *Prog Lipid Res.* 2003;42:544-568.

Dagnelie P, Sschuurman A, Goldbohm R, et al. Diet, anthropometric measures and prostate cancer risk: a review of prospective cohort and intervention studies. *BJU Int.* 2004;8: 1139-1150.

Di Nunzio M, Valli V, Bordoni A. Pro- and anti-oxidant effects of polyunsaturated fatty acid supplementation in HepG2 cells. *Prostaglandins Leukot Essent Fatty Acids.* 2011;85:121-127.

Dyerberg J, Bang HO, Hjorne N. Fatty acid composition of the plasma lipids in Greenland Eskimos. *Am J Clin Nutr*. 1975;28:958-966.

Dyerberg J, Bang HO. Haemostatic function and platelet polyunsaturated fatty acids in Eskimos. *Lancet*. 1979;2:433-435.

Erkkilä A, de Mello VD, Risérus U. Dietary fatty acids and cardiovascular disease: an epidemiological approach. *Prog Lipid Res*. 2008;47:172-187.

Esteve E, Ricart W, Fernández-Real JM. Dyslipidemia and inflammation: an evolutionary conserved mechanism. *Clin Nutr*. 2005;24:16-31.

Fantini J, Yahi N. Molecular insights into amyloid regulation by membrane cholesterol and sphingolipids: common mechanisms in neurodegenerative diseases. Expert Rev Mol Med. 2010;12:e27.

Fassett RG, Gobe GC, Peake JM, Coombes JS. Omega-3 polyunsaturated fatty acids in the treatment of kidney disease. *Am J Kidney Dis*. 2010;56:728-742.

Gay G, Andre JL, Pierson M, et al. Effect of a normocaloric, high fat, low carbohydrate diet on hyperlipoproteinemia in children with chronic renal insufficiency treated by periodic hemodialysis. *Nouv Presse Med*. 1977;6:2166.

Genton L, Melzer K, Pichard C. Energy and macronutrient requirements for physical fitness in exercising subjects. *Clin Nutr*. 2010;29:413-423.

Gerber M. Omega-3 fatty acids and cancers: a systematic update review of epidemiological studies. *Br J Nutr*. 2012;107 Suppl 2:S228-S239.

Gofman JW, Lindgren F. The role of lipids and lipoproteins in atherosclerosis. *Science*. 1950;111:166-171

Gómez Candela C, Bermejo López LM, Loria Kohen V. Importance of a balanced omega 6/omega 3 ratio for the maintenance of health: nutritional recommendations. *Nutr Hosp*. 2011;26:323-329.

González-Mañán D, Tapia G, Gormaz JG, et al. Bioconversion of α-linolenic acid to n-3 LCPUFA and expression of PPAR-alpha, acyl coenzyme A oxidase 1 and carnitine acyl transferase I are incremented after feeding rats with α-linolenic acid-rich oils. *Food Funct*. 2012. http://pubs.rsc.org/en/content/articlelanding/2012/FO/C2FO30012E

Gormaz JG, Rodrigo R, Videla LA, et al. Biosynthesis and bioavailability of long-chain polyunsaturated fatty acids in non-alcoholic fatty liver disease. *Prog. Lipid Res*. 2010;49:407-419.

Gormaz JG, Rodrigo R. Nonalcoholic steatohepatitis. Oxidative stress and antioxidants: their role in human disease (Rodrigo R., Ed.). *Nova Science Publishers Inc., New York, USA*, 2009 pp. 223–256.

Guallar E, Sanz-Gallardo MI, van't Veer P, et al. Mercury, fish oils, and the risk of myocardial infarction. *N Engl J Med*. 2002;347:1747-1754.

Han SF, Zhang H, Zhai CK. Protective potentials of wild rice (Zizania latifolia (Griseb) Turcz) against obesity and lipotoxicity induced by a high-fat/cholesterol diet in rats. *Food Chem Toxicol*. 2012;50:2263-2269.

Haslam D. Obesity: a medical history. *Obes Rev*. 2007;8 Suppl 1:31-36.

Hellerstein MK. Carbohydrate-induced hypertriglyceridemia: modifying factors and implications for cardiovascular risk. *Curr Opin Lipidol*. 2002;13:33-40.

Hofmann AF. The enterohepatic circulation of bile acids in mammals: form and functions. *Front Biosci*. 2009;14:2584-2598.

Houstis N, Rosen ED, Lander ES. Reactive oxygen species have a causal role in multiple forms of insulin resistance. *Nature*. 2006;440:944-8.

Huncharek M, Kupelnick B. Dietary Fat Intake and Risk of Epithelial Ovarian Cancer: A Meta-Analysis of 6,689 Subjects From 8 Observational studies. *Nutrition and Cancer*. 2001;2:87–91.

Junker R, Pieke B, Schulte H, et al. Changes in hemostasis during treatment of hypertriglyceridemia with a diet rich in monounsaturated and n-3 polyunsaturated fatty acids in comparison with a low-fat diet. *Thromb Res*. 2001;101:355-366.

Kaul D. Cholesterol-receptor-mediated genomics in health and disease. *Trends Mol Med*. 2003;9:442-449.

Keys A. Prevention of coronary heart disease. Official recommendations from Scandinavia. *Circulation*. 1968 Aug;38(2):227-8.

Khan M, Singh J, Gilg AG, et al. Very long-chain fatty acid accumulation causes lipotoxic response via 5-lipoxygenase in cerebral adrenoleukodystrophy. *J Lipid Res*. 2010;51:1685-1695.

Kuipers RS, de Graaf DJ, Luxwolda MF, et al. Saturated fat, carbohydrates and cardiovascular disease. *Neth J Med*. 2011;69:372-378.

Kusunoki, M., Cooney, G. J., Hara, T. et al. Amelioration of high-fat feeding-induced insulin resistance in skeletal muscle with the antiglucocorticoid RU486. *Diabetes*. 1995:44;718-720.

Li ZZ, Berk M, McIntyre TM, et al. Hepatic lipid partitioning and liver damage in nonalcoholic fatty liver disease: role of stearoyl-CoA desaturase. J Biol Chem. 2009;284:5637-5644.

Luckner G, Renz P. On the phospholipase activity in bovine seminal vesicles and its possible role in the regulation of the prostaglandin biosynthesis. *Z Naturforsch C*. 1975;30:429-433.

Malhotra JD, Kaufman RJ. Endoplasmic reticulum stress and oxidative stress: a vicious cycle or a double-edged sword? *Antioxid Redox Signal*. 2007;9:2277-2293.

McGandy RB, Hegsted DM, Stare FJ. Dietary fats, carbohydrates and atherosclerotic vascular disease. *N Engl J Med*. 1967;277:186-192.

Mercer LP. The determination of nutritional requirements: mathematical modeling of nutrient-response curves. *J Nutr*. 1992;122 Suppl 3:706-708.

Molendi-Coste O, Legry V, Leclercq IA. 2011. Why and How Meet n-3 PUFA Dietary Recommendations? *Gastroenterol Res Pract*. 2011;2011:364040.

Molina V, Rodrigo R. Atherosclerosis. Oxidative stress and antioxidants: their role in human disease (Rodrigo R., Ed.). *Nova Science Publishers Inc., New York, USA*, 2009 pp 63-90.

Neuschwander-Tetri BA. Hepatic lipotoxicity and the pathogenesis of nonalcoholic steatohepatitis: the central role of nontriglyceride fatty acid metabolites. *Hepatology*. 2010;52:774-788.

Nolan CJ, Larter CZ. Lipotoxicity: why do saturated fatty acids cause and monounsaturates protect against it? *J Gastroenterol Hepatol*. 2009;24:703-706.

Nordmann A, Nordmann A, Briel M, Keller U, Yancy, Jr W, Brehm B, Bucher H. Effects of Low-Carbohydrate vs. Low-Fat Diets on Weight Loss and Cardiovascular Risk Factors A Meta-analysis of Randomized Controlled Trials. *Arch Intern Med*. 2006;166:285-293.

Nordmann A, Suter-Zimmermann K, Bucher H, et al. Meta-Analysis Comparing Mediterranean to Low-Fat Diets for Modification of Cardiovascular Risk Factors. *The American Journal of Medicine.* 2011; 124:841-851.

Nosadini R, Tonolo G. Role of oxidized low density lipoproteins and free fatty acids in the pathogenesis of glomerulopathy and tubulointerstitial lesions in type 2 diabetes. Nutr Metab *Cardiovasc Dis.* 2011;21:79-85.

Odermatt A. The Western-style diet: a major risk factor for impaired kidney function and chronic kidney disease. Am J Physiol Renal Physiol. 2011;301:F919-F931.

Ortega RM, Rodríguez-Rodríguez E, López-Sobaler AM. Effects of omega 3 fatty acids supplementation in behavior and non-neurodegenerative neuropsychiatric disorders. *Br J Nutr.* 2012;107 Suppl 2:S261-S270.

Parker HM, Johnson NA, Burdon CA, et al. Omega-3 supplementation and non-alcoholic fatty liver disease: a systematic review and meta-analysis. *J Hepatol.* 2012;56:944-951.

Patrick L. Beta-carotene: the controversy continues. *Altern Med Rev.* 2000;5:530-545.

Peluffo RO, Brenner RR, Mercuri O. Action of linoleic and arachidonic acids upon the eicosatrienoic acid level in rat heart and liver. *J Nutr.* 1963;81:110-116.

Pérez-Martínez P, García-Ríos A, Delgado-Lista J, et al. Mediterranean diet rich in olive oil and obesity, metabolic syndrome and diabetes mellitus. *Curr Pharm Des.* 2011;17:769-777.

Pilz S, März W. Free fatty acids as a cardiovascular risk factor. Clin Chem Lab Med. 2008;46:429-34.

Puri P, Mirshahi F, Cheung O, et al. Activation and dysregulation of the unfolded protein response in nonalcoholic fatty liver disease. *Gastroenterology.* 2008;134:568-576.

Ralston R, Lee J, Truby H, et al. A systematic review and meta-analysis of elevated blood pressure and consumption of dairy foods. *Journal of Human Hypertension.* 2012; 26: 3–13.

Ramesh BN, Rao TS, Prakasam A, et al. Neuronutrition and Alzheimer's disease. *J Alzheimers Dis.* 2010;19:1123-1139.

Rifkind BM. Lipid Research Clinics Coronary Primary Prevention Trial: results and implications. *Am J Cardiol.* 1984;54:30C-34C.

Rocha M, Banuls C, Bellod L, et al. A review on the role of phytosterols: new insights into cardiovascular risk. *Curr Pharm Des.* 2011;17:4061-4075.

Rodrigo R. Prevention of postoperative atrial fibrillation: novel and safe strategy based on the modulation of the antioxidant system. *Front Physiol.* 2012;3:93.

Roth EM, Harris WS. Fish oil for primary and secondary prevention of coronary heart disease. *Curr Atheroscler Rep.* 2010;12:66-72.

Russell RM. Setting dietary intake levels: problems and pitfalls. *Novartis Found Symp.* 2007;282:29-36

Sardi F, Fassina L, Venturini L, et al. Alzheimer's disease, autoimmunity and inflammation. The good, the bad and the ugly. *Autoimmun Rev.* 2011;11:149-153.

Schaefer O. Glucose tolerance testing in Canadian Eskimos: a preliminary report and a hypothesis. *Can Med Assoc J.* 1968;99:252-262.

Schwingshackl L, Strasser B, Hoffmann G. Effects of Monounsaturated Fatty Acids on Cardiovascular Risk Factors: A Systematic Review and Meta-Analysis. *Ann Nutr Metab.* 2011;59:176-186.

Seneviratne AN, Sivagurunathan B, Monaco C. Toll-like receptors and macrophage activation in atherosclerosis. *Clin Chim Acta*. 2012;413:3-14.

Siri-Tarino P, Sun Q, Hu F et al. Meta-analysis of prospective cohort studies evaluating the association of saturated fat with cardiovascular disease. *Am J Clin Nutr*. 2010;91:535-546.

Skeaff M and Miller J. Dietary Fat and Coronary Heart Disease: Summary of Evidence from Prospective Cohort and Randomized Controlled Trials. *Ann Nutr Metab*. 2009;55:173-201.

Solfrizzi V, Panza F, Frisardi V, et al. Diet and Alzheimer's disease risk factors or prevention: the current evidence. *Expert Rev Neurother*. 2011;11:677-708.

Stanley WC, Dabkowski ER, Ribeiro RF Jr, et al. Dietary fat and heart failure: moving from lipotoxicity to lipoprotection. *Circ Res*. 2012;110:764-776.

Stemmer K, Perez-Tilve D, Ananthakrishnan G, et al. High-fat-diet-induced obesity causes an inflammatory and tumor-promoting microenvironment in the rat kidney. *Dis Model Mech*. 2012. http://dmm.biologists.org/ content/early/2012/03/15/dmm.009407.long.

Stewart CP, Gaddie R, Dunlop DM. Fat metabolism in muscular exercise. *Biochem J*. 1931;25:733-748.

Summers SA. Ceramides in insulin resistance and lipotoxicity. Prog Lipid Res. 2006;45:42-72.

Thompson AK, Minihane AM, Williams CM. Trans fatty acids, insulin resistance and diabetes. *Eur J Clin Nutr*. 2011;65:553-564.

Tovar AR, Torres N. The role of dietary protein on lipotoxicity. *Biochim Biophys Acta*. 2010;1801:367-371.

Trauner M, Arrese M, Wagner M. Fatty liver and lipotoxicity. *Biochim Biophys Acta*. 2010;1801:299-310.

Truman JP, Al Gadban MM, Smith KJ, et al. Differential regulation of acid sphingomyelinase in macrophages stimulated with oxidized low-density lipoprotein (LDL) and oxidized LDL immune complexes: role in phagocytosis and cytokine release. *Immunology*. 2012;136:30-45.

Tsiaousi ET, Hatzitolios AI, Trygonis SK, et al. Malnutrition in end stage liver disease: recommendations and nutritional support. *J Gastroenterol Hepatol*. 2008;23:527-533.

Turner L. A Meta-analysis of Fat Intake, Reproduction, and Breast Cancer Risk: An Evolutionary Perspective. *Am J Hum Biol*. 2011;23:601-608.

Tvrzicka E, Kremmyda LS, Stankova B, et al. Fatty acids as biocompounds: their role in human metabolism, health and disease--a review. Part 1: classification, dietary sources and biological functions. *Biomed Pap Med Fac Univ Palacky Olomouc Czech Repub*. 2011;155:117-130.

Vainio S, Ikonen E. Macrophage cholesterol transport: a critical player in foam cell formation. *Ann Med*. 2003;35:146-155.

Valentine RC, Valentine DL. Omega-3 fatty acids in cellular membranes: a unified concept. Prog *Lipid Res*. 2004;43:383-402.

Valenzuela, R Gormáz JG, Masson L, et al. Evaluation of the hepatic bioconversion of a-linolenic acid (ALA) to eicosapentaenoic acid (EPA) and docosahexaenoic acid (DHA) in rats fed with oils from chia (Salvia hispánica) or rosa mosqueta (Rosa rubiginosa). Grasas y Aceites. 2012:63;61-69.

Vuorio AF, Turtola H, Piilahti KM, et al. Familial hypercholesterolemia in the Finnish north Karelia. A molecular, clinical, and genealogical study. *Arterioscler Thromb Vasc Biol.* 1997;17:3127-3138.

Wanders RJ, Ferdinandusse S, Brites P, et al. Peroxisomes, lipid metabolism and lipotoxicity. *Biochim Biophys Acta.* 2010;1801:272-280.

Weeks JR, Sekhar NC, Ducharme DW. Relative activity of prostaglandins E1, A1, E2 and A2 on lipolysis, platelet aggregation, smooth muscle and the cardiovascular system. *J Pharm Pharmacol.* 1969;21:103-108.

Wielkoszyński T, Gawron K, Strzelczyk J, et al. Cellular toxicity of oxycholesterols. *Bioessays.* 2006;28:387-398.

Wu JH, Micha R, Imamura F, et al. Omega-3 fatty acids and incident type 2 diabetes: a systematic review and meta-analysis. *Br J Nutr.* 2012;107 Suppl 2:S214-S227.

Yvan-Charvet L, Wang N, Tall AR. Role of HDL, ABCA1, and ABCG1 transporters in cholesterol efflux and immune responses. *Arterioscler Thromb Vasc Biol.* 2010;30:139-143.

In: Low and High-Fat Diets: Myths vs. Reality
Editors: J. E. Ferreira and N. Muniz

ISBN: 978-1-62257-797-2

Chapter V

The Efficacy and Safety of Low-Fat Diets in Children

María Navarro-Solera[1], Raquel Simó-Jordá[2] and Pilar Codoñer-Franch*[1,2]

[1]Department of Pediatrics, Obstretrics and Gynecology, University of Valencia, Valencia, Spain

[2]Department of Pediatrics, Dr. Peset University Hospital, Valencia, Spain

Abstract

The dramatic increase in obesity worldwide remains a public health challenge and underscores the urgent need to test the effectiveness and safety of several widely used weight-loss diets, especially in children. Dietary guidelines recommend a reduction in total dietary fat to less than 30% of energy intake to help reduce the prevalence of obesity, cardiovascular disease (CVD) and certain cancers. Which diets result in safe weight loss, have positive long-term effects on chronic disease risk factors, and are sustainable? This question has been only partially answered. Numerous cross-sectional studies have clearly demonstrated a positive correlation between the proportion of total energy intake provided by fat and obesity. Subjects exposed to high-fat foods tend to overconsume energy. This effect depends largely on the high energy density of high-fat foods. A large body of short-term studies on appetite and energy intake unequivocally shows that fat is less satiating than carbohydrate and protein and that high-fat foods are more likely to induce passive overconsumption and weight gain than low-fat foods. Reducing the consumption of saturated fatty acids is one of the basis of international dietary recommendations to reduce the risk of cardiovascular disease. Recent studies of healthy individuals indicate that a single meal high in saturated fat causes immediate increases in triglycerides, oxidative stress, and inflammation. In general, the most efficient triggers of postprandial inflammatory response appear to be triglycerides and saturated fatty acids. On the other hand, the most important modulators of postprandial immune response appear to be polyunsaturated fatty acids (PUFA), and the n-3 to n-6

---

* Corresponding author: Pilar Codoñer-Franch. Department of Pediatrics, Dr. Peset University Hospital, Avda Gaspar Aguilar 90, 46017 Valencia, Spain

ratio is especially important. In general, n-3 PUFAs suppress postprandial inflammation, whereas n-6 PUFAs promote it. However, several critical questions remain regarding the relationship between saturated fatty acids consumption and cardiovascular risk. First, the health effects of reducing saturated fatty acids consumption can vary depending on whether the replacement nutrient is a carbohydrate, monounsaturated fat, or polyunsaturated fat. In this sense, another type of low-fat diet is the so called "high-protein diet," of which there are several variations. The diets are based on reduced carbohydrate and fat intake and high protein intake. These diets are effective for short-term weight loss, but this efficacy is counteracted by the negative effects on kidney function, both short and long term, and other secondary effects, such as hypercalciuria and osteopenia. Macrobiotic and vegetarian diets are also low-fat diets. Macrobiotic diets are characterized by reducing the percentage of fat and increasing complex carbohydrate and fiber intake. Macrobiotic diets also replace animal protein with vegetable protein. The composition of vegetarian diets depends on the type: vegan, lacto-vegetarian, ovo-vegetarian, lacto-ovo-vegetarian or semivegetarian. These diets may be deficient in vitamins and minerals (calcium, protein, iron, zinc, vitamins D and B12, riboflavin) and essential fatty acids that are necessary for growing children. In this way, considerable concerns have been raised about the safety of long-term low-fat diets in children.

Keywords: Children, low-carbohydrate diet, low-fat diet, Mediterranean diet, obesity

Introduction

Obesity, a chronic recurrent systemic and inflammatory disease, is the second leading cause of preventable death; consequently it is considered to be a true epidemic of the 21st century [1]. In fact, obesity represents the most common metabolic disorder in Western industrialized countries, and it has become a significant problem in developing countries [2]. It is a major health problem that is best controlled by early detection and prevention.

Likewise, childhood obesity has increased alarmingly in the last three decades [1], as have the consequences of obesity that arise in adult life. Given the disease burden associated with obesity, treatment is crucial for reducing comorbidities. Dieting, with the aim of shifting a positive energy balance to a negative energy balance by reducing energy intake, is the most important component of treatment. However, there is a controversy regarding the percentages of macronutrients that children on calorie-restricted diets should consume.

Many diets have been developed to achieve weight loss or maintain weight and reduce the metabolic impact on obese patients, but not all are suitable for children.

The recommended daily intake for healthy people is based on the macronutrient composition of a diet: 50-60% carbohydrate, 30% fat and 15% protein.

Hence, the traditional approach to reducing energy intake is to focus on low-fat diets because fats are energy rich. In this way, dietary guidelines recommend a reduction in total dietary fat content to less than 30% of energy intake to help reduce the prevalence of obesity, cardiovascular disease and certain cancers [3,4].

However, there are some concerns about the efficacy of low-fat diets, and alternative diets have been proposed for weight loss. Low-carbohydrate diets that are relatively high-protein, high-fat diets have been compared with low-fat, energy-restricted diets [5]. Some specific diets such as the vegetarian diet [6], the Southern European Atlantic Diet (SEAD) rich in w3 fatty acids [7] and the Mediterranean diet [8] have been claimed to prevent specific disorders associated with obesity.

Which diets result in safe weight loss, have positive effects on chronic disease risk factors, and are sustainable? This question has been only partly answered, especially in children whose continuous growth and maturation renders them more susceptible to secondary effects.

The purpose of this article is to review and assess several types of diet commonly recommended for weight reduction in children, with particular attention to low-calorie and low-fat diets in terms of efficacy and safety.

Low-Fat Diet: Indications

Weight Reduction

The most controversial issue in human nutrition is the impact of different macronutrients (fats, carbohydrates and proteins) on energy balance. If one macronutrient contributes more energy than another, it is more likely to induce a positive energy balance; this observation could be a basis for recommendations for both achieving weight loss in obese subjects and for the prevention of excess weight gain in the general population. Numerous cross-sectional studies have clearly demonstrated positive associations between the proportion of total energy intake covered by fat and body fatness [9,10]. A high-fat diet works against the goals of healthy eating. Subjects exposed to high-fat foods for several weeks tend to overconsume energy. This effect depends largely on the high energy density of high-fat foods. Even with small amounts of food, the energy consumed is elevated.

In addition, diet-induced thermogenesis associated with high-fat diets is much lower than that associated with high-protein and high-carbohydrate diets. This difference is partly due to the lower energy cost of converting dietary fat into adipose tissue. With long-term intake of a high-fat diet, satiety hormones become dysregulated, and hunger increases [11]. A large body of short-term studies on appetite and energy intake unequivocally shows that fat is less satiating than carbohydrate and protein joule for joule [12] and that high-fat foods are more likely to induce passive overconsumption and weight gain than low-fat foods with higher levels of carbohydrate and protein because the energy intake required to achieve satiety is higher. In turn, body weight also increases.

Hence, an energy-restricted low-fat diet remains the conventional therapy used to treat obesity [13]. In this sense, low-fat diets (20-25% of total energy) can lower mean energy intake by100 kcal/day, which is enough to stop the tendency toward overweight and obesity [14]. Eating less fat, particularly less saturated and trans fats, which are common in fast foods, easily reduces energy intake. Low-fat diets that are well balanced and are not restricted in carbohydrate or protein allow for weight loss, and they do not have any adverse effects on cardiovascular risk factors. In fact, they have been shown to decrease mortality among high-risk subjects [15]. To achieve satiety, these diets frequently have increased levels of carbohydrates. The basis of the high carbohydrate content of low-fat diets should come mainly from the complex carbohydrates of vegetables, fruits and whole grains, which are more satiating for fewer calories than fatty foods and are good sources of vitamins, minerals, trace elements and fiber. Less fat and more fruits, vegetables, and whole grains facilitate weight loss and the maintenance of healthy weight.

However, low-fat diets have some disadvantages. Energy-restricted diets with a diminished intake of fats are difficult to follow because they are not palatable and they do not curb the appetite if the intake of carbohydrates is not increased; therefore, they require a sustained commitment that many people, particularly children, find difficult to maintain. Moreover, several studies, including a Cochrane revision [16, 17] concluded that such diets are no better than other calorie-restricted diets in achieving and maintaining weight loss.

This lack of full effectiveness, the difficulty of maintaining low-fat diets and the continuing increase in obesity at the population level have led to a resurgence of interest in low-carbohydrate and low-glycemic-index diets, which in turn, are high in protein.

Low-carbohydrate/high-protein diets may induce a stronger satiating effect than high-carbohydrate/low-protein diets because protein is the most satiating of the macronutrients. In fact, satiety after a meal appears to be inversely related to the glycemic and insulinemic response [18]. Diets that induced a lower insulin response to ingested carbohydrate may also decrease hunger and hence promote weight loss because the energy intake is secondarily decreased. With these diets, weight loss is rapid in the first months, but the long-term effects on body weight are controversial.

One of the mechanisms by which a diet low in carbohydrates facilitates weight loss is by inducing ketosis, a metabolic state also generated by fasting. This state can produce nausea, vomiting, decreased appetite and an increase in urine output that provokes a high diuresis. A diet that induces ketosis has advantages over other low-calorie diets because of the decrease in insulin and the increase in energy expenditure favored by the thermal effect of food. In turn, it decreases triglycerides, increases HDL and leads to the dissolution of glycogen stores.

The effectiveness and safety of a low-carbohydrate approach as an alternative to a low-fat, high-carbohydrate diet have been examined. Researchers have concluded that reducing dietary carbohydrate improves glucose control, insulin response, atherogenic dyslipemia, and other cardiovascular risk factors in addition to decreasing energy intake without increasing hunger [19].

Other studies have compared the efficacy for weight loss of the low-carbohydrate diet versus the low-fat diet. Volek et al. have shown that a carbohydrate-restricted diet can provide a significant reduction in the clinical risk factors associated with Metabolic Syndrome [20]. Low-carbohydrate, non-restricted diets appear to be more effective than low-fat, energy-restricted diets At 24 weeks, weight loss was greater in the low-carbohydrate diet group than in the low-fat diet group in a randomized trial [21].

What are the mechanisms of weight loss on a low-carbohydrate diet? According to some investigators, weight loss occurs because energy expenditure increases when the subject is on a low-carbohydrate diet. Authors have described an increase in energy expenditure when protein intake increases and replaces carbohydrates. Carbohydrate restriction depletes glycogen stores, leading to greater weight loss. This depletion is associated with loss of water. However, the success of these types of diets may be due to their skill to reduce spontaneous energy intake.

Nevertheless, there is some concern about the long-term health effects and potential risks of low-carbohydrate diets: they are low in fiber, poor in calcium, potassium, magnesium, and iron and deficient in folates, thiamine, and other vitamins. In addition, low-carbohydrate diets are usually rich in saturated fatty acids, which can promote cardiovascular risk. Persons on these diets also present with a number of complaints, such as halitosis, constipation, headache, muscle cramps, diarrhea, asthenia and lack of concentration [22].

Furthermore, if children are fed such a diet, the protein content is a source of concern. There are several metabolic consequences that are associated with the high acid load from the excess protein, which contributes to bone resorption [23] (bone calcium is mobilized to offset 1 mEq of acid/day, which would lead to a 15% reduction of calcium in the bones over 10 years). The main amino acids that contribute to acidification are methionine and cysteine, which are part of animal proteins. The consequences of this chronic metabolic acidosis can be loss of magnesium and increased protein degradation. In the kidneys, glomerular hyperfiltration occurs, and phosphorus and calcium excretion is promoted in the urine. Additionally, citrate excretion decreases, leading to a decrease in urinary pH and an increase in the risk of stones. Moreover, in children, the diet is associated with later obesity (high protein intake in infants 12 to 24 months is related to higher BMI and body fat percentage at age 7). This is the "early protein hypothesis," according to which insulin and IGF1 synthesis are stimulated [24].

In summary, low-carbohydrate, high-protein diets, whether low-glycemic-index or not, appear to be at least as effective in the short-term as conventional energy-restricted low-fat regimens, but their long-term effects are unknown [25]. Long-term studies are necessary to measure changes in nutritional status and body composition in persons eating a low-carbohydrate, high-protein diet and to assess side effects, postprandial cardiovascular risk factors, fasting and other adverse effect. Without this information, low-carbohydrate diets cannot be recommended for children because data on effectiveness and safety are limited.

Other Indications

In addition to their role in weight management, low-fat diets are recommended for dyslipemias and cardiovascular disease control. In general, there is a reduction in cardiovascular risk in individuals consuming less fat [9]. Reducing the intake of saturated fatty acids is the basis of international dietary recommendations to reduce the risk of atherosclerosis. However, several critical questions remain about the relationship between consumption of saturated fatty acids and cardiovascular risk. First, do the health effects of reducing saturated fatty acids vary depending on whether the replacement nutrient is carbohydrate, monounsaturated fat or polyunsaturated fat? Public health emphasis on reducing saturated fat consumption without considering the replacement nutrient is unlikely to produce substantial, intended benefits. Secondly, and no less importantly, there are many other food-based risk factors for cardiometabolic disease that should be taken into account such as fiber or antioxidant (polyphenolics) content.

Low-Fat Diets: Type of Fat

The quality of dietary fat, and not just its quantity, may also be related to the risk of obesity [26]. Animal studies have shown that dietary short- and medium-chain fatty acids appear to promote weight loss better than long-chain fatty acids [27]. Similarly, monounsaturated fatty acids appear to favor weight loss more than saturated fatty acids in human studies [28]. The amount of fat should be limited to control obesity and secondary cardiovascular risk, but the type of fat consumed is more important for children.

Low-Fat Diets and Cardiovascular Risk

The type of fat consumed is also more important than the amount in reducing cardiovascular risk. In general, there is reduction in cardiovascular risk in individuals consuming less saturated fat and more polyunsaturated fat [9]. There is a negative effect on the lipid profile after consuming a diet rich in fat and carbohydrate. These diets are associated with increased levels of triglycerides, low-density lipoprotein (LDL) and lipoprotein(a) and low levels of high-density lipoprotein (HDL). Although the precise mechanisms by which unsaturated fatty acids reduce cardiovascular risk are still not fully understood, those identified so far include effects on blood lipid concentrations, blood pressure, inflammatory response, arrhythmia and endothelial function [29].

Diets low in fat with an increased intake of complex carbohydrates are beneficial, and they induce the following effects: a reduction in the consumption of carbohydrates with a high glycemic index, trans-fatty acids and linoleic acid; an increased consumption of fish, vegetables and fruit and a reduction in the chronic systemic low-grade inflammation that promotes the development of atherosclerosis. Furthermore, it has been shown that polyunsaturated fatty acids can influence cardiovascular disease by preventing serious arrhythmias, such as ventricular tachycardia or ventricular fibrillation [30]. However, eating an excessive amount of n-6 has been associated with a prothrombotic and proaggregatory effect [31]. All of these issues should be considered in estimating the type of fat recommended.

Low-Fat Diets and Oxidative Stress

Diet affects different mechanisms of oxidative stress, whose establishment depends on an imbalance between oxidant/antioxidant systems. Oxidative stress has been linked to chronic diseases, the onset or "imprinting" of which may begin in childhood, such as diabetes, obesity, neurodegenerative disorders, cardiovascular disease and even cancer [32].

There is scientific evidence for the relationship between oxidative stress and increased metabolic risk markers [33]. The diet is an important factor modulator.

There are diets that act not only on body weight but also on oxidative stress. Energy-restricted diets generally decrease lipid peroxidation [34] A diet low in fat, especially saturated fat, and rich in fiber has potent antioxidative effects due to the high antioxidant content of vegetables. The antioxidative effects could arise from various dietary components, such as vitamins, minerals, polyphenols and carotenoids, among others. These compounds can prevent the formation of free radicals, inhibit the activity of free radicals, or contribute to the repair of cellular damage.

The lipophilic vitamins A (or its precursor beta-carotene) and E and the hydrophilic vitamin C (ascorbic acid) have high antioxidant powers. The same goes for carotenoids (e.g., lycopene), zinc, selenium, magnesium, copper and other antioxidants derived from plants (phytochemicals), such as resveratrol, catechins (contained in green tea), quercetin (contained in black tea and onions), phenolic acids (found in wine) and hydrotyrosol and tyrosol (found in olive oil). In addition, olive oil contains fatty-acid esters of plant sterols and dietary diaglycerol that influence the tendency for lipoperoxidation of the hypercholesterolemic subjects [35]. The key role of antioxidants is to protect proteins, lipids and DNA from oxidation. This function is well known, but the recommended intakes and the extent such substances are needed to prevent oxidative stress are not well known. Additionally, a diet rich in fiber and vegetables decreases homocysteine levels, a well known factor influencing cardiovascular risk [36].

Low-Fat Diets and Inflammatory Response

Obesity is linked to a chronic inflammatory response that in turn can promote endothelial damage, the initial mechanism for atherosclerosis. A specific dietary pattern that may reduce this inflammatory response is thus of great importance. Low-calorie diets positively influence the levels of inflammatory markers [37]. However, the effects of low-fat diets besides the loss of body weight could be less important.

The type of fat consumed also influences the inflammatory response. A diet rich in eicosapentanoic or docosahexanoic acids (n-3 polyunsaturated acids) can decrease various inflammatory markers, such as fibrinogen, inflammatory interleukins and tumor necrosis factor-alpha [38]. There is an inverse correlation between levels of LDL and the oleic acid content of the diet as well as between the consumption of polyunsaturated fatty acids and monocyte adhesion [39].

Furthermore, diets enriched with oleic acid reduce accumulation of triglycerides in the liver and lower insulin resistance, which are the first steps of an inflammatory response in the liver.

Type of Fat and Postprandial Inflammatory Response

There are nutrient-dependent factors, particularly the lipid profile of a meal, that influence postprandial inflammation. In general, the most efficient triggers of postprandial inflammatory response appear to be triglycerides and saturated fatty acids [40]. Indeed, triglycerides and saturated fatty acids induce a significant postprandial inflammatory response, whereas monounsaturated fat improves postprandial oxidative stress [41]. However, the most important modulators of postprandial immune response appear to be polyunsaturated fatty acids, especially the n-3 to n-6 ratio [42].

In general, the n-3 polyunsaturated fatty acids suppress postprandial inflammation, whereas the n-6 polyunsaturated acids promote it. Recent studies of healthy individuals have shown that a single meal high in saturated fat will cause immediate increases in triglycerides, oxidative stress, and inflammation, which cause postprandial endothelial dysfunction, vasoconstriction, and an increase in systolic blood pressure [43].

Special Diets

Macrobiotic Diets

Macrobiotic diets are low in fat and rich in fiber, with moderate levels of protein and complex carbohydrate. They replace animal protein with vegetable protein and encourage the intake of natural foods, organic and whole foods. Although these diets are generally rich in vitamins, antioxidant phyto-compounds and fiber, the more strict macrobiotic diets can be deficient in vitamins B1, B12 or C and iron. Because they are high in folic acid, they lower homocysteine concentrations in the blood; thus, they lower cardiovascular risk. They are rich in calcium and have a good relationship between calcium and phosphorus. They contain prebiotics and probiotics, have strong antioxidative power and favor metabolic alkalinity. However, because they can be deficient in essential nutrients, they are not recommended for young children [44].

Vegetarian Diets

Depending on the type of vegetarian diet (lacto-vegetarian, ovo-vegetarian, lacto-ovo-vegetarian or vegan), certain nutrients will be lost to a greater or lesser extent. These diets, when properly planned, can meet the needs of young children for nutrition and normal growth [45]. However, if the diet excludes eggs and dairy products, vitamins and minerals must be supplemented, particularly vitamin B12. Studies carried out in children have shown that the nutritional status of vegetarian children is in general satisfactory, and the diet prevents subsequent obesity [46]. Products of animal origin have a greater amount of fat, protein and saturated fatty acid, and the absence of meat from the diet may be responsible for a better lipid profile. The presence of a considerable amount of fruits, grains, nuts and vegetables can account for other protective factors such as fiber and antioxidants.

However, they are very energy-restricted, and strict supervision and monitoring of such diets by health professionals is necessary to avoid any irreversible effects on growing children.

Mediterranean Diet

The effects and safety of the so-called Mediterranean diet are well known, not only in the control of weight but also in the prevention of diseases such as cardiovascular disease in adults [47]. The consumption of certain components of the Mediterranean diet (rich in olive oil, nuts, whole grains, legumes, fish, fruits and vegetables and low in red meat and refined sugars) is associated with low serum levels of inflammatory markers, the prevention of vascular disease and beneficial effects on endothelial function [48]. Olive oil, the main source of fat in the Mediterranean diet, has been shown a positive influence on ageing and be effective against the oxidative stress associated with certain diseases, [49]. The Mediterranean diet, which is not energy-restricted when compared with low-fat diets, has a more favorable effects on lipids and glycemic control, and it seems to be effective in the prevention of diabetes in subjects at high risk for cardiovascular disease [49]. In this way, the Mediterranean diet may be a safe alternative to low-fat diets [50]. Personal preferences and metabolic considerations might inform individualized tailoring of dietary interventions.

Table 1. Efficacy and safety of the different diets

TYPE OF DIET	CHARACTERISTICS	Effects		EFFICACY	SECURITY
		Positive	Negative		
LOW-FAT-DIET (LFD)	Energy restricted < 20-25% Fat 50%-60% CH (complex carbohydrates-vegetables,fruits, whole grains) 15% Protein Rich in fiber.Potent antioxidant effect	> impact on inflammatory markers > positive influence on postprandial inflammatory markers Decrease cardiovascular risk Decrease lipid peroxidation Good sources of vitamin and minerals.	<palatable than LCD < loss weight than LCD	+	+
LOW-CARBOHYDRATE DIET (LCD)	Energy intake non restricted No restriction of Protein Low carbohydrate (3%-10%) No restriction on saturated fat intake/ low fat	Effective on short-term weight loss Decrease hunger Secondarily decrease calorie intake Decrease insulin and HOMA index Rise the energy expenditure.	Associated to later obesity in children Low Fiber Poor in Ca, Mg,K,Fe, deficient in folates, thiamine and others vitamins. Halitosis, Constipation, Headache, Muscle cramps, Diarrhea, Asthenia Lack of concentration.	+++	---
VEGETARIAN DIET (VD)	Ovo-vegetarian, Lacto-ovo-vegetarian	Better profile of fats than normal diet		+	--
	Lacto-vegetarian, Vegetarian,	Better profile of fats Satisfactory nutritional status (prevent children obesity)	Decient in vitamins and minerals (D, B12, Riboflavin, calcium, iron, zinc), Protein and essential fatty acids could to be supplemented.	+	--
MEDITERRANEAN DIET (MD)	Energy intake non restricted 50-60% HC (whole grains, fruits and vegetables) 15% Protein 30% Fat (virgin olive oil, nuts)	Prevention cardiovascular diseases. Low serum levels of inflammatory markers. Decrease inflammation and endothelial dysfunction.		+	+++

Low-Fat Diets: Safety

Low-fat diets do not induce satiety, which predisposes children to inappropriate consumption of other macronutrients, such as carbohydrates or protein, with metabolic consequences arising from this overconsumption. When there is a change in the amount of one macronutrient, it may change the proportions of the other two, leading to side effects. Low-fat diets can predispose those consuming them to deficient absorption of fat-soluble vitamins, leading to visual or neurological deficits.

The amount of fat that a food contains alters physical and nutritional characteristics, including palatability, plasticity, texture and satiety. The poor palatability of low-fat diets hinders their maintenance in the pediatric population [51].

Given the importance of essential fatty acids for cellular structure and function, low-fat diets can be insufficient and result in the "essential fatty acid deficiency syndrome", characterized by skin lesions, scaliness, hair loss, and, in animals, fertility problems. In addition to linoleic acid and linolenic fatty acids, other long-chain n-3 polyunsaturated fatty acids such as eicosapentanoic or docosahexanoic fatty acid are considered to be of fundamental importance for the central nervous system and brain development as well as for better cognitive properties, not only during the fetal and early neonatal periods but throughout the whole life.

Cholesterol is a component of almost all cell membranes. Although there is no doubt about its relationship with cardiovascular disease, cholesterol has a major role in the synthesis of bile acids, vitamin D and steroidal hormones. In studies with non-human primates as well as in experiments *in vitro*, low cholesterol content in the diet leads to lower serotoninergic activity [52]. Because high serotoninergic activity is associated with less impulsivity and aggression, it has been suggested that low-cholesterol diets could increase the risk of external-cause mortality [53]. It seems reasonable, therefore, to presume a certain relationship between the cholesterol content of the brain and brain function.

It is important not to maintain a low-fat diet for the management of obesity over a long period of time. Preserving the intake of an appropriate ratio of saturated, monounsaturated and polyunsaturated fatty acids is of great importance to assure adequate cellular metabolism and function.

In the Table 1 there are a summary of the efficacy and safety of different diets claimed to be used in children.

Conclusion

The diets that have been analyzed are based on the restriction of the percentage of some of the macronutrients. However, obese children need all macronutrients, vitamins and minerals provided by foods for normal growth. There is little evidence to support the current recommendation of a low-fat, energy-restricted diet at long-term, either in terms of efficacy or safety. In the same way, there is no reason to recommend a low-carbohydrate diet in children.

An alternative approach is to increase healthy eating while reducing energy intake and avoiding energy-dense foods [54]. A greater intake of foods that are not energy-dense may increase fullness without limiting any macronutrients. There are several mechanisms that should be tested in future research, such as the action and direct or indirect effects of foods that are not energy-dense on satiety.

It is better to encourage positive than negative behaviors, focusing on healthy eating and emphasizing what the child can eat rather than what the child cannot. The change in emphasis can influence children's food choices and may enhance weight loss. We suggest that this is an important target in pediatric weight-control programs.

There is no single therapy for the treatment of obese children. Dietary changes should be tailored to food preferences and must allow for flexible approaches to reducing caloric intake so that children will be likely to continue the diet. Additionally, the genetic predisposition to obesity in some children must be recognized to give a specific and effective treatment [55].

Furthermore, the support of the family is critical. Children learn behaviors through observation and imitation of models, such as parents, siblings, other family members, friends, and also famous people [56]. Family participation and collaboration is an essential component of treatment [57].

The effectiveness of different dietary strategies is only achieved when they are coupled with behavioral therapy and ongoing support [58]. A strong association between adherence to a diet and clinically significant weight loss has been found, suggesting that "sustained adherence to a diet" rather than "following a certain type of diet" is the key to successful weight management [59].

There is an urgent need for well designed intervention studies of the long-term effectiveness of alternative diets that can provide support for evidence-based recommendations.

Addressing childhood obesity involves a multifactorial and multidisciplinary treatment regimen in which it is necessary to consider the family, physical activity, and the psychological and social situation as well as the participation of different health professionals. Dietary factors remain the cornerstone of treatment, but dietary recommendations should be individualized and balanced to avoid deficiencies.

References

[1] Mitchell NS, Catenacci VA, Wyatt HR, Hill JO. Obesity: overview of an epidemic. *Psychiatr. Clin. North Am.* 2011;34:717-32.

[2] Prentice AM. The emerging epidemic of obesity in developing countries. *Int. J. Epidemiol.* 2006;35:93-9.

[3] Scholl J. Traditional dietary recommendations for the prevention of cardiovascular disease: do they meet the needs of our patients? *Cholesterol.* 2012;2012:367898.

[4] Fung TT, Hu FB, Wu K, Chiuve SE, Fuchs CS, Giovannucci E. The Mediterranean and Dietary Approaches to Stop Hypertension (DASH) diets and colorectal cancer. *Am. J. Clin. Nutr.* 2010;92:1429-35.

[5] Klement RJ, Kämmerer U. Is there a role for carbohydrate restriction in the treatment and prevention of cancer? *Nutr Metab* (Lond) 2011;8:75.

[6] Thedford K, Raj S. A vegetarian diet for weight management. *J. Am. Diet Assoc.* 2011;111:816-8.

[7] Oliveira A, Lopes C, Rodríguez-Artalejo F. Adherence to the Southern European Atlantic Diet and occurrence of nonfatal acute myocardial infarction. *Am. J. Clin. Nutr.* 2010;92:211-7.

[8] Schröder H. Protective mechanisms of the Mediterranean diet in obesity and type 2 diabetes. *J. Nutr. Biochem.* 2007;18:149-60.

[9] Zarraga IG, Schwarz ER. Impact of dietary patterns and interventions on cardiovascular health. *Circulation* 2006;114:961-73.

[10] Labayen I, Martínez JA. Distribution of macronutrients from the diet and regulation of weight and body composition: role of lipids intake in obesity. *An. Sist. Sanit Navar.* 2002;25 Suppl 1:79-90.

[11] Maljaars J, Peters HP, Masclee AM. Review article: The gastrointestinal tract: neuroendocrine regulation of satiety and food intake. *Aliment Pharmacol. Ther.* 2007;26 Suppl 2:241-50.

[12] Westerterp-Plantenga MS. The significance of protein in food intake and body weight regulation. *Curr. Opin. Clin. Nutr. Metab. Care* 2003;6:635-8.

[13] Blackburn GL. The low-fat imperative. *Obesity* (Silver Spring). 2008;16:5-6.

[14] Imayama I, Ulrich CM, Alfano CM, Wang C, Xiao L, Wener MH, Campbell KL, Duggan C, Foster-Schubert KE, Kong A, Mason CE, Wang CY, Blackburn GL, Bain CE, Thompson HJ, McTiernan A. Effects of a caloric restriction weight loss diet and exercise on inflammatory biomarkers in overweight/obese postmenopausal women: a randomized controlled trial. *Cancer Res.* 2012;72:2314-26.

[15] Howard BV, Van Horn L, Hsia J, Manson JE, Stefanick ML, Wassertheil-Smoller S, Kuller LH, LaCroix AZ, Langer RD, Lasser NL, Lewis CE, Limacher MC, Margolis KL, Mysiw WJ, Ockene JK, Parker LM, Perri MG, Phillips L, Prentice RL, Robbins J, Rossouw JE, Sarto GE, Schatz IJ, Snetselaar LG, Stevens VJ, Tinker LF, Trevisan M, Vitolins MZ, Anderson GL, Assaf AR, Bassford T, Beresford SA, Black HR, Brunner RL, Brzyski RG, Caan B, Chlebowski RT, Gass M, Granek I, Greenland P, Hays J, Heber D, Heiss G, Hendrix SL, Hubbell FA, Johnson KC, Kotchen JM. Low-fat dietary pattern and risk of cardiovascular disease: the Women's Health Initiative Randomized Controlled Dietary Modification Trial. *JAMA* 2006;295:655-66.

[16] Gibson LJ, Peto J, Warren JM, dos Santos Silva I. Lack of evidence on diets for obesity for children: a systematic review. *Int. J. Epidemiol.* 2006;35:1544-52.

[17] Whitlock EP, Williams SB, Gold R, Smith PR, Shipman SA. Screening and interventions for childhood overweight: a summary of evidence for the US Preventive Services Task Force. *Pediatrics.* 2005;116:e125-44.

[18] Trout DL, Hallfrisch J, Behall KM. Atypically high insulin responses to some foods relate to sugars and satiety. *Int. J. Food Sci. Nutr.* 2004;55:577-88.

[19] Hite AH, Berkowitz VG, Berkowitz K. Low-carbohydrate diet review: shifting the paradigm. *Nutr. Clin. Pract.* 2011;26:300-8.

[20] Volek JS, Phinney SD, Forsythe CE, Quann EE, Wood RJ, Puglisi MJ, Kraemer WJ, Bibus DM, Fernandez ML, Feinman RD. Carbohydrate restriction has a more favorable impact on the metabolic syndrome than a low fat diet. *Lipids* 2009;44:297-309.

[21] Yancy WS Jr, Olsen MK, Guyton JR, Bakst RP, Westman EC. A low-carbohydrate, ketogenic diet versus a low-fat diet to treat obesity and hyperlipidemia: a randomized, controlled trial. *Ann. Intern Med.* 2004;140:769-77.

[22] McClernon FJ, Yancy WS Jr, Eberstein JA, Atkins RC, Westman EC. The effects of a low-carbohydrate ketogenic diet and a low-fat diet on mood, hunger, and other sel f-reported symptoms. *Obesity* (Silver Spring) 2007;15:182-7.

[23] Bonjour JP. Protein intake and bone health. *Int. J. Vitam Nutr. Res.* 2011;81:134-42.

[24] Larnkjær A, Mølgaard C, Michaelsen KF. Early nutrition impact on the insulin-like growth factor axis and later health consequences. *Curr. Opin. Clin. Nutr. Metab. Care.* 2012;15:285-92.

[25] Strychar I. Diet in the management of weight loss. *CMAJ* 2006;174: 56-63.

[26] Moussavi N, Gavino V, Receveur O. Could the quality of dietary fat, and not just its quantity, be related to risk of obesity? *Obesity* (Silver Spring) 2008;16:7-15.

[27] Moussavi N, Gavino V, Receveur O. Is obesity related to the type of dietary fatty acids? An ecological study. *Public Health Nutr.* 2008;11:1149-55.

[28] Abete I, Goyenechea E, Zulet MA, Martínez JA. Obesity and metabolic syndrome: potential benefit from specific nutritional components. Nutr *Metab. Cardiovasc. Dis.* 2011;21 Suppl 2:B1-15.

[29] Baum SJ, Kris-Etherton PM, Willett WC, Lichtenstein AH, Rudel LL, Maki KC, Whelan J, Ramsden CE, Block RC. Fatty acids in cardiovascular health and disease: A comprehensive update. *J. Clin. Lipidol.* 2012;6:216-34.

[30] Abdukeyum GG, Owen AJ, McLennan PL. Dietary (n-3) long-chain polyunsaturated fatty acids inhibit ischemia and reperfusion arrhythmias and infarction in rat heart not enhanced by ischemic preconditioning. *J. Nutr* 2008;138:1902-9.

[31] Hankey GJ. Nutrition and the risk of stroke. *Lancet Neurol.* 2012;11: 66-81.

[32] Codoñer-Franch P, Boix-García L, Simó-Jordá R, Del Castillo-Villaescusa C, Maset-Maldonado J, Valls-Bellés V. Is obesity associated with oxidative stress in children? *Int. J. Pediatr. Obes* 2010;5:56-63.

[33] Codoñer-Franch P, Tavárez-Alonso S, Murria-Estal R, Tortajada-Girbés M, Simó-Jordá R, Alonso-Iglesias E. Elevated advanced oxidation protein products(AOPPs) indicate metabolic risk in severely obese children. *Nutr. Metab. Cardiovasc. Dis.* 2012;22:237-43.

[34] Löhrke B, Derno M, Hammon H, Metges C, Melcher J, Viergutz T, Jentsch W, Zühlke H. Nutritional level and energetic source are determinants of elevated circulatory lipohydroperoxide concentration. *Br. J. Nutr.* 2008;99:1255-65.

[35] Masella R, Giovannini C, Varì R, Di Benedetto R, Coni E, Volpe R, Fraone N, Bucci A. Effects of dietary virgin olive oil phenols on low density lipoprotein oxidation in hyperlipidemic patients. *Lipids* 2001;36:1195-202.

[36] Veeranna V, Zalawadiya SK, Niraj A, Pradhan J, Ference B, Burack RC, Jacob S, Afonso L. Homocysteine and reclassification of cardiovascular disease risk. *J. Am. Coll. Cardiol.* 2011;58:1025-33.

[37] Montero D, Walther G, Perez-Martin A, Roche E, Vinet A. Endothelial dysfunction, inflammation, and oxidative stress in obese children and adolescents: markers and effect of lifestyle intervention. *Obes. Rev.* 2012;13:441-55.

[38] Yang Y, Lu N, Chen D, Meng L, Zheng Y, Hui R. Effects of n-3 PUFA supplementation on plasma soluble adhesion molecules: a meta-analysis of randomized controlled trials. *Am. J. Clin. Nutr.* 2012;95:972-80.

[39] Sneddon AA, McLeod E, Wahle KW, Arthur JR. Cytokine-induced monocyte adhesion to endothelial cells involves platelet-activating factor: suppression by conjugated linoleic acid. *Biochim. Biophys. Acta* 2006;1761:793-801.

[40] Dekker MJ, Wright AJ, Mazurak VC, Marangoni AG, Rush JW, Graham TE, Robinson LE. Fasting triacylglycerol status, but not polyunsaturated/saturated fatty acid ratio, influences the postprandial response to a series of oral fat tolerance tests. *J. Nutr. Biochem.* 2009;20:694-704.

[41] Perez-Martinez P, Garcia-Quintana JM, Yubero-Serrano EM, Tasset-Cuevas I, Tunez I, Garcia-Rios A, Delgado-Lista J, Marin C, Perez-Jimenez F, Roche HM, Lopez-Miranda J. Postprandial oxidative stress is modified by dietary fat: evidence from a human intervention study. *Clin. Sci. (Lond)* 2010;119:251-61.

[42] Margioris AN. Fatty acids and postprandial inflammation. *Curr. Opin. Clin. Nutr. Metab. Care* 2009;12:129-37.

[43] Peairs AD, Rankin JW, Lee YW. Effects of acute ingestion of different fats on oxidative stress and inflammation in overweight and obese adults. *Nutr. J.* 2011;10:122.

[44] Kirby M, Danner E. Nutritional deficiencies in children on restricted diets. *Pediatr. Clin. North Am.* 2009;56:1085-103.

[45] Van Winckel M, Vande Velde S, De Bruyne R, Van Biervliet S. Clinical practice: vegetarian infant and child nutrition. *Eur. J. Pediatr.* 2011;170:1489-94.

[46] Thedford K, Raj S. A vegetarian diet for weight management. *J. Am. Diet Assoc.* 2011;111:816-8.

[47] Martínez-González MA, García-López M, Bes-Rastrollo M, Toledo E, Martínez-Lapiscina EH, Delgado-Rodriguez M, Vazquez Z, Benito S, Beunza JJ. Mediterranean diet and the incidence of cardiovascular disease: a Spanish cohort. *Nutr. Metab. Cardiovasc. Dis.* 2011;21:237-44.

[48] Marin C, Ramirez R, Delgado-Lista J, Yubero-Serrano EM, Perez-Martinez P, Carracedo J, Garcia-Rios A, Rodriguez F, Gutierrez-Mariscal FM, Gomez P, Perez-Jimenez F, Lopez-Miranda J. Mediterranean diet reduces endothelial damage and improves the regenerative capacity of endothelium. *Am. J. Clin. Nutr.* 2011;93:267-74.

[49] Pérez-Martínez P, García-Ríos A, Delgado-Lista J, Pérez-Jiménez F, López-Miranda J. Mediterranean diet rich in olive oil and obesity, metabolic syndrome and diabetes mellitus. *Curr. Pharm. Des*. 2011;17:769-77.

[50] Domínguez LJ, Bes-Rastrollo M, de la Fuente-Arrillaga C, Toledo E, Beunza JJ, Barbagallo M, Martínez-González MA. Similar prediction of decreased total mortality, diabetes incidence or cardiovascular events using relative- and absolute-component Mediterranean diet score: The SUN cohort. *Nutr. Metab. Cardiovasc. Dis.* 2012 Mar 6. [Epub ahead of print] PubMed PMID: 22402062.

[51] Perica MM, Delas I. Essential fatty acids and psychiatric disorders. *Nutr. Clin. Pract.* 2011;26:409-25.

[52] Kaplan JR, Shively CA, Fontenot MB, Morgan TM, Howell SM, Manuck SB, Muldoon MF, Mann JJ. Demonstration of an association among dietary cholesterol, central serotonergic activity, and social behavior in monkeys. *Psychosom. Med.* 1994;56:479-84.

[53] Zhang J. Epidemiological link between low cholesterol and suicidality: a puzzle never finished. *Nutr. Neurosci.* 2011;14:268-87.

[54] Epstein LH, Paluch RA, Beecher MD, Roemmich JN. Increasing healthy eating vs. reducing high energy-dense foods to treat pediatric obesity. *Obesity* (Silver Spring) 2008;16:318-26.

[55] Corella D, Arnett DK, Tucker KL, Kabagambe EK, Tsai M, Parnell LD, Lai CQ, Lee YC, Warodomwichit D, Hopkins PN, Ordovas JM. A high intake of saturated fatty acids strengthens the association between the fat mass and obesity-associated gene and BMI. *J. Nutr.* 2011;141:2219-25.

[56] Contento IR, Williams SS, Michela JL, Franklin AB. Understanding the food choice process of adolescents in the context of family and friends. *J. Adolesc. Health* 2006;38:575-82.

[57] Panagiotopoulos C, Ronsley R, Al-Dubayee M, Brant R, Kuzeljevic B, Rurak E, Cristall A, Marks G, Sneddon P, Hinchliffe M, Chanoine JP, Mâsse LC. The centre for healthy weights--shapedown BC: a family-centered, multidisciplinary program that reduces weight gain in obese children over the short-term. *Int. J. Environ. Res. Public Health* 2011;8:4662-78.

[58] Niemeier HM, Leahey T, Palm Reed K, Brown RA, Wing RR. An acceptance-based behavioral intervention for weight loss: a pilot study. *Behav. Ther.* 2012;43:427-35.

[59] Makris A, Foster GD. Dietary approaches to the treatment of obesity. *Psychiatr. Clin. North Am.* 2011;34:813-27.

In: Low and High-Fat Diets: Myths vs. Reality
Editors: J. E. Ferreira and N. Muniz

ISBN: 978-1-62257-797-2

Chapter VI

The Comparison of Lipid Profiling in Mouse Brain and Liver after Starvation and a High-Fat Diet: A Medical Systems Biology Approach*

Vincent J. T. van Ginneken[1,†], Elwin Verheij[2], Maarten Hekman[2], Jan van der Greef[2], E. J. M. Feskens[3] and Robert E. Poelmann[1]

[1]Department of Anatomy and Embryology,
Leiden University Medical Center (LUMC) RC, Leiden, The Netherlands
[2]TNO Pharma, Analytical Systems Biology, PAJ Zeist, The Netherlands
[3]Division of Human Nutrition, Section Nutrition and Epidemiology,
Wageningen University, Wageningen, The Netherlands

And after fasting forty days and forty nights, he was hungry.

(Matthew 4:2)

Abstract

We investigated with LC-MS techniques, measuring approximately 109 lipid compounds, in mouse brain and liver tissue after 48 hours of starvation and a High-Fat Diet if brain and liver lipid composition changed. We measured Cholesterolesters (ChE), Lysophosphatidyl-cholines (LPC), Phosphatidylcholine (PC), Sphingomyelin (SPM) and Triacylglycerols (TG's) for liver tissue while for brain tissue we had an extra lipid

* A version of this chapter also appears in *Biology of Starvation in Humans and Other Organisms*, edited by Todd C. Merkin, published by Nova Science Publishers, Inc. It was submitted for appropriate modifications in an effort to encourage wider dissemination of research.

† Corresponding author: Ginneken van, V. J. T. (Vincent.vanginneken@wur.), Tel. 0031 317 481 742, fax. 0031 317 48 10 47. Department of Anatomy and Embryology, Leiden University Medical Center (LUMC) P.O.Box 9600, 2300 RC, Leiden, The Netherlands.

compound the Plasmalogens. In addition, dynamics of hepatic steatosis were determined in an *in vivo* mouse model with localized non-invasive Magnetic Resonance Spectroscopy (^{1}H-MRS) techniques. In the experimental design Male C57bl6 mice (age 8-12 weeks) were exposed to three treatments: A: They were fed a chow Diet for a period of approximately 40 days (Control group); B: They were fed a High-Fat Diet, containing 0.25% cholesterol (Ch) and 24% energy from bovine lard for a period of approximately 40 days, C: Or they were exposed to 48 hours of starvation. For whole brain tissue of these mice groups the LC-MS techniques indicated that the brain was rather invulnerable to Dietary intervention. The (phospho-) lipid-composition of the brain was unchanged in the starvation group but the cholesterol-ester content was significantly increased in the high High-Fat Diet group. These observations suggest that the brain lipid composition is insensitive to starvation but can be affected by a high High-Fat Diet. In contrast, for liver tissue both 24 h starvation and the 40 day High-Fat Diet resulted in exponential hepatic fat accumulation, although their time course (measured with ^{1}H MRS) techniques was distinctly different. Mass spectrometry (LC-MS) demonstrated for liver tissue remarkable differences in lipid profiles between treatments. ^{1}H-MRS proved to be a reliable method for frequent, repetitive determination of hepatic fat *in vivo* and a noninvasive alternative to biopsy. Moreover, LC-MS and Principal Component Analysis (PCA) demonstrated that in liver tissue different lipid end products are formed as result of Dietary composition Apparently, for liver tissue starvation and a High-Fat Diet result in a process called hepatic steatosis which is regulated under both conditions via different metabolic pathways. In addition, ^{1}H-MRS techniques demonstrated for liver that the relative amount of unsaturated bindings is significantly higher in the High-Fat Diet group ($P \leq 0.001$), which can be deducted from the relative intensities of the (CH=CH) elements and their conjugated unsaturated elements ($C\text{-}CCH_2C{=}C$). We conclude, comparing brain *vs.* liver tissue that both tissues have a totally different metabolic response to both treatments. The brain is insensitive to starvation but can be affected by a High-Fat Diet while in liver tissue both treatments result paradoxically in a hepatic steatosis. However, for the liver, the dynamics and the lipid profiles of this process of this hepatic steatosis under starvation or a High-Fat Diet are totally different.

Keywords: Mice, starvation, high-fat diet, brain, cholesterol-ester, liver, hepatic steatosis, lipid compounds, triacylglycerols, LC-MS, localized non-invasive Magnetic Resonance Spectroscopy (^{1}H-MRS) techniques

Introduction

Brain: The brain contains about 100 billion brain cells interrelated by axons and dendrites leading electrical impulses coding for information from or to the periphery. Lipids cover about 60% of the brain's dry weight making brain tissue the second most lipid-dense tissue after adipose tissue (Bryhn, 2003). Besides cholesterol, phospholipids are the main lipid component of the neurons. Phospholipids (PL) are phosophodiesters linked to a base, in the brain usually ethanolamine, as phosphatidylethanolamine (PE). PE binds two different types of fatty acids, namely unsaturated (palmic and stearic acid) and polyunsaturated fatty acids (arachidonic and docosahexaenoic acid). The fatty acid pattern differs inside the brain with different concentrations in the grey and white matter. The grey matter, localised to the grain cortex with mainly brain cells, contains more saturated fatty acids and docosahexaenoic acid (DHA) compared to the white matter. The white matter is located in the sub-cortical region and contains more oleic acid (OA) and docosatetraenoic acid (DTA) (Söderberg et al. 1991).

The myelin sheet covering the nerve axon, which is very rich in polyunsaturated fatty acids, helps conduction of electrical impulses along the axons. This conductivity is about 50 times higher compared to non-myelinated axons. Degenerative diseases of the myelin sheets such as multiple scleroses may therefore cause serious neurological defect.

Lipids play a key role in determining membrane fluidity, and changes in lipid and fatty acids composition have been reported to alter important cellular functions (Stubbs and Smith 1984, Boure et al. 1991).

We hypothesize that a High-Fat Diet may have functional and structural consequences in the brain. In order to investigate this question we used a mouse model after a period of 48 hours starvation or 40 days of High-Fat Diet in comparison to a Control group (normal chow).

With LC-MS techniques we measured Cholesterolesters (ChE), lysophosphatidylcholines (LPC), phosphatidylcholine (PC), sphingomyelin (SPM) and Triacylglycerols (TG's) and plasmalogens in these mouse groups. Changes in biochemical composition of the brain of the different mice groups might explain the observed behavioral changes after nutritional intervention in animal behavior studies which were observed in other studies (see discussion).

Liver: Hepatic steatosis was long seen as a symptom of alcoholic liver disease. In recent years, however, steatosis was found in absence of alcohol abuse and led to the definition of disorders ranging from nonalcoholic fatty liver (NAFL) to nonalcoholic steatohepatitis (NASH) (Bradbury, 2006). Currently, evidence exists that nonalcoholic fatty liver disease (NAFLD) is a component of metabolic syndrome (Marchesin, *et al.*, 2005). Metabolic syndrome affects about 20% of the US population (Ford, *et al.*, 2002) and its prevalence is strongly increasing due changing life styles and Diet (Dallman, *et al.*, 2004) combined with genetic susceptibility (Lakka, *et al.*, 2002). It is a risk factor for type 2 diabetes, premature atherosclerosis, and coronary heart disease (Baird, *et al.*, 2002). Little is known of the etiology connecting the different symptoms of metabolic syndrome, but a striking contribution of both environmental and genetic factors has been shown in animals (Den Boer, *et al.*, 2004) and humans (Lakka, Laaksonen, Lakka, Niskanen, Kumpusalo, Tuomilehto and Salonen, 2002). NAFLD is 1. the major cause of abnormal liver function in the Western world, 2. is associated with obesity and diabetes, and 3. is characterized by insulin resistance (IR). Since numerous etiological, environmental, nutritional and metabolic factors are involved in chronic liver disease (CLD), pathogenic mechanisms underlying the relationship between insulin resistance or diabetes and chronic liver disease remain to be elucidated (Picardi, *et al.*, 2006).

Hepatic steatosis is caused by increased fatty acid flux to the liver, the result of high availability of plasma Free Fatty Acids (FFA) in relation to peripheral oxidative requirements. This is observed under two conditions. First, an increase of exogenous fat, i.e. High-Fat feeding, increases liver TG (TG) content (Gauthier, *et al.*, 2003). Second, excessive influx of fatty acids into the liver, resulting from hydrolysis of stores of body adipose under conditions of overnight starvation, predisposes to hepatic steatosis. This was observed in dogs starvation overnight (Basso and Havel, 1970) and in rodents (Hashimoto, *et al.*, 2000). It is probably characteristic for all mammals under starvation, when switching from a carbohydrate to fat metabolism. The main question remains unsolved: under what Dietary conditions (restriction vs. abundance) will hepatic steatosis deteriorate from a beneficial survival strategy to the onset of pathogenesis including diabetes-2 and insulin insensitivity? In addition, the pathophysiology that leads to NAFLD is poorly understood; especially those factors that lead to progressive hepatocellular damage after TG accumulation (Adams, *et al.*, 2005).

We hypothesize that hepatic steatosis due to High-Fat Diet or starvation follows different pathways and wanted to determine the dynamics of hepatic TG accumulation using Liquid Chromatography Mass Spectroscopy (LC-MS). Moreover, as liver biopsy's have drawbacks (invasive, infection risk, haematoma formation, potentially biliary leakage) (Piccinino *et al.* 1987) and errors may occur due to inhomogeneous fatty infiltration (result of small sample volume), there is a need for new diagnostic tools that help to quantify intrahepatocellular lipid content. Here, we compared Magnetic Resonance Spectroscopy (MRS) with High Performance Thin Layer (HPTLC)-chromatography.

Material and Methods

Brain

Experimental Animals

In order to determine differences in fat composition brain under different feeding regimes, we had three treatments. Two different Diets (one regular and one High-Fat Diet) and a 48 hours starvation group. Purebred male wild-type C57bl6 mice (age 8-12 weeks), obtained from Charles River (Maastricht, The Netherlands) were used. Animal experiments were approved by the animal experimentation committee of the Leiden University Medical Centre (The Netherlands).The C57BL/6 mice strain was used as it has extensively been studied as model of control of environmental induced starvation (van Ginneken et al. 2007) and the determination of blood composition was one of the other objectives using these animals (not reported here). We had three treatments: Two feeding regimes were compared: i.) a regular Control-Chow diet Table 1 and ii.) a high-dietary situation reflected by the High-Fat diet of which the composition is given in Table 1 and Annex 1.

The High-Fat diet mice group received this diet for a period of 40 days From other studies we know that this strain wlid-type C57b16 becomes insulin insenstive after 40 days on this High-Fat Diet. For the brain experiment the mouse were starved for 48 hours which is a long period for rodents with their high metabolic rate (Blaxter 1989).

In total, 21 rodents were used: 7 mice in the Control group, 7 in the High-Fat Diet group and 7 in the 48 Starvation group. Mice were housed in a temperature-controlled room (21°C) on a 10-hour dark/14-hour light cycle.

Diet

Mice in the Control group were fed a Control-Chow standard diet (SDS.3, Special Diet Services, Witham, UK) containing about 4.3 energy percent fat (Table 1). The High-Fat Diet that was fed to mice in the High-Fat treatment group and contained 21.4 % protein, 36% carbohydrates, 24% fat, 6% fibers and 5.7% water (weight-percentages).

Before the experiment started animals of both the control group and the treatment group received unrestricted amounts of food and water. The Diet contained approximately the same caloric content: Control-Chow Diet 17 kJ/ g dm *versus* High-Fat Diet 21 kJ/ g dm (Table 1).

In Annex 1 the LC-MS lipid composition of the Control-Chow and the High-Fat Diet are given determined according to the method described further in this paragraph under the following section.

Table 1. Food constitution of the mice chow: "Normal Chow" for the Control group (Special Diet Services, SDS No.3, Witham, UK) and the High-Fat Diet (Arie Blok, food code 4032.05, Woerden, The Netherlands) based on bovine lard and 0.25% cholesterol

Proximate Analysis	Control-Chow (SDS.3)	Proximate Analysis	High-Fat Diet (4032.05)
Moisture (%)	10.00	Moisture (%)	5.74
Crude Oil (%)	4.25	Crude Fat (Bovine Lard) (%)	24.00
Crude Protein (%)	22.39	Crude Protein (%)	21.44
Crude Fiber (%)	4.21	Crude Fiber (%)	6.16
Minerals	7.56	Minerals	2.25
Nitrogen Free Extract	51.20	Nitrogen Free Extract	36.19
-----	-	Cholesterol	0.25
TOTAL	99.61	TOTAL	96.03
Measured Energy (Bombcalorimetry, [kJ/g dm]	16.86	Measured Energy (Bombcalorimetry, [kJ/g dm]	21.46

Mass Spectrometry: LC-MS of Lipids and Fatty Acids of Food Composition (Control-Vs. High-Fat Diet)

With LC-MS techniques (see further), the lipid composition of the Standard (mean ± SD (n=5)) and the High-Fat Diet (mean ± SD (n=5)) was determined as described below for brain tissue (results see Annex 1).

Brain-Tissue Sampling and Pretreatment for LC-MS

The whole mouse brain was removed from the skull. A tissue homogenate (~10% wet weight/ vol) in PBS (phosphate-buffered saline) was made by stirring the tissue in a closed tube with small glass globules.

Mass Spectrometry: LC-MS of Lipids and Fatty Acids in Brain Tissue

After brain removal, fifty µl of the well mixed tissue homogenate (brain tissue) was extracted with 300 µl of isopropanol and was mixed with 1000 µl IPA containing 4 internal standards standards (IS: C17:0 lysophosphatidylcholine, di-C12:0 phosphatidylcholine, tri-C17:0 glycerol ester, C17:0 cholesterol ester and heptadecanoic acid (C17:0)) and placed in an ultrasonic bath for 5 minutes. Thereafter, samples were centrifuged at 10000 rpm for 3 minutes followed by injection of 10 µl on a Thermo LTQ (linear ion-trap) LC-MS Instrument (Thermo Electron, San JoAfter mixing and centrifugation the supernatant was transferred to autosampler vial. Lipids were separated on a 150 x 3.2 mm i.d. C4 Prosphere column (Alltech, US) using a methanol gradient in 5 mM ammonium acetate and 0.1% formic acid (mobile phase A: 5% methanol, mobile phase B: 90% methanol). The flowrate was 0.4 ml/min and the gradient was as follows: 0-2 min – 20%B, 2-3 min – 20% to 80%B, 3-15 min

– 80% to 100%B, 15-25 min – hold 100%B, 25-32 min –condition at 20% B. The instrument used was a Thermo LTQ equipped with a Thermo Surveyor HPLC pump. Data were acquired by scanning the instrument from m/z 300 to 1200 at a scan rate of approximately two scans/s in positive ion ESI mode. The FFA LC-MS platform employs the same sample and similar HPLC conditions as the lipid method. The ammonium acetate concentration is 2 mM instead of 5 mM and no formic acid was added. The gradient: 0-2 min – 30%B, 2-3 min – 30% to 70%B, 3-10 min – 70% to 100%B, 10-15 min – hold 100%B, 15-20 min –condition at 30% B. Detection of FFA is performed in negative ion ESI mode. Combined the two methods provide (semi)quantitative data for approximately 200 different identified lipids and FFA. Each extract was injected three times (10 μl), once for the LC-MS FFA platform and two times for the LC-MS lipid platform. Furthermore, a quality control (QC) sample was prepared by pooling the samples. The pool was divided into 10 μl aliquots that were extracted the same as the study samples. The QC samples were placed at regular intervals in the analysis sequence (one QC after every 10 samples). The QC samples served two purposes. The first is a regular quality control sample to monitor the LC-MS response in time. After the response has been characterized, the QC samples were used as standards of unknown composition to calibrate the data . The 6 dominant lipid classes observed with these two methods are the lyso-phosphatidylcholines (IS used: C17:0 lyso-phosphatidylcholine), phosphatidylcholines (IS used: di-C12:0 phosphatidylcholine), sphingomyelines (IS used: di-C12:0 phosphatidylcholine), cholesterolesters (IS used: C17:0 cholesterol ester), triacylglycerols (TG's) (IS used: tri-C17:0 glycerol ester), and free fatty acids (IS used: C17:0 FFA). In addition to these lipids, the extracts also contain minor lipids, but these were either not detected (concentration too low relative to very abundant lipids like phosphatidylcholines and TG's) or they were not included in data processing. The LC-MS lipid and LC-MS FFA data were processed using the LC-Quan software (Thermo).

Analysis of Plasmalogens in Brain Tissue

Analysis of Cholesterolesters (ChE), Lysophosphatidyl-cholines (LPC), Phosphatidylcholine (PC), Sphingomyelin (SPM) and TG's were performed by LC-MS techniques based on molecular mass and retention time using internal standards (see paragraph above). Because for the Plasmalogens no standards exists mass lists determined by (Hsu and Turk, 2005), using atmospheric pressure chemical ionization (APCI) and electrospray inonization (ESI) mass spectrometry (MS) techniques were used. These mass lists were published on internet www.byrdwell.com/plasmogensandwww.byrdwell.com/-Phosphatidyl-Ethanolamine.

Calculations and Statistics for Brain Tissue

For all measured lipid parameters of whole brain tissue given in Table 2 and Annex 2, the mean value of the Control mice group was compared to the mean value of the Starvation and High-Fat Diet mice groups. Statistics were performed via SAS (Statistical Analyzing Software) using an one-way ANOVA for differences between control and starvation groups. $P \leq 0.05$ was considered as statistically significant. Normality of the data and homogeneity of variances were checked by Kolmogorov-Smirnov and F_{max} tests, respectively. Principal Component Analysis (PCA) was carried out on the parameters of lipid metabolism measured via reversed phase liquid chromatography coupled to mass spectrometry. This type of analysis allows one to simultaneously examine the relative state of individuals according to three or more variables. We used Principal Component Analysis (PCA) statistical methods, which are specially developed, for application in biomedical research (van der Greef et al., 2007, 2008) using TNO IMPRESS, EQUEST and WINLIN software.

Principal components analysis (PCA) is a classic statistical technique used to reduce multidimensional data sets to lower dimensions for analysis (Jackson 1991). The applications include exploratory data analysis and data for generating predictive models. PCA involves the computation of the eigenvalue decomposition or singular value decomposition of a data set, usually after mean centering the data for each attribute.

The results of a PCA are usually discussed in terms of scores and loadings. The score and loading vectors give a concise and simplified description of the variance present in the dataset (Jackson 1991).

A principal component is a linear combination of the original variables (in this case: lipid concentrations) and the magnitude of its eigenvalue is a measure of the explained variance. Typically only a few principal components are required to explain >90% of the total variance in the data. In other words PCA is a dimension reduction method, e.g. from >100 lipid attributes in the data to only a 4 principal components, which simplifies data visualization.

Liver

Experimental Set Up

All three experiments were approved by the Animal Authorization Committee of Leiden University Medical Centre (The Netherlands).

Liver-Experiment 1: MRS-Test

Male, 12-16 weeks old C57Bl/6 mice (N_{total}=63) were housed in a temperature-controlled room (21°C) on a 10-hour dark/14-hour light cycle. Before the experiment started all animals had unrestricted access to food and water. Three treatments were compared: *Treatment A* (Control, n=33) received ad libitum standard mouse chow (RM3, Special Diet Services, Witham, UK) and water; *Treatment B* (24h starvation, n=24) only water; and *Treatment C* (n=6) an ad-lib High-Fat Diet (4032.05, Arie Blok, Woerden, The Netherlands) and water. The standard lab chow contained about 12 energy percent fat, while the High-Fat Diet contained 24% protein, 39% carbohydrates, 24% fat, 6% fibers, 7% water (weight-percentages) and 0.25% cholesterol. Mice under *Treatment A* were fasted 4 hours before the experiment to standardize their metabolic rate.

Mice under *Treatment A* were used to validate the use of the ^{1}H MRS method compared to HPTLC. After measuring a voxel of the liver *in vivo* in the Bruker 9.4 Tesla magnet their livers were removed under anesthesia. Liver samples were homogenized in phosphate buffered saline (~10% wet weight/vol) and their protein content was measured by a Lowry assay (Lowry*, et al.*, 1951). Lipid content was determined using the Bligh and Dyer extraction method (Bligh and Dyer, 1959) and by separating the lipids using High Performance Thin Layer Chromatography (HPTLC) on silica gel plates (Havekes*, et al.*, 1987), followed by TINA2.09 software analysis (Raytest Isotopen Meβgeräte GmbH, Straubenhardt, Germany) (Post*, et al.*, 1997). Enzymatic assays of the TG content were performed with a Roche Diagnostics kit.

Mice under *Treatment B* were used to study dynamics of TG accumulation during a period of starvation. Four separate groups of mice fasted for 0, 5, 12 or 24 hrs. (6 mice for each time point, total 24). Four groups were used as handling and anesthesized animals within 24 hours would have too much impact on their metabolism. Qualification and quantification of the lipid resonance spectra were performed in the comparison t=0 *vs.* t=24 hrs. Livers were not removed.

Treatment C aimed to study TG accumulation dynamics during a High-Fat Diet. On day t=0 the initial status of the animals (n=6) was measured. On day 4, 12, 18, 28 and 40 a repetitive liver lipid spectrum was made using ^{1}H-MRS; in this way each animal served as its own control over time. Qualification and quantification of lipid resonance spectra were performed in the comparison t=0 *vs.* t=40 days.

In Vivo Localized Magnetic Resonance Spectroscopy of Liver Tissue

For imaging, mice were induced with 4% isoflurane in air (50%) and O_2 (50%) and anesthesia was maintained with ~1.5% isoflurane. All images and spectra were respiration-gated using an air-pressure cushion connected to a laptop using Biotrig software (Bruker, Rheinstatten, Germany). Anesthesia depth was constantly regulated to maintain a stable respiration rate during the experiment. *In vivo* ^{1}H MRS localized spectroscopy was carried out on a 9.4 T vertical bore imaging system equipped with an Avance console controlled by ParaVision 3.01 software, Bruker Biospin (Karlsruhe, Germany). A Bruker Micro2.5 gradient system of 1 T/m was used with a solenoidal 30 mm I.D. RF volume coil in transmit/receive mode. Animal placement in the magnet was assessed by three orthogonal slices acquired with a gradient echo protocol (TE 4.0, TR 200 ms, 1 average, FLASH, hermite pulse, 30¡, 3.0cm FOV, 128X128 matrix giving resolution 0.234mm, slice thickness 1.0mm, with respiratory triggering).

The animal position was adjusted to center the liver in the coil. A second gradient echo protocol (TE 4.0, TR 220 ms, 1 average, FLASH, hermite pulse, 30¡, 3.0cm FOV, 128X128 matrix giving resolution 0.234mm, slice thickness 0.8mm, with respiratory triggering) with 6-9 x 1 mm axial slices transecting the liver was used to localize the voxel of interest. The global shim was optimized manually with a gated single pulse method (90¡ block pulse excitation, 500ms repetition time. Global shimming was used as cardiac motion and low signal to noise made localized shimming difficult. Spectra were acquired with a PRESS protocol.

Parameters were: TE/TR = 50/3000ms, 256 averages, 0.5 ms hermite pulses, $(2.5)^3$ mm voxel, 4K FID, 6009.6154 Hz spectral width, no outer volume suppression. Preliminary spectra of 3 scout voxels (2.5mm cubed, 32 scans) were acquired from apparently homogeneous regions of the liver as seen on the axial gradient echo slices. Voxels were placed near the liver margins to avoid significant blood vessels and to obtain more homogeneous tissue. Spectra from scout voxels were compared for line width and apparent lipid concentration. A voxel with narrow, undistorted line shapes and a representative lipid concentration was chosen.

Assessment of MRS Data

Spectra were Fourier transformed with 10 Hz exponential line broadening and baseline corrected. Spectroscopic evaluation of hepatic steatosis was limited to quantification of two dominant peaks in the MRS spectrum: water at 4.6 ppm and TG's (TG) at 1.2 ppm, to calculate the fat/water ratio. This method is based on two assumptions: i). methylene proton signals estimated by spectroscopy are specific for the total mobile TG fraction; ii). water content is usable as concentration standard.

For validation, we measured TG in mice with different degrees of liver fattening using our *in vivo* ^{1}H MRS protocol. The integration limits were slightly varied depending on the signal line widths in the final spectrum. The obtained spectral resolution allowed identification of resonances arising from saturated and unsaturated fatty acid moieties assigned according to the spectrum of Corbin et al. (Corbin, *et al.*, 2004).

Liver-Experiment 2: Determination of the T2 of Fat and Water Components

A T2 measurement was performed to assess the influence of T2 weighing on the fat/water ratio for some animals under each treatment (N=3 for each group). The PRESS protocol was applied with an increasing echo time of 46, 66, and 86 ms. Water and CH_2 lipid peaks were quantified as above and T2 was determined assuming mono-exponential decay, using the function $S(t) = A + S(0) * \exp(-t/T2)$.

Liver-Experiment 3: LC-MS of Lipids and Fatty Acids

Eighteen mice were randomly assigned to one of three treatments. *Treatment A* was the control group (n=6) and received ad-lib standard lab chow and water during 40 days. During *Treatment B,* animals were deprived from food for 24 hours (n=5). *Treatment C* were animals that received a High-Fat Diet during 40 days (n=7).

Mass Spectrometry LC-MS of Lipids and Fatty Acids in Liver Tissue

Lipids and free fatty acids (FFA) in liver tissue were analyzed with electrospray LC-MS as described above for brain tissue.

Calculations and Statistics for Liver Tissue

For all with LC-MS techniques measured lipid compounds given in Annex 2, the mean value of the Control mice group was compared to the mean value of the Starvation and High-Fat Diet mice groups as described above for brain tissue.

Results

Control Chow and the High-Fat Diet: The chromatogram of a sample with run on the LC-MS with a Control-Chow food sample and a High-Fat diet food sample is displayed in Figure 1. Three groups of chemical compounds can be clearly distinguished in this Figure 1: A). After 9-11 minutes retention time the lysophosphatidylcholines (LPC) become visible with at 11.5 minutes the Internal Standard di-lauroyl-phoshatidylcholine (IS); B). After 13-16 minutes the plasmalogens, phosphatidyl cholines (PC), Sphingomyelins (SPM) and phosphatidylethanolamines (PE) become visible; and C). After 18-19 minutes the TG's and Cholesterol-esters (ChE).

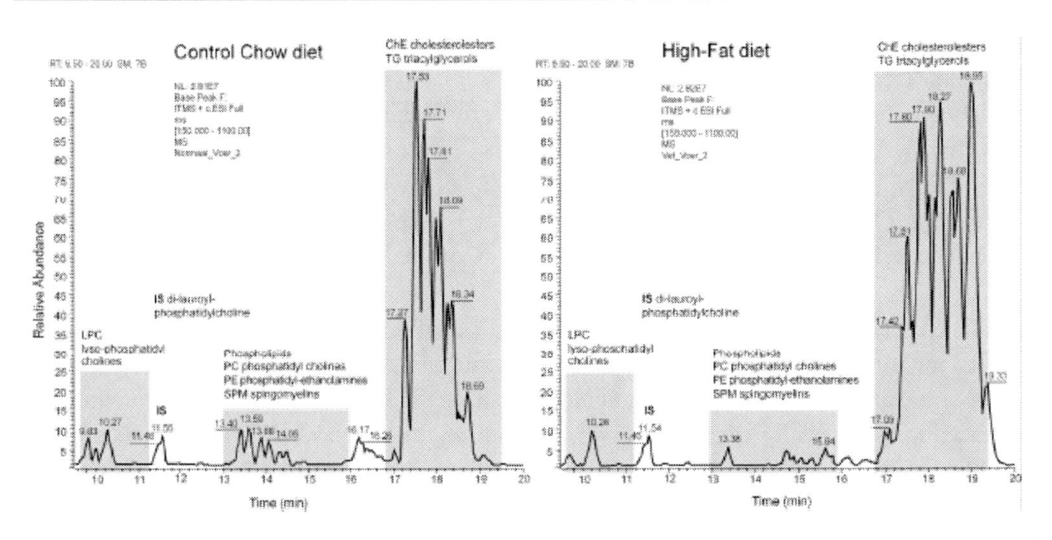

Figure 1. Chromatogram with run on the LC-MS with a Control-Chow food sample (left) and a High-Fat diet food sample (right). Separation of the different lipid compounds is based on molecular mass and retention time using internal standards.

In Annex 1 are in detail the different lipid compounds for both diets given. The following highly significant differences between the two diets can be observed:

1. *1000%-10,000%:* The following compounds are in the range 1000%-10,000% higher in the High-Fat diet in comparison to the Control-Chow diet: C26-1-DG, C36-0-DG, C22-0-SPM, C44-2-TG, C44-3-TG, C46-3-TG, C46-4-TG, C48-0-TG, C48-3-TG, C48-4-TG, C50-1-TG, C50-2-TG, C50-3-TG, C50-4-TG, C52-1-TG, C54-2-TG, C56-1-TG, C56-9-TG.
2. *> 10,000%:* The following compounds are in the range > 10,000% higher in the High-Fat diet in comparison to the Control-Chow diet: C44-0-TG, C44-1-TG, C46-0-TG, C46-1-TG, C46-2-TG, C48-1-TG, C48-2-TG, C50-0-TG, C54-1-TG.

So comparing the diet composition of the two used diets for lipid compounds (Annex 1), we can conclude that the major differences in the High-Fat diet, in comparison to the Control-Chow diet, are mainly in the TG's compounds and mainly the elongated ones (>10,000% increase).

Brain: The chromatogram of mouse brain (Control animal) is displayed in Figure 2. Three groups of chemical compounds can be clearly distinguished in this Figure 2: A). After 9-11 minutes retention time the lysophosphatidylcholines (LPC) become visible with at 11.5 minutes the Internal Standard di-lauroyl-phoshatidylcholine (IS); B). After 13-16 minutes the plasmalogens, phosphatidyl cholines (PC), Sphingomyelins (SPM) and phosphatidylethanolamines (PE) become visible; and C). After 18-19 minutes the TG's (TG) and Cholesterol-esters (ChE).

The most important observation of this study was that the Cholesterol-esters in High-Fat diet exposed brains are significantly increased (Table 2). Out of eight Cholesterol-esters five showed a strong significant increase ($P \leq 0.0009$-$P \leq 0.0013$) (Table 2). The compound 20:3-ChE of the High-Fat Diet group increased with 318% in the High-Fat Diet group in comparison with the Control group while the compound 18:2-ChE of the Control group increased with 209% in the High-Fat Diet group (Table 2). Control *vs.* Starvation showed no significant changes while this was also not the case for Starvation group *vs.* High-Fat Diet group (*vide* Annex 2)

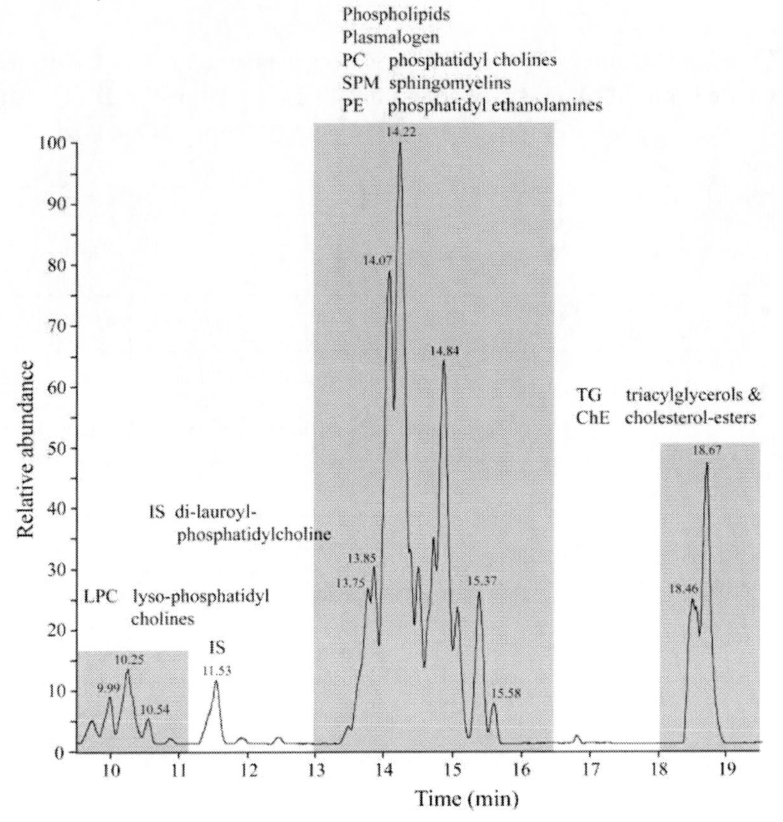

Figure 2. Chromatogram obtained by LC-MS technique of the whole brain homogenate of a mouse from the Control group.

In Annex 2 minor changes in whole brain of a High-Fat diet and 48 h Starvation exposed groups are given. No other tendency could be observed.

Control versus Starvation group: For LPC, SPM, DG, PC, PE, Plasmalogen's and TG's the most significant changes were observed between the Starvation and the High-Fat Diet group without tendency were 12 out of 61 compounds (Annex 2).

Control versus High-Fat Diet group: For LPC, SPM, DG, PC, PE, Plasmalogen's and TG's the most significant changes were observed between the Starvation and the High-Fat Diet group without tendency were 5 out of 61 compounds (Annex 2).

Starvation versus High-Fat Diet group: For LPC, SPM, DG, PC, PE, Plasmalogen's and TG's the most significant changes were observed between the Starvation and the High-Fat Diet group without tendency were 23 out of 61 compounds (Annex 2).

Principal Component Analysis (PCA) was carried out on different 50 compounds. In Figure 3 the score plot (PC1 and PC2) for starvation, fatty brain *vs.* control brain is shown. Principal components 1 accounted for 61 % PC of the total variance. Principal components 2 accounted for 22 % PC of the total variance while.

It is evident from Figure 3 that the Control, Starvation and High-Fat Diet exposed mice groups are not separated for LC-MS measured lipid composition in whole brain despite the significant increase in Cholesterol-esters in High-Fat Diet exposed brain (Table 2).

Table 2. Significant changes in Cholesterol-esters measured with LC-MS techniques in the whole brain of black six mice fed for 40 days a High-Fat Diet containing 0.25% cholesterol (Ch) and 24% energy from bovine lard

Compound	Control Diet (A) (Mean ± SD)	Starvation (B) (Mean ± SD)	High-Fat Diet (C) (Mean ± SD)	Kruskal – Wallis	P-value			Change in %		
					A vs. B	A vs. C	B vs. C	A vs. B	A vs. C	B vs. C
C16-0-ChE	0.0028 ± 0.0005	0.0069 ± 0.0086	0.0049 ± 0.0011	*0.022	0.2716	***0.0009	0.5624	245.24	175.90	71.73
C16-1-ChE	0.0060 ± 0.0008	0.0130 ± 0.0196	0.0102 ± 0.0024	**0.005	0.4079	**0.0021	0.7184	215.47	169.51	78.67
C18-0-ChE	0.0149 ± 0.0009	0.0160 ± 0.0016	0.0161 ± 0.0017	0.580	0.1571	0.1563	0.9220	107.43	108.00	100.53
C18-1-ChE	0.0229 ± 0.0017	0.0407 ± 0.0443	0.0314 ± 0.0046	**0.004	0.3483	**0.0013	0.5915	178.01	137.35	77.16
C18-2-ChE	0.0042 ± 0.0016	0.0163 ± 0.0314	0.0087 ± 0.0029	*0.017	0.3663	**0.0058	0.5351	392.15	209.09	53.32
C20-3-ChE	0.0010 ± 0.0004	0.0026 ± 0.0035	0.0032 ± 0.0010	**0.002	0.3049	***0.0004	0.6531	255.21	318.29	124.72
C20-4-ChE	0.0118 ± 0.0043	0.0156 ± 0.0078	0.0201 ± 0.0037	**0.006	0.3110	**0.0032	0.1818	131.56	169.98	129.20
C22-6-ChE	0.0057 ± 0.0026	0.0250 ± 0.0508	0.0077 ± 0.0013	0.154	0.3743	0.1005	0.3847	440.97	135.14	30.65

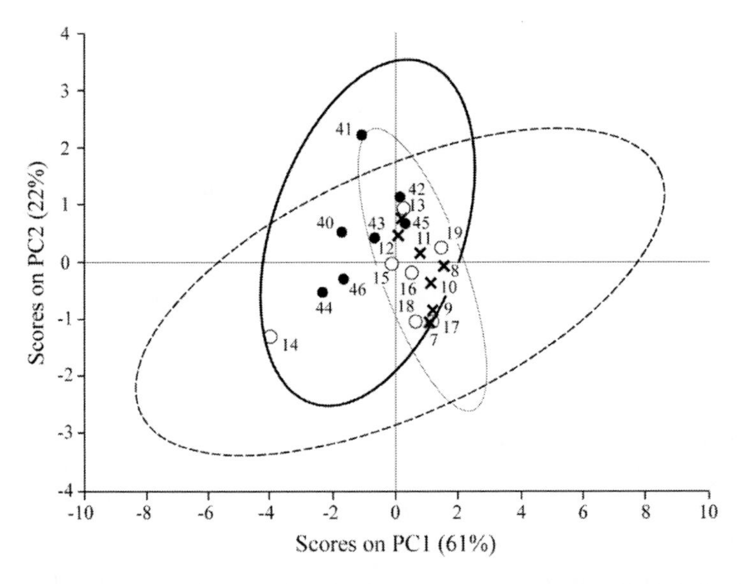

Figure 3. Canonical correlation of LC-MS (ES) data is a study of the lipid analysis in brain homogenate of a control mouse group (○), one group starved 48 hours (●), and one was exposed 40 days to a High-Fat Diet (x). Principal component analysis (PCA) was performed on the lipid components in the brain homogenate of the three groups. Each data point on the plot represents a separate measurement of metabolites in brain homogenate with LC-MS techniques on 1 animal.

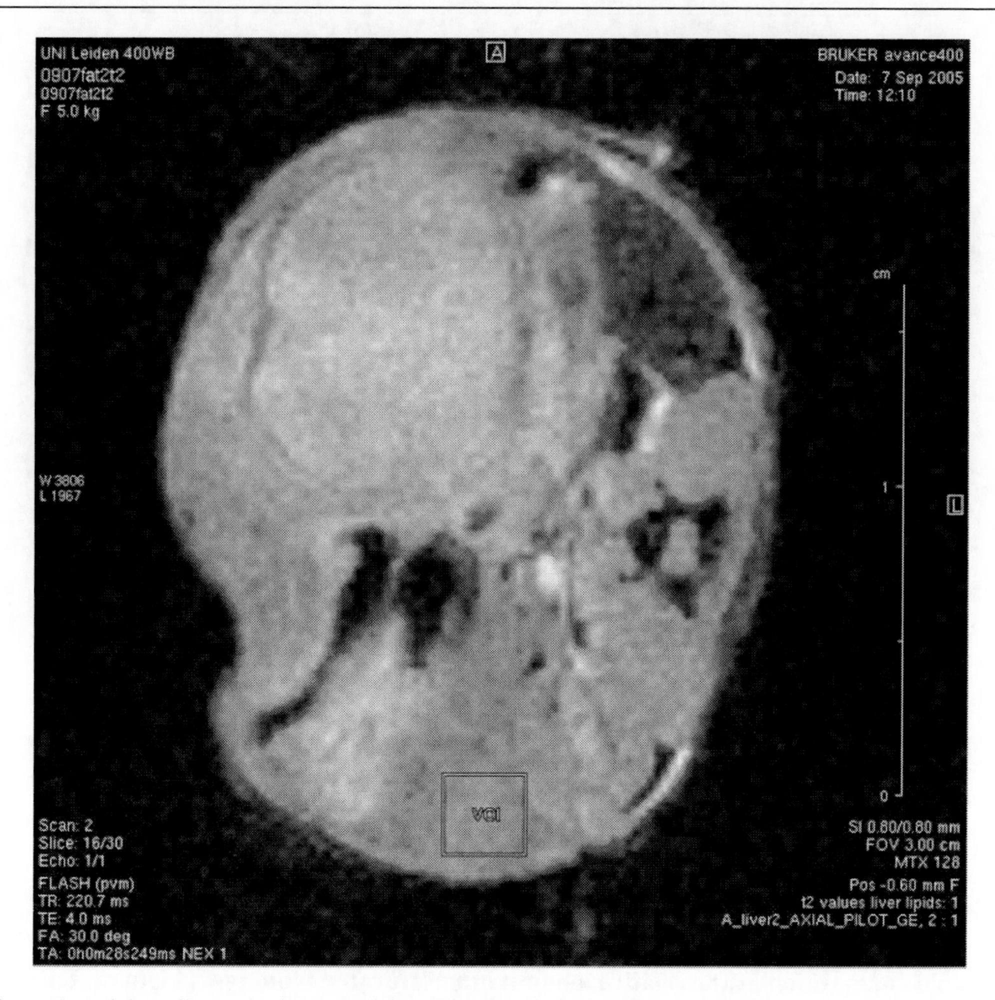

Figure 4. Axial gradient echo images of the abdomen of a Control male C57bl6 mouse (age 8-12 weeks). Selected voxel in liver tissue, 2.5 x 2.5 x 2.5 mm.

Liver

Liver-Experiment 1: MRS-Test

In Figure 4 an image of a cross section of the liver of an anaesthetized mouse is given with a selected voxel. In Figure 5 the two dominant peaks (water at 4.6 ppm and TG's at 1.2 ppm) are visualized of the selected voxel (≈localized spectroscopy). Using Foley's protocol (Browning and Horton, 2004), all lipid resonances were quantified separately at the begin and end of each experiment.

Treatment B (starvation) *vs. Treatment C* (High-Fat Diet) revealed different lipid compositions: the relative amount of unsaturated bindings was higher under *Treatment* C ($P \leq 0.001$), which can be deducted from the relative intensities of the (CH=CH) elements and their conjugated unsaturated elements ($C\text{-}CCH_2C\text{=}C$) (*vide* Table 3).

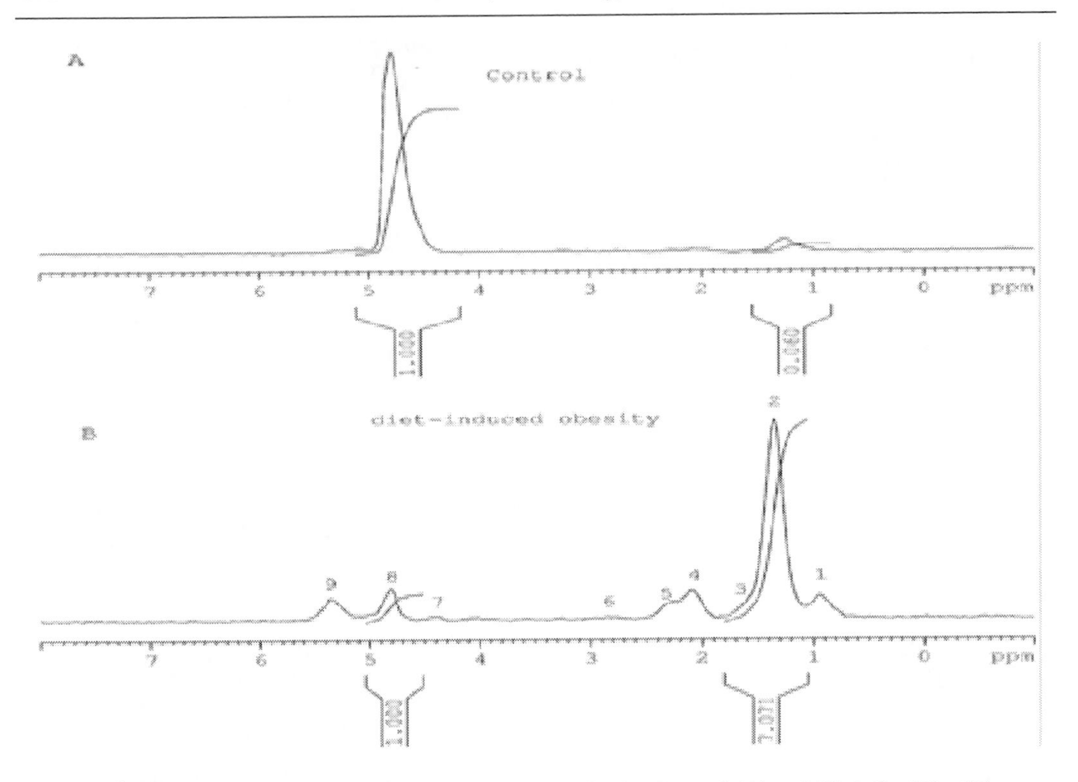

Figure 5. ^{1}H MRS-spectrum of liver tissue from a mouse in the Control (A) and High-Fat Diet (B) groups. Lipid resonances are: 1: triacylglycerol terminal methyl; 2: methylene $(CH_2)_n$; 3: CH_2CH_2CO; 4: $CH_2C=C$; 5: CH_2CO; 6: $C=CCH_2C=C$; 7: CH_2OCOR; 8: H_2O 9: CH=CH.

Table 3. Shows neutral lipid resonances in vivo in liver measured with localized MRS spectroscopy. The comparison of treatment B vs. C revealed important differences in lipid composition as the relative amount of unsaturated bindings is higher after Treatment C (P≤0.001). This is deduced from the relative intensities of the (CH=CH) elements and their conjugated unsaturated elements (C-CCH2C=C)

Nr.	Compound	Treatment A (Control)	Treatment B (Starvation) before	Treatment B (Starvation) after	Treatment C (High-Fat Diet) before	Treatment C (High-Fat Diet) after
1	Triacylglycerol terminal methyl	0	0	0.33 ± 0.01	0	0.33 ± 0.36
2	Methylene $(CH_2)n$	0.08 ± 0.01	0.11 ± 0.04	3.00 ± 1.41**	0.12 ± 0.05	3.35 ± 3.42 **
3	CH_2CH_2CO	0	0	0.07 ± 0.02	0	0.10 ± 0.07
4	$CH_2CH=C$	0	0	0	0	0.45 ± 0.45
5	CH_2CO	0	0	0	0	0.29 ± 0.28
6	$C=CCH_2C=C$	0	0	0.03 ± 0.09	0	0.14 ± 0.26
7	CH_2OCOR	0	0	0	0	0.08 ± 0.06
8	Water (H_2O)	1	1	1	1	1
9	CH=CH	0	0	0.05 ± 0.04	0	0.36 ± 0.38

**denotes significantly difference $P \leq 0.001$.

Liver-Experiment 2: Determination of the T2 of Fat and Water Components

The T2 of the fat and water components was determined to assess the influence of T2-weighting on the fat/water ratio (*vide* Table 4). The water T2 was significantly shorter than that of fat for both regimes. The fat T2 significantly decreased after starvation ($p<0.05$), which reflects differences in fat composition.

Liver-Experiment 3: LC-MS of Lipids and Fatty Acids

The chromatogram of mouse liver (Control animal) is displayed in Figure 6. Three groups of chemical compounds can be clearly distinguished in this Figure 6: A). After 9-11 minutes retention time the lysophosphatidylcholines (LPC) become visible with at 11.5 minutes the Internal Standard di-lauroyl-phoshatidylcholine (IS); B). After 13-16 minutes the plasmalogens, phosphatidyl cholines (PC), Sphingomyelins (SPM) and phosphatidy-lethano-lamines (PE) become visible; and C). After 18-19 minutes the TG's and Cholesterol-esters (ChE). For comparison see the chromatogram of the liver of a mouse exposed to 24h of fasting in (van Ginneken et al. 2007: figure 2, page 1267).

Table 4. T2 values of water and fat with increasing echo time (n=3 per treatment)

Treatment	Water T2 (ms)	Fat T2 (ms)
A (Control)	16.6 ± 2.10	34.2 ± 5.31
B (Starvation)	15.9 ± 3.58	22.0 ± 5.88
C (High-Fat Diet)	17.8 ± 3.37	32.0 ± 7.74

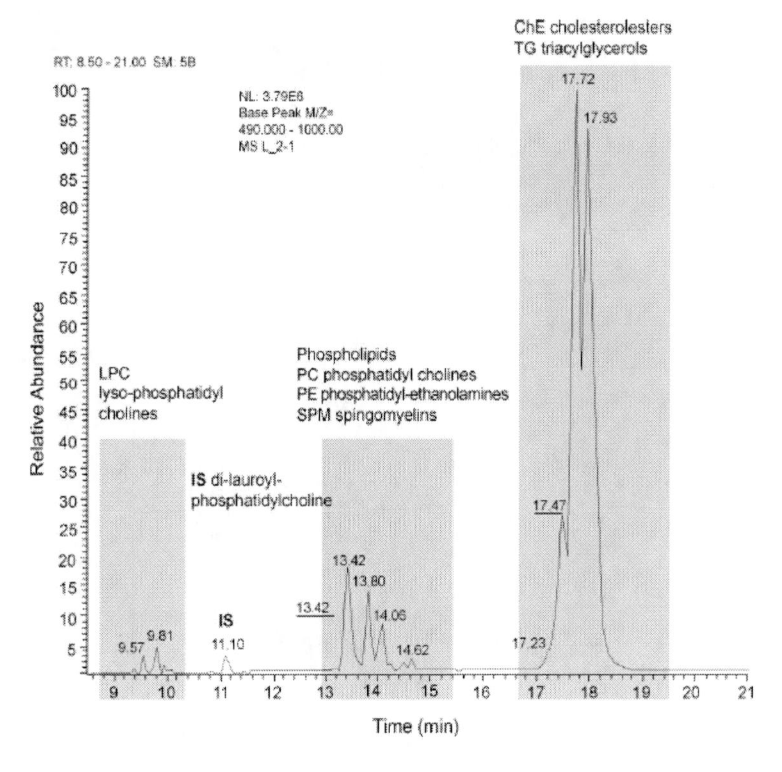

Figure 6. Chromatogram obtained by LC-MS technique of a mouse liver of a Control animal.

The 3-D images of LC-MS measurements are displayed in Figure 7. Three main lipid compounds were identified: lysophospatidylcholines, phosphatidylcholines and TG's. Note the difference in TG's between the starvation and High-Fat Diet exposed livers. Next, a within-subject comparison was made using conventional High Performance Thin layer Chromatography on excised liver tissue (*vide* Figure 8). We found a very high correlation coefficient (r = 0.97, $p \leq 0.001$). The dynamics of TG accumulation during starvation is described by the formula $Y=0.0473e^{0.1343x}$ ($R^2=0.9827$, *vide* Figure 9). Similar accumulation took place when mice were exposed to a 40-day period of High-Fat Diet (*vide* Figure 10). This process can be described by an e-function: $Y=0.0983e^{0.0586x}$ ($R^2=0.8941$). Thus, TG accumulation in the liver follows an exponential course both during starvation and a High-Fat Diet. All lipid compounds measured with LC-MS techniques in the liver of the different mouse groups: *Treatment A* (Control), *Treatment B* (24 h Starvation), and *Treatment C* (High-Fat Diet exposed) are given in Annex 3.

Liver: Treatment A (Control) Vs. Treatment B (Starvation)

When comparing *Treatment A* (Control) *vs. Treatment B* (Starvation) we found that all lysophosphatidylcholines in liver tissue increased (P≤0.0001), except for 20:3-LPC that decreased under *Treatment B* (Annex 3).

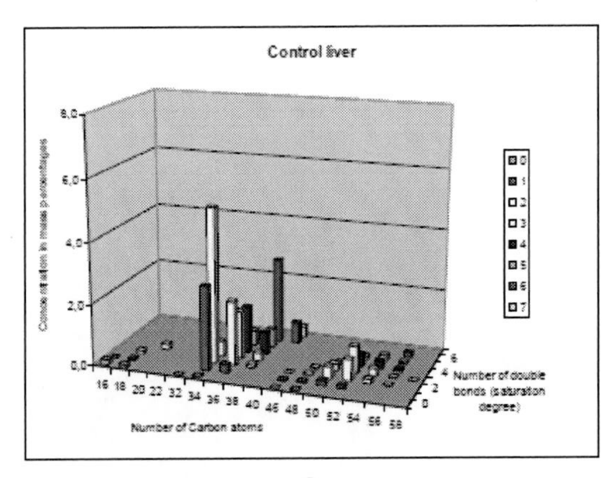

a

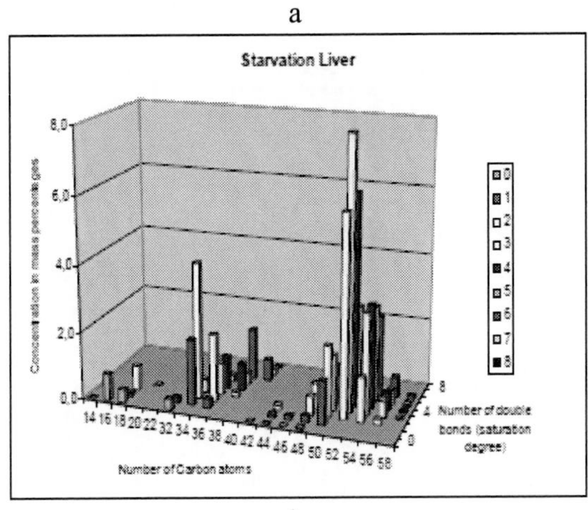

b

Figure 7. (Continued).

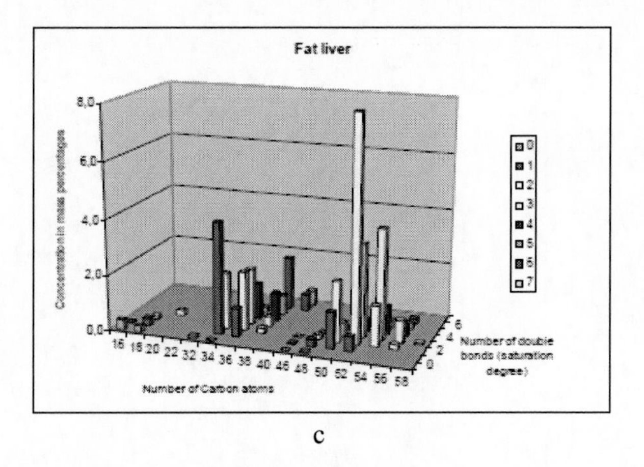

c

Figure 7. 3D-graphs of LC-MS measurements under Treatment A (Control), Treatment B (Starvation) and Treatment C (High-Fat Diet).

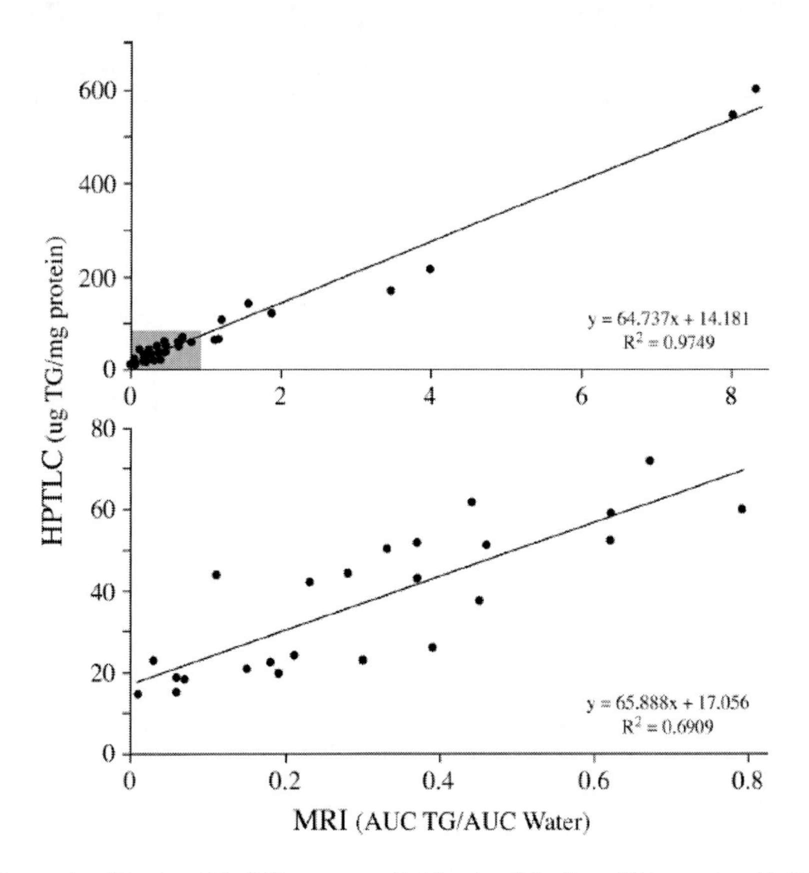

Figure 8. Comparing 33 mice with different water/lipid ratio of the liver. TG content with 1H- MRS vs. High Performance Thin Layer (HPTLC)-chromatography on whole liver homogenate.

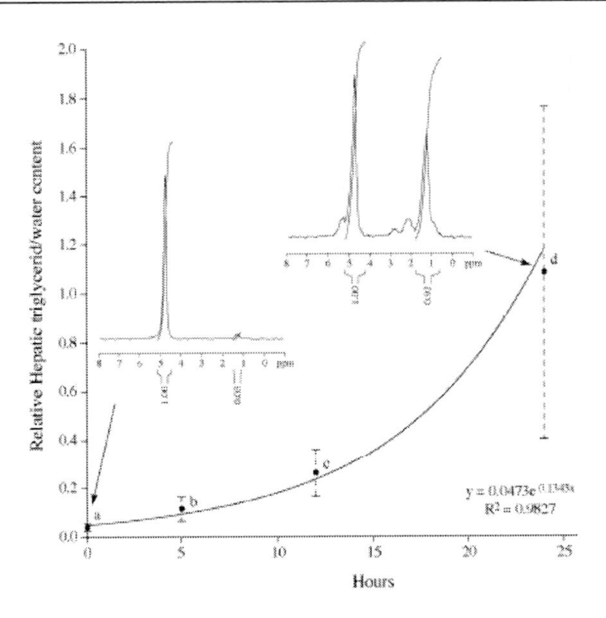

Figure 9. Relative TG/water ratio in mice (N=24) under Treatment B (starvation) as measured by 1H-MRS. Each point: mean ± SD. Measuring points t=0, 5, 12 and 24 hours. Significance: a-d: $P \leq 0.0001$; b-d: $P \leq 0.0001$, c-d: $P \leq 0.001$.

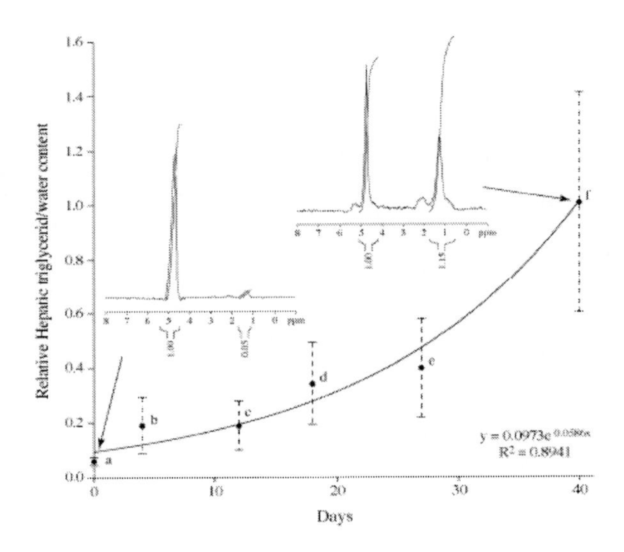

Figure 10. Relative TG/water ratio in mice (N=6) after Treatment C (High-Fat Diet) as measured by 1H-MRS. Each point: mean ± SD. Measuring points t=0, 4, 12, 18, 27 and 40 days. Significance: a-d: $P \leq 0.021$; a-e: $P \leq 0.007$; a-f: $P \leq 0.0001$; b-f: $P \leq 0.0001$, c-f: $P \leq 0.0001$, d-f: $P \leq 0.0001$, e-f: $P \leq 0.0001$.

Twelve out of 15 measured phosphatidylcholines remained unchanged. Only three (34:1-PC, 34:2-PC and 34:4-PC) showed a significant drop after starvation (Annex 3). Two of four cholesterol esters showed a remarkable increase under *Treatment B:* 18:1-ChE (1637%) and 18:2-ChE (1187%), making them possible biomarker candidates. Twenty-five TG's were measured in liver tissue of animals under Treatment B. All showed significant increases, except 46:0-TG. Three candidate biomarkers were identified: 46:2-TG, 50:4-TG and 52:5-TG increased with 9088%, 2634% and 2894% respectively.

Liver: Treatment A (Control) Vs. Treatment C (High-Fat Diet Exposed)

When comparing *Treatment A* (Control) *vs.* Treatment C (High-Fat Diet exposed liver) 6 of 7 lysophosphatidylcholines increased. *Treatment C* did not affect 18:2-LPC (Annex 3). Five phosphatidylcholines (out of 17) declined with *Treatment C* (32:0-PC, 34:2-PC, 34:3-PC, 36:5-PC, and 38:6-PC), while five others increase (34:1-PC, 36:1-PC, 36:3-PC, 38:2-PC and 40:7-PC) (Annex 1). Seven phosphatidylcholines in liver tissue (34:0-PC, 36:2-PC, 36:4-PC, 38:3-PC, 38:5-PC and 40:6-PC) are unaffected (Annex 3). The increase of 36:1PC (378%) after *Treatment C* is remarkable. Another study (Van Ginneken et al., unpublished results) revealed that this compound increased in heart muscle (400%) and blood plasma (1493%), making it a biomarker candidate. All 5 cholesterol esters showed an increase (Annex 3). Compound 16:1-ChE increased with 799% after *Treatment C*, while compound 18:1-ChE increased with 722%. Twenty-two out of 26 TG's increased after *Treatment C*. Only four TG's (50:4-TG, 52:4-TG, 54:5-TG and 56:6-TG) showed no change.

Liver: Treatment B (Starvation) Vs. Treatment C (High-Fat Diet Exposed)

Five out of 6 lysophosphatidylcholines dropped after *Treatment C* (16:0-LPC, 18:0-LPC, 18:2-LPC and 22:6-LPC), while 2 (18:1-LPC and 20:3-LPC) increased significantly (Annex 3). Four out of 15 phosphatidylcholines 4 (32:0-PC, 34:2-PC, 34:3-PC and 36:5-PC) dropped, 2 remained unaffected (36:2-PC, 40:6-PC) and 9 increased. Four cholesterol esters showed a significant decrease (Annex 3). Twenty-five TG's were measured. Three (46:0-TG, 54:3-TG, 56:3-TG) increased after Treatment C but not after Treatment B. For 7 TG's (48:0-TG, 48:1-TG, 50:1-TG , 50:2-TG, 54:2-TG, 56:2-TG and 58:3-TG no significant changes were observed (Annex 3). Fifteen TG's dropped significantly in the fatty livers, which implies they increased to a higher content in the starvation livers compared to the fatty livers. Principal Component Analysis (PCA) was carried out on 50 different compounds. In Figure 11 the score plot is shown. TG accumulation (PC#1) accounted for 44.39% of total variance, while the absolute fat concentration (PC#2) accounted for 31.92% of total variance.

Discussion

Brain

The most important observation of this study is that the brain can be affected by a High-Fat Diet while starvation nearly has no impact on the lipid brain composition in a mouse model. We are aware of the fact that we used whole brain and that splitting it up in white *versus* gray or cortex *versus* brain stem would for reductionist more meaningful.

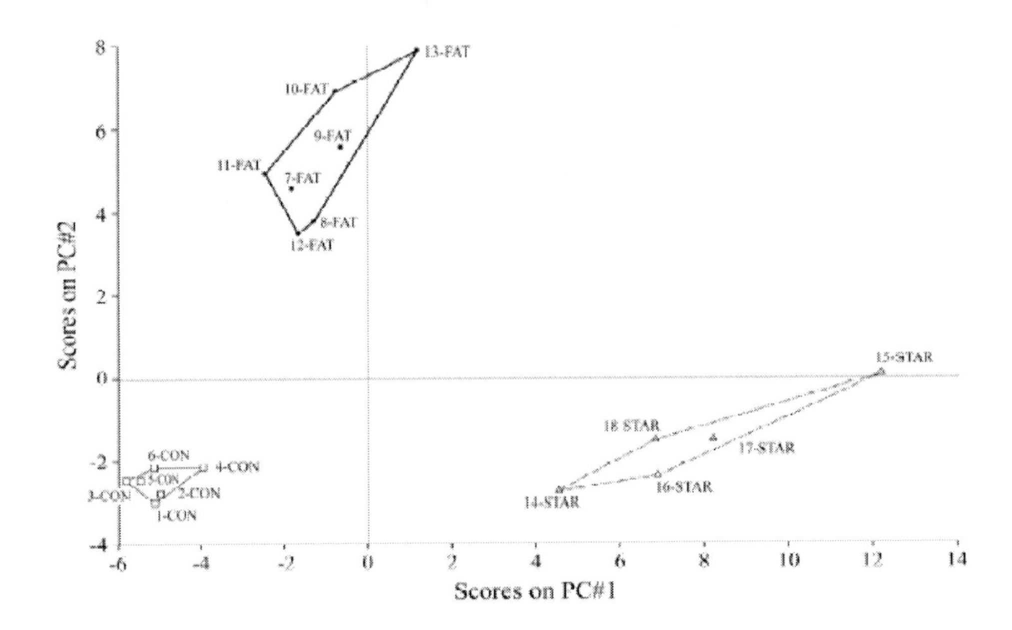

Figure 11. Canonical correlation of LC-MS data after Principal Component Analysis. Each point represents a separate measurement of metabolites in liver homogenate on 1 animal. CON = Treatment A (Control), STAR= Treatment B (starvation), FAT= Treatment C (High-Fat Diet). PC#1: TG Accumulation, PC2#: Absolute concentration of all lipids.

However this is the first study were the brain of murents is studied on lipid composition after a High-Fat Diet intervention and Starvation via LCMS techniques. In studies which are performed at this moment, using the same LCMS techniques and brain (white versus gray) and blood material of male post mortem subjects (Control; n=8; 73.5±10.5 years; Diabetes-2 (DM-2); n=8; 77.3±7.2 years) from the 'Netherlands Brain Bank', we are quantifying 109 lipid compounds.

In this unpublished study we want to investigate whether mental disorders occur more frequently than expected. in (post-mortem) diabetes type-2 patients by investigating the lipid composition of homogenized brain tissue by LC-MS techniques. It is not known whether this "diabetic encephalopathy" develops as a result of aberrant lipid metabolism (van Ginneken et al. unpublished results). So this study with a black-six mouse model is our first experiment with brain and LCMS- techniques under controlled experimental conditions.

The "systems Biology" approach aims to understand phenotypic variation to assemble comprehensive data and models of cellular organization and biochemical function, and to elucidate interactions and pathways (Kitano, 2002). An important area in which metabolomics has great potential is the discovery of biomarkers related to metabolic processes or a disease. In our approach we used biomarkers from the lipid fraction like Phosphatidylcholine (PC), Sphingomyelin (SPM), Lysophosphatodylcholine (LPC), Cholesterol-esters (ChE), TG's.

Although we found ChE which could serve as biomarkers this is of no value for the brain because until now the detection of these compounds in brain tissue is invasive and destructive. Possibly that non-invasive NMR techniques in future studies can be used.

In this study a new groups of lipid compounds were observed in brain tissue with LCMS techniques. Plasmalogens have a "vinylether" linkage, which is an oxygen atom next to a *cis* double bond on the alkenyl chain. This combination of an ether oxygen plus a double bond is what makes plasmalogens different from normal glycerophospholipids (Salway 2006). Most Plasmalogens are Phosphatidyl-Ethanolamine Plasmogens or Plasmenyl-Ethanolamines. On the other hand, Plasmanylcholines have a quaternary amine group and do not have the *cis* double bound on the first carbon of the alkyl chain at the *sn*-1 position.

Dietary essential fatty acids affects membrane phospholipids acyl chains in all mammalian tissues. To date, numerous animal studies have been performed to determine the relevance between Dietary essential fatty acids and the effects on the central nervous system, brain, retina, and other mental health problems.

We will summarize a couple of animal studies to give an impression of the different studies that have been done regarding the effect of a High-Fat Diet on mainly polyunsaturated fatty acids, TG's and Cholesterol. The found results between the different studies are not uniform and often conflicting. One study gave a positive protective effect on brain (Sullivan et al. 2003), one study gave (despite significant changes in brain composition) no behavioral changes (Barcelo-Coblijn 2003) and one study points in the direction of epigenesis.

A High-Fat Diet during pregnancy may bring about changes in the offspring's brain that makes them more prone to over-eating and obesity throughout their lives (Chang et al. 2008). We are aware of the fact that our study was only biochemical without any behavioural aspects but brain literature on only lipidonomics concerning the compounds we selected is scarce. Most are dealing with omega 3 and 6 (Sinclair et al. 2007). Ethological studies in future has to prove what are the consequences of changed ChE content in the brain on the behaviour of rodents.

In the following section the earlier mentioned studies will be described in detail.

A positive effect of a High-Fat Diet was observed on newborn brain by Sullivan et al.(2003).. They found that very high levels of a protein called uncoupling protein2 (UCP2) in the brains of newborn rats. UCP2 production is stimulated by fatty acids, which are the products of Dietary fat metabolism.

This high level of UCP2 may provide the protection from brain damage seen in infants who have seizures. Sullivan et al. (2003) hypothesized that uncoupling proteins –specifically UCP2 found in mitochondrial membranes- reduce the formation of reactive oxygen compounds and decrease the potential for cell injury in the brains of immature rats.

They found that UCP2 function and levels were greater in immature animals. UCP2 production is increased by fatty acids, the breakdown products of Dietary fats, and rat pups obtain most of their nutrition from maternal milk, which is very rich in fat.

Barcelo-Coblijn (2003) tried to study the dynamics of long polyunsaturated fatty acids in the rat brain. Therefore several feeding experiments were done and fatty acid and molecular composition of brain lipids were determined. The Diet consisted in normal rat chow enriched in different oils depending on their composition.

Fish oil, perilla and soyabean oil were use to have Diets rich in DHA, linolenic acid and linoleic acid, respectively. Essential fatty acids sufficient rats of different ages were fed from conception with oils rich either in LNA, EPA + DHA or with a mixture of oils giving a ratio of LA to LNA 8.2 or 4.7. Phospholipids were extracted and separated depending on their hydrophilic head by thin layer chromatography from brain, cerebellum and hypocampus. Their composition in fatty acids was determined by gas chromatography after transmethylation.

Barcelo-Coblijn (2003) found that brain fatty acid and molecular species composition, particularly of PE can be modified by a Diet depending manner. The major finding was that the response of brain Dietary fatty acids, like LA, LNA and DHA is faster than that was described so far by others.

Despite of this alteration in molecular composition in brain membranes did not performed better in Morris water maze test. Therefore, it was concluded that accumulation of DHA alone can not explain the beneficial effects of long chain polyunsaturated fatty acids in cognitive functions in rat.

A High-Fat Diet during pregnancy may bring about changes in the offspring's brain that makes them more prone to over-eating and obesity throughout their lives, according to the study of Chang et al. (2008) that may explain the rise in childhood obesity.

The work of Chang et al. (2008) provides the first evidence for a fetal program that links high levels of fat circulating in the mother's blood during pregnancy to the overeating and increased weight gain of offspring after weaning. The researchers believe that the high levels of TG's that the fetuses are exposed to during pregnancy cause the growth of the neurons earlier and much more than is normal.

In this was we are programming our children to be fat because there is vulnerability in the developing brain and Chang et al. (2008) have identified the site of this action where new neurons are born.

In Conclusion for Brain Tissue

Lipids play a key role in determining membrane fluidity, and changes in lipid composition have been reported to alter cellular functions (Stubbs and Smith 1984, Boure et al. 1991. Our data show that the brain is affected by a High-Fat Diet for Cholesterol-esters.

Membrane lipid composition appears to influence the state of mental health and is likely to exert its effects through lipid-protein interactions within the membrane. Such interactions may include effects upon neurotransmitter release and reuptake, and membrane receptors (Hulbert et al. 2005).

Perspectives-brain studies: In future studies we want to investigate whether a High-Fat Diet induces key enzymes in cholesterol metabolism (ACAT, LCAT, HMG-CoA) (Salway 2006) at the mRNA level and whether the brains of hyperlipidemic (ApoE2 knock-in mice) are more sensitive to such a Diet which would be indicative for posttranslational regulation.

Furthermore we want to investigate if changed Cholesterol-esters in the brain due to a High-Fat Diet have impact on behavioral changes.

Liver

Develop a Diagnostic Tool to Quantify Intrahepatocellular Content

Also a method for the detection, diagnosis, the stage and degree of fibrosis accurately is important for management and study of liver fibrosis. Until now liver biopsy was the current gold standard for the diagnosis of liver fibrosis. However, this procedure has numerous disadvantages. It is highly invasive and is associated with potential morbidity and mortality (Piccinino et al. 1986).

Luckily, recent studies of Wang et al. (2009) found that liver stiffness (which is correlated with fibrosis) can be measured using acoustic radiation force and in this way can provide a quantitative assessment of the extent of fibrosis in the liver.

In three studies the ^{1}H MRS method has been validated against direct determination of TG-content of liver biopsies. One study with dogs and rabbits gave a correlation of $r = 0.934$, $p \leq 0.0001$; slope 0.98 between both methods (Thomas, *et al.*, 2005), while during a study in humans a correlation was found between fat concentration of liver biopsies and the concentration calculated from spectroscopic experiments ($r = 0.9$, $p \leq 0.001$) (Garbow, *et al.*, 2001). In a study with 48 mice, the TG content was plotted against MRS-determined lipid content and a correlation coefficient of r^2=0.91 was found (Siegelman and Rosen, 2001).

Effective techniques are needed to investigate the potential and range of NAFDL towards NASH in animal and human studies. Especially the relation between hepatic steatosis and its association with obesity and type II diabetes needs further research. Proton magnetic resonance spectroscopy (^{1}H MRS) is a non-invasive method for measurement of tissue fat content, including intrahepatocellular lipids (IHCL) and intramyocellular lipids (IMCL). From the study of Thomas et al. (2005) it became clear that hepatic steatosis appears to be closely related to body adiposity, especially central obesity. In addition the separation of histologically defined steatohepatistis from simple steatosis is clinically important (Cobbold 2009).

Recently, magnetic resonance (MR) techniques using chemical shift imaging have provided a quantitative assessment of the degree of hepatic fatty infiltration, which correlates well with liver biopsy in the same animals (Thomas et al. 2005) casu quo patients (Garbow *et al.* 2001, Taylor-Robinson 2008).

Similarly in vivo ^{1}H MRS is a fast, safe, non-invasive method for the quantification of intrahepatocellular lipid (IHCL) levels (Mehta et al. 2008, Cobbold et al. 2009). Both techniques will be useful tools in future longitudinal clinical studies, either in examining the natural history of conditions causing hepatic steatosis (Cortez-Pinto and Machado 2008, Mehta et al. 2008), or in testing new treatments for these conditions (Mehta et al. 2008).

This study demonstrates that volume-selective localized spectroscopy is a useful method for qualitative and quantitative assessment of the fat fraction in diffuse fat accumulation of the liver. With this method we described the dynamics of TG liver influx in mice with different Diets. Comparison of ^{1}H MRS with HPTLC measurements demonstrated a close correlation ($r^2 = 0.975$ $p \leq 0.001$) which shows the technique is reliable and that a MRS voxel of $(2.5\ mm)^3$ is sufficient to overcome local differences in liver fat content.

Due to a long echo time the fat/water ratios in this study were heavily T2-weighted. A T2 correction was not applied as this could introduce a larger bias than the original T2-weighting error. The T2 decrease during starvation means an overestimation of the fat/water ratio for high levels of accumulation, but remains within the standard deviation of the experiment.

We conclude that localized ^{1}H MRS spectroscopy is a suitable non-invasive diagnostic tool for qualifying and quantifying liver fat concentration. Fatty infiltration dynamics in the liver showed similar patterns for TG under starvation and High-Fat Diet (e-power function).

Characteristics/pathways of hepatic steatosis: Broadly, hepatic steatosis is derived from a combination of factors: aberrations in insulin-related postprandial lipolysis with increased free fatty acid delivery to the liver, excess Dietary carbohydrate resulting in de novo fatty acid synthesis in the liver, and impairment of mitochondrial β oxidation and the complex mechanisms of TG assembly and export. Free fatty acids are also toxic (Day, 2002; Sanyal et al. 2001).

FFA are toxic via three mechanisms: a). They are substrate for ROS-generating enzymes and thus increase hepatocyte ROS production; b). Oxidized FA themselves can also catalyze lipid peroxidation reactions that are directly cytotoxic; c). They might affect global changes in liver gene expression (reviewed: Yamaguchi et al. 2007).

A few years ago Dr. A. Schiel (European Lipoprotein Club, 2005, Session IV), looked at differentially expressed genes using the program "Gene Map", for Gene Microarray Pathway Profiles (Gladstone Institutes, US) for the same black six mouse model as in this study (given the same feeding and sampling protocol).

She found at a $P \leq 0.01$ that only 41 genes were differentially expressed between Control and High-Fat groups, 281 genes between Control and 24 hours starvation and 324 genes between 24 hours starvation and the High-Fat Diet. At a $P \leq 0.05$ only 72 genes were differentially expressed between Control and High-Fat groups, 452 genes between Control and 24 hours starvation and 530 genes between 24 hours starvation and the High-Fat Diet. Her three major conclusions were: a). Hepatic steatosis due to starvation and a High-Fat Diet follow different biochemical pathways; b). a High-Fat Diet induces less different hepatic gene expression compared to a long period of starvation; c). Long starvation result in changes in expression of genes mainly involved in carbohydrate catabolism, lipid metabolism, lipid transport and cholesterol absorption (European Lipoprotein Club, 2005, Session IV).

With respect to hepatic TG accumulation, recent evidence in a murine model would suggest that hepatic TG content correlates poorly with the disease progression or hepatic damage and that TG's may represent a safe "bystander" (Yamaguchi et al. 2007). The authors demonstrate that TG-synthesis actually helps to protect hepatocytes from lipotoxicity by buffering the accumulation of FFA (Yamaguchi et al. 2007).

The factors leading from NAFLD to NASH are still largely unknown (Marra 2008). Recent findings indicate that a). Inflammation is a marker of the progression from simple steatosis to steatohepatitis, and is greatly involved in the generation of hepatic damage (Marra 2008). The other two characteristics are: b). Hepatocyte damage and c). Fibrosis.

a): Both obesity and insulin resistance are considered chronic inflammatory states. (Arkan *et al.*, 2005) The multifactorial and interrelated metabolic mechanisms and inflammatory mediators that link obesity, insulin resistance, and, in selected subjects with as intermediate result hepatic steatohepatitis with fibrosis are topics of intense investigation using a variety of animal models (Cobold et al. 2009) and sophisticated human metabolic studies (Rigazio et al. 2008).

Thus in both conditions, just like in reaction to an infection or an injury, cytokines (IL-6 and TNF-α) are released from the site of tissue injury (Tilg and Hotamisligil 2006).

These cytokines promote an acute-phase response. This response is characterised by the production of a range of proteins, primarily from hepatocytes (liver cells), but also from other cells such as monocytes (precursors to macrophages), fibroblasts (connective tissue cells) and adipocytes (fat cells). (Arkan *et al.*, 2005).

Production of cytokines is one of the earliest events in many types of liver injury, triggering the production of other cytokines that together recruit inflammatory cells and initiate a healing process in the liver that includes fibrogenesis (Tilg and Hotamisligil 2006). Although inflammation was not the topic of this study we will mention it briefly because it can lead to hepatocyte damage.

b): The pathological changes that develop in e.g. hepatocytes are often ascribed to oxidative stress due to fatty-acid oxidation (Fernandez-Checa and Kaplowitz 2005). It has been proved that the transition from steatosis to steatohepatitis is established by the role of reactive oxygen species (ROS) (Sanyal et al. 2001), lipid peroxidation and oxidative stress, impaired mitochondrial respiratory chain function and adenosine triphosphate depletion, and production of the proinflammatory cytokines, including tumor necrosis factor-alpha (TNF-α) (reviews: Cortez-Pinto and Machado 2008, Marra 2008).

This oxidative stress may result in a mitochondrial dysfunction (Pessayre, 2001), but increased oxidation of long chain fatty acids is reportedly a major source of ROS in NASH. Recent concepts of the cellular, subcellular, and metabolic pathways known or proposed to promote and perpetuate the cycles(s) of hepatocellular injury and fibrogenesis in NASH have been reviewed (Cortez-Pinto and Machado 2008, Marra 2008).

c): Although we demonstrated that volume-selective localized spectroscopy is a useful method for qualitative and quantitative assessment of the fat fraction in diffuse fat accumulation of the liver, the distinction between steatosis and steatohepatitis, and the assessment of the severity of the disease appears to be correlated with the stage of fibrosis (Saadeh et al. 2002) and rely on liver histology alone (Ratziu et al, 2005, Ahmed 2006).

In Conclusion for Liver Tissue

We applied ^{1}H-MRS techniques demonstrated for liver that the relative amount of unsaturated bindings is significantly higher in the High-Fat Diet group ($P \leq 0.001$), which can be deducted from the relative intensities of the (CH=CH) elements and their conjugated unsaturated elements ($C\text{-}CCH_2C\text{=}C$) we demonstrated quantitatively that different resonances arising from saturated and unsaturated fatty acid moieties could be assigned to the spectrum (Table 3) and different end products are formed as result of different Diets.

With LC-MS techniques, using advanced PCA-analysis, we demonstrated that the lipid compounds in the Control, Starvation and High-Fat Diet were at totally different positions in the factorial plane (Figure 11) reflecting their totally different biochemical position.

In Conclusion: Comparing Brain Vs. Liver Tissue

Hence, the major observation of this study, in which we investigated the effect of starvation and a High-Fat Diet on liver- and brain- lipid composition, is that the brain is invulnerable for starvation but can be affected by a Fat-Diet mainly in the Cholesterol-ester component.

Application of LC-MS and PCA demonstrated huge differences between treatments on the biochemical composition of the liver.

Apparently, different biochemical pathways are involved in the process of hepatic steatosis due to Starvation and a High-Fat Diet.

Final conclusion: The organ specific response of brain and liver to starvation (the brain's incapacity to utilize energy sources other than glucose and ketone bodies and the liver which produces ketone bodies as by-products of excess lipid catabolism) constitutes a mechanism of protecting the organism from self-destruction and maintaining its integrity, at the expense of the rest of the body, during starvation.

ANNEX 1. LC-MS constitution of a Normal (Control) Diet (DSD.3. Special Diet Services. Witham. UK) (mean ± SD. n=5) and a Fat Diet (Arie Blok. food code 4032.05. Woerden. The Netherlands) based on bovine lard and 0.25% cholesterol (mean ± SD. n=5)

Compound	Control-Chow (Mean ± SD)	High-Fat (Mean ± SD)	Kolmogorov-Smirnov	P-value	Change in %
C14-0-LPC	0.0148 ±0.0027	0.0014 ± 0.0003	**0.005	***0.0000	9.43
C16-0-LPC	0.4340 ± 0.0812	0.1289 ± 0.0261	**0.005	***0.0000	29.71
C16-1-LPC	0.0109 ± 0.0028	0.0046 ± 0.0009	*0.031	***0.0004	42.45
C18-0-LPC	0.0121 ± 0.0027	0.0052 ± 0.0009	**0.005	***0.0002	42.73
C18-1-LPC	0.0554 ± 0.0107	0.0190 ± 0.0039	**0.005	***0.0000	34.23
C18-2-LPC	0.7058 ± 0.1275	0.1189 ± 0.0218	**0.005	***0.0000	16.85
C20-1-LPC	0.0035 ± 0.0007	0.0012 ± 0.0004	*0.031	***0.0000	33.61
C20-4-LPC	0.0041 ± 0.0006	0.0002 ± 0.0001	**0.005	***0.0000	4.32
C18-2-MG	0.0010 ± 0.0002	0.0013 ± 0.0002	1.000	*0.0325	130.10
C20-2-MG	0.0014 ± 0.0005	0.0014 ± 0.0005	1.000	0.9688	100.86
C20-3-MG	0.0002 ± 0.0001	0.0002 ± 0.0001	1.000	0.9934	100.23
C22-2-MG	0.0001 ± 0.0001	0.0002 ± 0.0001	1.000	0.6240	120.57
C22-3-MG	0.0004 ± 0.0001	0.0005 ± 0.0001	0.893	0.5880	114.74
C24-2-MG	0.0001 ± 0.0001	0.0001 ± 0.0000	1.000	0.1841	57.84
C24-3-MG	0.0001 ± 0.0001	0.0001 ± 0.0000	1.000	0.3739	62.93
C24-4-MG	0.0002 ± 0.0001	0.0007 ± 0.0004	0.441	*0.0363	299.72
C24-1-DG	0.0006 ± 0.0002	0.0010 ± 0.0002	0.893	**0.0038	174.27
C26-1-DG	0.0006 ± 0.0003	0.0057 ± 0.0010	**0.005	***0.0000	1018.38
C28-0-DG	0.0109 ± 0.0030	0.0232 ± 0.0034	**0.005	***0.0001	213.07
C28-1-DG	0.0007 ± 0.0004	0.0073 ± 0.0010	**0.005	***0.0000	992.66
C28-2-DG	0.0003 ± 0.0001	0.0034 ± 0.0008	**0.005	***0.0000	1186.01
C30-0-DG	0.0139 ± 0.0027	0.0821 ± 0.0136	**0.005	***0.0000	590.72
C30-1-DG	0.0059 ± 0.0019	0.0336 ± 0.0054	**0.005	***0.0000	569.73
C30-2-DG	0.0009 ± 0.0005	0.0038 ± 0.0011	*0.031	***0.0002	406.15
C32-0-DG	0.0551 ± 0.0129	0.1959 ± 0.0328	**0.005	***0.0000	355.79
C32-1-DG	0.0332 ± 0.0060	0.1485 ± 0.0265	**0.005	***0.0000	446.74
C32-2-DG	0.0131 ± 0.0021	0.0293 ± 0.0049	**0.005	***0.0000	223.15
C32-3-DG	0.0012 ± 0.0005	0.0026 ± 0.0005	0.139	***0.0006	211.31
C34-0-DG	0.0166 ± 0.0033	0.1850 ± 0.0382	**0.005	***0.0000	1112.38
C34-1-DG	0.1893 ± 0.0399	0.7559 ± 0.1571	**0.005	***0.0000	399.29
C34-2-DG	0.5271 ± 0.1165	0.1496 ± 0.0319	**0.005	***0.0000	28.38
C34-3-DG	0.0629 ± 0.0141	0.0208 ± 0.0040	**0.005	***0.0000	33.00
C34-4-DG	0.0033 ± 0.0011	0.0010 ± 0.0005	*0.031	**0.0011	31.82
C36-0-DG	0.0040 ± 0.0010	0.0633 ± 0.0145	**0.005	***0.0000	1583.64
C36-1-DG	0.0497 ± 0.0103	0.4046 ± 0.0805	**0.005	***0.0000	814.80
C36-2-DG	0.2500 ± 0.0528	0.4861 ± 0.0953	**0.005	***0.0003	194.39
C36-3-DG	0.4775 ± 0.1103	0.0787 ± 0.0166	**0.005	***0.0000	16.48
C36-4-DG	0.8439 ± 0.1776	0.0214 ± 0.0039	**0.005	***0.0000	2.54
C36-5-DG	0.1508 ± 0.0312	0.0039 ± 0.0003	**0.005	***0.0000	2.60
C38-1-DG	0.0186 ± 0.0048	0.0045 ± 0.0012	**0.005	***0.0000	24.08
C38-2-DG	0.0279 ± 0.0059	0.0080 ± 0.0019	**0.005	***0.0000	28.71
C30-0-PC	0.0142 ± 0.0030	0.0369 ± 0.0019	**0.005	***0.0000	259.62
C32-0-PC	0.0455 ± 0.0097	0.0440 ± 0.0032	0.441	0.7369	96.82

Compound	Control-Chow (Mean ± SD)	High-Fat (Mean ± SD)	Kolmogorov-Smirnov	P-value	Change in %
C32-1-PC	0.0472 ± 0.0109	0.0169 ± 0.0011	**0.005	***0.0001	35.86
C34-0-PC	0.0122 ± 0.0027	0.0165 ± 0.0008	*0.031	**0.0033	135.95
C34-1-PC	0.3595 ± 0.0740	0.0822 ± 0.0040	**0.005	***0.0000	22.86
C34-2-PC	0.9184 ± 0.1830	0.0312 ± 0.0017	**0.005	***0.0000	3.40
C34-3-PC	0.1012 ± 0.0205	0.0051 ± 0.0005	**0.005	***0.0000	5.09
C36-1-PC	0.0753 ± 0.0156	0.0245 ± 0.0027	**0.005	***0.0000	32.59
C36-2-PC	0.2727 ± 0.0554	0.0401 ± 0.0023	**0.005	***0.0000	14.70
C36-3-PC	0.5573 ± 0.1129	0.0213 ± 0.0012	**0.005	***0.0000	3.82
C36-4-PC	1.2069 ± 0.2388	0.0119 ± 0.0015	**0.005	***0.0000	0.99
C38-4-PC	0.0057 ± 0.0020	0.0012 ± 0.0005	**0.005	***0.0004	21.96
C38-6-PC	0.1981 ± 0.0445	0.0022 ± 0.0010	**0.005	***0.0000	1.11
C38-7-PC	0.1599 ± 0.0308	0.0022 ± 0.0006	**0.005	***0.0000	1.38
C40-6-PC	0.0192 ± 0.0069	0.0027 ± 0.0014	**0.005	***0.0002	14.18
C40-7-PC	0.0250 ± 0.0057	0.0001 ± 0.0001	**0.005	***0.0000	0.34
C32-0-PE	0.0078 ± 0.0024	0.0010 ± 0.0003	**0.005	***0.0000	13.35
C32-1-PE	0.0256 ± 0.0068	0.0030 ± 0.0014	**0.005	***0.0000	11.78
C34-0-PE	0.0150 ± 0.0054	0.0008 ± 0.0005	**0.005	***0.0001	5.52
C34-1-PE	0.0379 ± 0.0098	0.0126 ± 0.0010	**0.005	***0.0001	33.31
C34-2-PE	0.0856 ± 0.0198	0.0091 ± 0.0009	**0.005	***0.0000	10.62
C36-1-PE	0.0159 ± 0.0027	0.0137 ± 0.0008	0.139	0.0877	86.44
C36-2-PE	0.0178 ± 0.0032	0.0389 ± 0.0027	**0.005	***0.0000	218.30
C36-3-PE	0.0257 ± 0.0059	0.0148 ± 0.0007	*0.031	**0.0011	57.63
C16-0-SPM	0.0077 ± 0.0029	0.0237 ± 0.0010	**0.005	***0.0000	308.92
C18-0-SPM	0.0018 ± 0.0008	0.0024 ± 0.0007	0.441	0.1534	138.35
C18-3-SPM	0.0008 ± 0.0006	0.0025 ± 0.0007	**0.005	***0.0008	317.06
C22-0-SPM	0.0012 ± 0.0013	0.0285 ± 0.0026	**0.005	***0.0000	2335.37
C23-0-SPM	0.0064 ± 0.0022	0.0224 ± 0.0015	**0.005	***0.0000	346.76
C24-0-SPM	0.0025 ± 0.0010	0.0174 ± 0.0008	**0.005	***0.0000	683.78
C24-1-SPM	0.0326 ± 0.0093	0.0042 ± 0.0012	**0.005	***0.0000	12.95
C14-0-ChE	0.0003 ± 0.0002	0.0010 ± 0.0007	0.139	*0.0461	318.74
C16-0-ChE	0.0050 ± 0.0013	0.0011 ± 0.0008	*0.031	***0.0001	22.21
C16-1-ChE	0.0052 ± 0.0008	0.0033 ± 0.0011	0.139	**0.0072	63.52
C18-0-ChE	0.0383 ± 0.0045	0.0163 ± 0.0013	**0.005	***0.0000	42.50
C18-1-ChE	0.0422 ± 0.0026	0.0109 ± 0.0020	**0.005	***0.0000	25.89
C18-2-ChE	0.0058 ± 0.0008	0.0071± 0.0018	0.893	0.1475	121.34
C18-3-ChE	0.0003 ± 0.0002	0.0021 ± 0.0009	**0.005	**0.0011	678.61
C20-3-ChE	0.0264 ± 0.0037	0.0002 ± 0.0002	**0.005	***0.0000	0.94
C20-4-ChE	0.0073 ± 0.0009	0.0000 ± 0.0000	**0.005	***0.0000	0.00
C20-5-ChE	0.0227 ± 0.0041	0.0004 ± 0.0002	**0.005	***0.0000	1.61
C22-6-ChE	0.0397 ± 0.0050	0.0009 ± 0.0003	**0.005	***0.0000	2.36
C44-0-TG	0.0134 ± 0.0028	2.0585 ± 0.8189	**0.005	***0.0001	15358.24
C44-1-TG	0.0116 ± 0.0029	1.6876 ± 0.6332	**0.005	***0.0001	14600.20
C44-2-TG	0.0041 ± 0.0009	0.3983 ± 0.1504	**0.005	***0.0001	9685.34
C44-3-TG	0.0019 ± 0.0004	0.0576 ± 0.0210	**0.005	***0.0001	3048.87
C46-0-TG	0.0179 ± 0.0022	4.8980 ± 1.2063	**0.005	***0.0000	27298.72
C46-1-TG	0.0407 ± 0.0086	6.3782 ± 2.2866	**0.005	***0.0000	15657.08
C46-2-TG	0.0146 ± 0.0033	1.7957 ± 0.7049	**0.005	***0.0001	12319.81
C46-3-TG	0.0043 ± 0.0010	0.2715 ± 0.1086	**0.005	***0.0001	6350.63
C46-4-TG	0.0025 ± 0.0006	0.0304 ± 0.0107	**0.005	***0.0001	1197.42

ANNEX 1. (Continued)

Compound	Control-Chow (Mean ± SD)	High-Fat (Mean ± SD)	Kolmogorov-Smirnov	P-value	Change in %
C48-0-TG	0.0427 ± 0.0066	3.1081 ± 0.3775	**0.005	***0.0000	7270.72
C48-1-TG	0.0977 ± 0.0119	13.3135 ± 2.5144	**0.005	***0.0000	13621.56
C48-2-TG	0.0826 ± 0.0129	10.3133 ± 3.3356	**0.005	***0.0000	12492.30
C48-3-TG	0.0267 ± 0.060	1.6247 ± 0.6402	**0.005	***0.0001	6086.66
C48-4-TG	0.0126 ± 0.0028	0.1928 ± 0.0800	**0.005	***0.0003	1535.68
C50-0-TG	0.0184 ± 0.0038	2.4463 ± 0.0393	**0.005	***0.0000	13307.73
C50-1-TG	0.5081 ± 0.0835	10.4197 ± 1.8209	**0.005	***0.0000	2050.88
C50-2-TG	1.2848 ± 0.1728	13.7411 ± 2.3466	**0.005	***0.0000	1069.51
C50-3-TG	0.2239 ± 0.0333	6.3849 ± 1.8181	**0.005	***0.0000	2851.56
C50-4-TG	0.0813 ± 0.0167	1.0902 ± 0.4023	**0.005	***0.0001	1341.52
C50-5-TG	0.0416 ± 0.0101	0.1173 ± 0.0473	**0.005	**0.0033	281.62
C50-6-TG	0.0180 ± 0.0041	0.1049 ± 0.0488	**0.005	**0.0015	582.76
C52-0-TG	0.0110 ± 0.0032	3.9343 ± 0.7037	**0.005	***0.0000	35678.23
C52-1-TG	0.2344 ± 0.0462	15.7798 ± 3.1203	**0.005	***0.0000	6730.91
C52-2-TG	1.8014 ± 0.2984	16.6112 ± 2.5970	**0.005	***0.0000	922.12
C52-3-TG	2.7313 ± 0.3834	9.7095 ± 1.6801	**0.005	***0.0000	355.49
C52-4-TG	3.9193 ± 0.5070	3.7768 ± 0.8095	0.893	0.7225	96.37
C52-5-TG	0.9671 ± 0.1554	0.8818 ± 0.2796	0.893	0.5286	91.18
C52-6-TG	0.1499 ± 0.0332	0.3078 ± 0.1328	*0.031	*0.0180	205.34
C54-1-TG	0.1105 ± 0.0271	27.9021 ± 7.4345	**0.005	***0.0000	25261.50
C54-2-TG	0.6759 ± 0.1267	15.6236 ± 3.0924	**0.005	***0.0000	2311.36
C54-3-TG	1.9100 ± 0.3247	5.8816 ± 0.9246	**0.005	***0.0000	307.94
C54-4-TG	3.0623 ± 0.4460	1.8426 ± 0.2935	**0.005	***0.0002	60.17
C54-5-TG	3.7421 ± 0.4576	1.0570 ± 0.1863	**0.005	***0.0000	28.25
C54-6-TG	4.8234 ± 0.7028	0.7781 ± 0.2591	**0.005	***0.0000	16.13
C54-7-TG	1.6223 ± 0.3455	0.8730 ± 0.3841	*0.031	**0.0052	53.81
C56-1-TG	0.0252 ± 0.0062	1.8684 ± 0.8086	**0.005	***0.0002	7409.93
C56-2-TG	0.2112 ± 0.0506	1.6670 ± 0.4833	**0.005	***0.0000	789.14
C56-3-TG	0.2870 ± 0.0575	0.5210 ± 0.1086	**0.005	***0.0009	181.53
C56-4-TG	0.1975 ± 0.0362	0.1230 ± 0.0237	*0.031	**0.0018	62.28
C56-5-TG	0.2153 ± 0.0337	0.0791 ± 0.0136	**0.005	***0.0000	36.75
C56-6-TG	0.1609 ± 0.0247	0.1591 ± 0.0230	0.893	0.8942	98.83
C56-7-TG	0.1276 ± 0.0164	0.3963 ± 0.1423	**0.005	***0.0010	310.52
C56-8-TG	0.0646 ± 0.0120	0.3882 ± 0.1402	**0.005	***0.0002	600.79
C56-9-TG	0.0461 ± 0.0114	0.5353 ± 0.2024	**0.005	***0.0001	1160.83
C58-10-TG	0.0480 ± 0.0094	0.0189 ± 0.0059	**0.005	***0.0001	39.25
C58-2-TG	0.0802 ± 0.0191	0.3990 ± 0.1693	**0.005	***0.0010	497.15
C58-3-TG	0.1580 ± 0.0379	0.1637 ± 0.0584	0.893	0.8431	103.66
C58-4-TG	0.1388 ± 0.0315	0.0262 ± 0.0070	**0.005	***0.0000	18.87
C58-5-TG	0.0795 ± 0.0148	0.0127 ± 0.0030	**0.005	***0.0000	16.02
C58-9-TG	0.0308 ± 0.0039	0.0285 ± 0.0111	0.893	0.6405	92.48
C60-2-TG	0.0198 ± 0.0040	0.0673 ± 0.0331	**0.005	**0.0058	339.73
C60-3-TG	0.0602 ± 0.0144	0.0496 ± 0.0219	0.441	0.3456	82.41
C60-4-TG	0.0388 ± 0.0094	0.0179 ± 0.0068	*0.031	**0.0013	46.06

ANNEX 2. Measured compounds in whole brain of mice with LC-MS techniques like Lysophosphatidyl-cholines (LPC), Phosphatidylcholine (PC), Spingomyelin (SPM), Triacylglycerols (TG) and Phosphatidyl-Ethanolamine- or Plasmenyl-Ethanolamine Plasmogens

Compound	Control (A) (Mean ± SD)	48h Starvation (B) (Mean ± SD)	High-Fat (C) (Mean ± SD)	Kruskal – Wallis	P-value			Change in %		
					A vs. B	A vs. C	B vs. C	A vs. B	A vs. C	B vs. C
C16_0_LPC	0.4876 ± 0.1272	0.6967 ± 0.0686	0.5191 ± 0.0612	***0.001	**0.0018	0.5719	***0.0002	142.88	106.44	74.50
C16_1_LPC	0.0095 ± 0.0022	0.0098 ± 0.0015	0.0114 ± 0.0009	0.091	0.7078	0.0579	*0.0335	104.01	120.42	115.78
C18_0_LPC	0.2551 ± 0.0715	0.4587 ± 0.0722	0.2735 ± 0.0328	***0.001	***0.0002	0.5535	***0.0000	179.79	107.19	59.62
C18_1_LPC	0.1727 ± 0.0465	0.2016 ± 0.0319	0.2056 ± 0.0194	0.335	0.1908	0.1141	0.7788	116.76	119.07	101.98
C20_1_LPC	0.0150 ± 0.0036	0.0275 ± 0.0107	0.0173 ± 0.0011	***0.001	*0.0184	0.1386	*0.0261	183.04	115.00	62.83
C16_0_SPM	0.0576 ± 0.0161	0.0582 ± 0.0277	0.0654 ± 0.0040	0.372	0.9626	0.2429	0.5139	101.06	113.42	112.23
C18_0_SPM	0.7943 ± 0.1578	0.5870 ± 0.1367	0.9427 ± 0.1032	**0.004	*0.0219	0.0664	***0.0001	73.90	118.67	160.59
C34_0_DG	0.0665 ± 0.0174	0.0594 ± 0.0143	0.0878 ± 0.0096	**0.004	0.4151	*0.0174	***0.0006	89.26	132.08	147.97
C34_1_DG	0.1942 ± 0.0331	0.1727 ± 0.0470	0.2466 ± 0.0733	0.056	0.3595	0.1362	*0.0348	88.93	126.96	142.77
C36_0_DG	0.0089 ± 0.0026	0.0173 ± 0.0086	0.0104 ± 0.0020	**0.005	*0.0395	0.2550	0.0580	195.54	117.18	59.92
C36_1_DG	0.2644 ± 0.0776	0.2063 ± 0.0796	0.3184 ± 0.0382	*0.022	0.1967	0.1308	**0.0048	78.00	120.43	154.40
C36_2_DG	0.0456 ± 0.0077	0.0491 ± 0.0224	0.1000 ± 0.0908	*0.018	0.7213	0.1737	0.1472	107.70	219.48	203.80
C30_0_PC	0.3384 ± 0.1010	0.2734 ± 0.0432	0.4280 ± 0.0615	**0.002	0.1256	0.0748	***0.0001	80.79	126.48	156.55
C32_0_PC	6.8224 ± 1.1420	5.8046 ± 0.6325	7.0666 ± 0.5407	*0.017	0.0538	0.6228	**0.0012	85.08	103.58	121.74
C32_1_PC	1.0255 ± 0.2553	0.8733 ± 0.1486	1.2632 ± 0.1528	**0.003	0.1846	0.0621	***0.0002	85.16	123.18	144.64
C34_0_PC	2.6822 ± 0.4523	2.3096 ± 0.1914	2.6095 ± 0.1814	*0.013	0.0562	0.7022	**0.0084	86.11	97.29	112.98
C34_1_PC	9.4605 ± 1.1296	9.1603 ± 0.5799	9.9656 ± 0.1738	**0.007	0.5271	0.2646	**0.0037	96.83	105.34	108.79
C34_2_PC	0.5900 ± 0.1082	0.9793 ± 0.1994	0.5197 ± 0.0574	***0.000	***0.0010	0.1628	***0.0001	165.99	88.09	53.07
C36_1_PC	6.0130 ± 0.9461	5.9592 ± 0.4859	6.1931 ± 0.5978	0.425	0.8915	0.6844	0.4181	99.11	103.00	103.93
C36_2_PC	1.2090 ± 0.1844	1.4349 ± 0.1420	1.3701 ± 0.0448	*0.024	*0.0234	*0.0458	0.2700	118.68	113.33	95.49
C36_4_PC	2.0928 ± 0.4973	1.7801 ± 0.2713	2.2758 ± 0.3200	*0.044	0.1555	0.4395	**0.0063	85.06	108.75	127.85
C38_1_PC	0.4641 ± 0.1312	0.5646 ± 0.1668	0.4872 ± 0.0767	0.534	0.2472	0.7005	0.2811	121.66	104.97	86.29
C38_2_PC	1.1745 ± 0.2235	1.3548 ± 0.2524	1.4519 ± 0.0823	0.109	0.1907	*0.0107	0.3498	115.35	123.62	107.17
C38_4_PC	1.8154 ± 0.4715	1.5843 ± 0.2348	2.0648 ± 0.2869	*0.038	0.2491	0.2654	**0.0034	87.27	113.74	130.33
C40_1_PC	0.1020 ± 0.0332	0.1458 ± 0.0629	0.0906 ± 0.0188	0.095	0.1486	0.4539	*0.0442	143.00	88.85	62.13
C40_2_PC	0.1851 ± 0.0647	0.2631 ± 0.1142	0.2166 ± 0.0405	0.212	0.1615	0.3079	0.3273	142.10	117.00	82.34
C40_3_PC	0.0164 ± 0.0028	0.0183 ± 0.0032	0.0163 ± 0.0019	0.291	0.2706	0.9604	0.1806	111.64	99.60	89.22
C42_1_PC	0.0828 ± 0.0272	0.1403 ± 0.0692	0.0713 ± 0.0183	*0.035	0.0800	0.3851	*0.0242	169.48	86.15	50.83

ANNEX 2. (Continued)

Compound	Control (A) (Mean ± SD)	48h Starvation (B) (Mean ± SD)	High-Fat (C) (Mean ± SD)	Kruskal – Wallis	P-value			Change in %		
					A vs. B	A vs. C	B vs. C	A vs. B	A vs. C	B vs. C
C42_2_PC	0.0614 ± 0.0191	0.0938 ± 0.0418	0.0589 ± 0.0153	0.051	0.1054	0.7938	0.0574	152.73	95.84	62.75
C32_1_PE	0.0140 ± 0.0028	0.0146 ± 0.0040	0.0168 ± 0.0018	0.220	0.7448	0.0536	0.2226	104.60	119.74	114.48
C34_0_PE	0.1430 ± 0.0330	0.1144 ± 0.0181	0.1616 ± 0.0225	**0.007	0.0590	0.2530	***0.0006	80.00	113.03	141.28
C34_1_PE	0.3585 ± 0.0517	0.3712 ± 0.0560	0.3954 ± 0.0301	0.447	0.6721	0.1368	0.3268	103.55	110.30	106.52
C34_2_PE	0.0407 ± 0.0088	0.0518 ± 0.0100	0.0386 ± 0.0039	*0.016	0.0509	0.5844	**0.0062	127.46	94.93	74.48
C36_2_PE	0.4029 ± 0.0410	0.5356 ± 0.0726	0.4419 ± 0.0532	**0.004	**0.0018	0.1725	*0.0147	132.94	109.68	82.50
C36_3_PE	0.0858 ± 0.0163	0.1284 ± 0.0196	0.0927 ± 0.0044	***0.001	***0.0010	0.2994	***0.0004	149.65	108.07	72.21
C38_1_PE	0.1330 ± 0.0347	0.1763 ± 0.0571	0.1486 ± 0.0243	0.166	0.1279	0.3630	0.2552	132.54	111.69	84.27
C34_1_PCplas	0.1661 ± 0.0573	0.2031 ± 0.0604	0.2061 ± 0.0216	0.414	0.2686	0.1132	0.9029	122.30	124.11	101.48
C36_1_PCplas	0.1344 ± 0.0191	0.1998 ± 0.0485	0.1811 ± 0.0175	**0.007	**0.0092	***0.0008	0.3533	148.66	134.74	90.64
C38_1_PCplas	1.6800 ± 0.2165	1.9111 ± 0.2385	1.8189 ± 0.1573	0.188	0.0870	0.2079	0.4006	113.76	108.27	95.17
C40_1_PCplas	2.3260 ± 0.6000	2.8174 ± 0.5561	2.6419 ± 0.3146	0.325	0.1394	0.2491	0.4748	121.12	113.58	93.77
C42_1_PCplas	0.0370 ± 0.0149	0.0562 ± 0.0267	0.0441 ± 0.0078	0.200	0.1405	0.2928	0.2710	151.94	119.31	78.52
C34_1_PEplas	0.4456 ± 0.0749	0.5608 ± 0.1280	0.4942 ± 0.0551	0.130	0.0744	0.2057	0.2257	125.83	110.89	88.13
C34_2_PEplas	0.0190 ± 0.0040	0.0256 ± 0.0043	0.0222 ± 0.0015	*0.016	*0.0126	0.0704	0.0696	134.74	116.87	86.74
C36_1_PEplas	0.8454 ± 0.1440	0.9826 ± 0.1646	0.8939 ± 0.0807	0.265	0.1300	0.4600	0.2186	116.23	105.74	90.97
C36_2_PEplas	0.8109 ± 0.1437	1.0224 ± 0.2181	0.9693 ± 0.0980	0.124	0.0625	*0.0382	0.5643	126.08	119.53	94.81
C38_1_PEplas	0.3690 ± 0.1242	0.5301 ± 0.2650	0.4298 ± 0.1007	0.297	0.1956	0.3501	0.3641	143.69	116.48	81.07
C38_2_PEplas	0.4747 ± 0.1131	0.5901 ± 0.1807	0.5741 ± 0.0767	0.393	0.1964	0.0868	0.8319	124.30	120.93	97.29
C40_2_Peplas	0.0498 ± 0.0196	0.0806 ± 0.0490	0.0609 ± 0.0146	0.141	0.1741	0.2661	0.3259	161.82	122.28	75.57
C48_0_TG	0.0102 ± 0.0037	0.0048 ± 0.0031	0.0192 ±0.0163	**0.002	*0.0114	0.2159	*0.0287	46.91	187.89	400.51
C48_1_TG	0.0037 ± 0.0019	0.0041 ± 0.0050	0.0308 ± 0.0550	**0.010	0.8341	0.2558	0.1935	112.58	839.82	745.96
C48_2_TG	0.0020 ± 0.0013	0.0036 ± 0.0057	0.0189 ± 0.0346	*0.021	0.5224	0.2606	0.2380	178.68	937.68	524.79
C50_1_TG	0.0113 ± 0.0053	0.0123 ± 0.0164	0.0994 ± 0.1805	**0.006	0.8940	0.2603	0.1952	108.44	877.50	809.18
C50_2_TG	0.0104 ± 0.0088	0.0159 ± 0.0242	0.1267 ± 0.2440	*0.026	0.6079	0.2708	0.2215	153.13	1222.80	798.55
C50_3_TG	0.0041 ± 0.0043	0.0060 ± 0.0102	0.0379 ± 0.0743	*0.033	0.6739	0.2922	0.2488	147.09	925.75	629.39
C52_1_TG	0.0058 ± 0.0019	0.0055 ± 0.0062	0.0274 ± 0.0405	**0.005	0.9104	0.2211	0.1529	94.72	474.33	500.76
C52_2_TG	0.0104 ± 0.0065	0.0202 ± 0.0331	0.2643 ± 0.5121	**0.006	0.4923	0.2529	0.1993	194.17	2540.04	1308.18
C52_3_TG	0.0124 ± 0.0132	0.0224 ± 0.0372	0.1732 ± 0.3496	*0.024	0.5432	0.2871	0.2447	180.52	1392.86	771.60
C52_4_TG	0.0068 ± 0.0082	0.0073 ± 0.0115	0.0374 ± 0.0753	0.094	0.9198	0.3460	0.2832	108.40	551.81	509.03
C54_2_TG	0.0024 ± 0.0011	0.0060 ± 0.0098	0.0444 ± 0.0858	**0.008	0.3940	0.2590	0.2290	250.69	1859.78	741.87

Compound	Control (A) (Mean ± SD)	48h Starvation (B) (Mean ± SD)	High-Fat (C) (Mean ± SD)	Kruskal – Wallis	P-value			Change in %		
					A vs. B	A vs. C	B vs. C	A vs. B	A vs. C	B vs. C
C54_3_TG	0.0046 ± 0.0031	0.0130 ± 0.0216	0.1851 ± 0.3856	** 0.007	0.3654	0.2787	0.2273	284.92	4052.40	1422.32
C54_4_TG	0.0062 ± 0.0059	0.0134 ± 0.0226	0.0737 ± 0.1538	* 0.039	0.4654	0.3086	0.2908	216.06	1186.81	549.30
C56_3_TG	0.0006 ± 0.0003	0.0020 ± 0.0032	0.0078 ± 0.0137	* 0.012	0.2951	0.2278	0.2686	349.79	1338.59	382.68

ANNEX 3. Measured compounds in liver of mice with LC-MS techniques like Lysophosphatidyl-cholines (LPC), Phosphatidylcholine (PC), Spingomyelin (SPM), Triacylglycerols (TG)

Compound	Control (A) (Mean±SD)	24h Starvation (B) (Mean±SD)	High-Fat (C) (Mean±SD)	Kruskal – Wallis	P-value			Change (%)		
					A vs. B	A vs. C	B vs. C	A vs. B	A vs. C	B vs. C
16:0-LPC	0.181 ± 0.078	0.798 ± 0.138	0.359 ± 0.080	0.001 ***	0.000 ***	0.002 **	0.000 ***	440.88	198.34	44.99
16:1-LPC	0.018 ± 0.005	-	0.049 ± 0.009	0.003 **	-	0.000 ***	-	-	272.22	-
18:0-LPC	0.089 ± 0.034	0.399 ± 0.054	0.207 ± 0.046	0.001 ***	0.000 ***	0.000 ***	0.001 **	448.31	232.58	51.88
18:1-LPC	0.060 ± 0.022	0.108 ± 0.027	0.273 ± 0.073	0.001 ***	0.010 *	0.000 ***	0.001 ***	180.00	455.00	252.78
18:2-LPC	0.096 ± 0.037	0.736 ± 0.193	0.107 ± 0.025	0.005 **	0.000 ***	0.5127	0.000 ***	766.67	111.46	14.54
20:3-LPC	0.161 ± 0.007	0.023 ± 0.006	0.202 ± 0.017	0.001 ***	0.000 ***	0.000 ***	0.000 ***	14.29	125.47	878.26
22:6-LPC	0.085 ± 0.031	0.311 ± 0.051	0.149 ± 0.038	0.001 ***	0.000 ***	0.007 **	0.000 ***	365.88	175.29	47.91
32:0-PC	0.190 ± 0.026	0.305 ± 0.036	0.100 ± 0.015	0.001 ***	0.000 ***	0.000 ***	0.000 ***	160.53	52.63	32.79
34:0-PC	0.032 ± 0.004	-	0.034 ± 0.005	0.005 **	-	0.3942	-	-	106.25	-
34:1-PC	2.724 ± 0.574	1.972 ± 0.104	4.030 ± 0.584	0.002 **	0.019 *	0.002 **	0.000 ***	72.39	147.94	204.36
34:2-PC	5.064 ± 0.740	4.067 ± 0.258	1.997 ± 0.349	0.001 ***	0.019 *	0.000 ***	0.000 ***	80.31	39.44	49.10
34:3-PC	0.499 ± 0.078	0.397 ± 0.061	0.197 ± 0.028	0.001 ***	0.040 **	0.000 ***	0.000 ***	79.56	39.48	49.62
36:1-PC	0.269 ± 0.062	0.253 ± 0.027	1.014 ± 0.193	0.002 **	0.6096	0.000 ***	0.000 ***	94.05	376.95	400.79
36:2-PC	2.096 ± 0.405	2.000 ± 0.145	2.112 ± 0.407	0.878	0.626	0.9459	0.5712	95.42	100.76	105.60
36:3-PC	1.566 ± 0.317	0.957 ± 0.080	2.026 ± 0.276	0.005 **	0.002 **	0.017 *	0.000 ***	61.11	129.37	211.70
36:4-PC	1.499 ± 0.312	0.978 ± 0.105	1.284 ± 0.217	0.001 ***	0.006 **	0.171	0.016 *	65.24	85.66	131.29
36:5-PC	0.491 ± 0.086	0.241 ± 0.017	0.194 ± 0.021	0.001 ***	0.000 ***	0.000 ***	0.002 **	49.08	39.51	80.50
38:2-PC	0.093 ± 0.018	-	0.163 ± 0.025	0.003 **	-	0.000 ***	-	-	175.27	-
38:3-PC	0.261 ± 0.059	0.133 ± 0.018	0.358 ± 0.106	0.001 ***	0.001 ***	0.0725	0.001 ***	50.96	137.16	269.17
38:4-PC	0.710 ± 0.167	0.803 ± 0.061	1.004 ± 0.178	0.001 ***	0.27	0.011 *	0.037 *	113.10	141.41	125.03
38:5-PC	0.630 ± 0.114	0.339 ± 0.028	0.707 ± 0.098	0.001 ***	0.000 ***	0.218	0.000 ***	53.81	112.22	208.55
38:6-PC	2.773 ± 0.488	1.510 ± 0.068	1.914 ± 0.245	0.001 ***	0.000 ***	0.002 **	0.005 **	54.45	69.02	126.75
40:6-PC	0.693 ± 0.145	0.633 ± 0.031	0.606 ± 0.090	0.003 **	0.39	0.211	0.535	91.34	87.45	95.73

ANNEX 3. (Continued)

Compound	Control (A) (Mean±SD)	24h Starvation (B) (Mean±SD)	High-Fat (C) (Mean±SD)	Kruskal – Wallis	P-value			Change (%)		
					A vs. B	A vs. C	B vs. C	A vs. B	A vs. C	B vs. C
40:7-PC	0.364 ± 0.071	0.172 ± 0.013	0.548 ± 0.063	0.001 ***	0.000 ***	0.000 ***	0.000 ***	47.25	150.55	318.60
16:1-ChE	0.009 ± 0.004	-	0.070 ± 0.024	0.003 **	-	0.000 ***	-	-	777.78	-
18:1-ChE	0.036 ± 0.005	0.595 ± 0.130	0.263 ± 0.085	0.001 ***	0.000 ***	0.000 ***	0.000 ***	1652.78	730.56	44.20
18:2-ChE	0.049 ± 0.008	0.578 ± 0.135	0.078 ± 0.019	0.001 ***	0.000 ***	0.006 **	0.000 ***	1179.59	159.18	13.49
20:4-ChE	0.017 ± 0.004	0.072 ± 0.030	0.045 ± 0.008	0.002 **	0.001 **	0.000 ***	0.040 *	423.53	264.71	62.50
22:6-ChE	0.015 ± 0.003	0.158 ± 0.053	0.028 ± 0.008	0.001 ***	0.000 ***	0.0040 **	0.000 ***	1053.33	186.67	17.72
46:0-TG	0.014 ± 0.003	0.009 ± 0.004	0.019 ± 0.004	0.030 *	0.054	0.001 **	0.001 **	64.29	135.71	211.11
46:1-TG	0.010 ± 0.003	0.120 ± 0.042	0.021 ± 0.007	0.010 **	0.000 ***	0.003 **	0.000 ***	1200.00	210.00	17.50
46:2-TG	0.006 ± 0.002	0.542 ± 0.259	0.010 ± 0.002	0.010 **	0.001 **	0.001 **	0.000 ***	9033.33	166.67	1.85
48:0-TG	0.026 ± 0.014	0.060 ± 0.013	0.051 ± 0.014	0.016 *	0.002 **	0.009 **	0.245	230.77	196.15	85.00
48:1-TG	0.055 ± 0.025	0.191 ± 0.076	0.246 ± 0.091	0.004 **	0.002 **	0.000 ***	0.295	347.27	447.27	128.80
48:2-TG	0.054 ± 0.017	0.564 ± 0.219	0.162 ± 0.052	0.001 ***	0.000 ***	0.000 ***	0.000 ***	1044.44	300.00	28.72
48:3-TG	0.017 ± 0.004	0.748 ± 0.327	0.026 ± 0.006	0.001 ***	0.000 ***	0.011 *	0.000 ***	4400.00	152.94	3.48
50:1-TG	0.169 ± 0.068	1.296 ± 0.376	1.296 ± 0.382	0.003 **	0.000 ***	0.000 ***	0.997	766.86	766.86	100.00
50:2-TG	0.379 ± 0.123	2.095 ± 0.663	2.175 ± 0.616	0.003 **	0.000 ***	0.000 ***	0.835	552.77	573.88	103.82
50:3-TG	0.228 ± 0.062	1.670 ± 0.692	0.473 ± 0.135	0.001 ***	0.000 ***	0.002 **	0.001 **	732.46	207.46	28.32
50:4-TG	0.044 ± 0.011	1.171 ± 0.481	0.045 ± 0.013	0.006 **	0.000 ***	0.9673	0.000 ***	2661.36	102.27	3.84
52:1-TG	0.083 ± 0.026	-	0.515 ± 0.197	0.003 **	-	0.000 ***	-	-	620.48	-
52:2-TG	0.702 ± 0.244	5.964 ± 1.590	7.979 ± 1.809	0.002 **	0.000 ***	0.000 ***	0.0739	849.57	1136.61	133.79
52:3-TG	0.887 ± 0.250	8.092 ± 1.762	3.346 ± 0.726	0.001 ***	0.000 ***	0.000 ***	0.000 ***	912.29	377.23	41.35
52:4-TG	0.409 ± 0.090	6.253 ± 1.449	0.422 ± 0.108	0.006 **	0.000 ***	0.8161	0.000 ***	1528.85	103.18	6.75
52:5-TG	0.097 ± 0.021	2.803 ± 0.964	0.049 ± 0.010	0.001 ***	0.000 ***	0.000 ***	0.000 ***	2889.69	50.52	1.75
54:2-TG	0.123 ± 0.033	1.326 ± 0.373	1.477 ± 0.477	0.003 **	0.000 ***	0.000 ***	0.57	1078.05	1200.81	111.39
54:3-TG	0.251 ± 0.083	2.991 ± 0.776	3.956 ± 0.708	0.002 **	0.000 ***	0.000 ***	0.049 *	1191.63	1576.10	132.26
54:4-TG	0.249 ± 0.079	3.078 ± 0.665	0.983 ± 0.200	0.001 ***	0.000 ***	0.000 ***	0.000 ***	1236.14	394.78	31.94
54:5-TG	0.208 ± 0.053	2.846 ± 0.534	0. 248 ± 0.055	0.004 **	0.000 ***	0.203	0.000 ***	1368.27	119.23	8.71
56:2-TG	0.018 ± 0.005	0.164 ± 0.060	0.178 ± 0.070	0.003 **	0.000 ***	0.000 ***	0.722	911.11	988.89	108.54
56:3-TG	0.050 ± 0.015	0.499 ± 0.157	0.783 ± 0.215	0.001 ***	0.000 ***	0.000 ***	0.031 *	998.00	1566.00	156.91
56:4-TG	0.057 ± 0.016	0.542 ± 0.134	0.354 ± 0.091	0.001 ***	0.000 ***	0.000 ***	0.016 *	950.88	621.05	65.31
56:5-TG	0.061 ± 0.017	0.457 ± 0.061	0.252 ± 0.061	0.001 ***	0.000 ***	0.000 ***	0.000 ***	749.18	413.11	55.14
56:6-TG	0.147 ± 0.046	0.620 ± 0.049	0.165 ± 0.027	0.003 **	0.000 ***	0.396	0.000 ***	421.77	112.24	26.61
58:3-TG	0.007 ± 0.001	0.063 ± 0.024	0.066 ± 0.024	0.003 **	0.000 ***	0.000 ***	0.828	900.00	942.86	104.76

Acknowledgments

This study was supported by a grant of Center for Medical Systems Biology (CMSB). Martin Brittijn and Martin Jansen are kindly acknowledged for drawing some of the drawings.

Conflicts of interests: None

References

Adams L., Angulo P. and Lindor K. (2005). Nonalcoholic fatty liver disease. *CMAJ* 172, 899-905.

Ahmed, M. (2006). Invasive and non-invasive investigations for non-alcoholic steatohepatitis (NASH) The need for biochemical markers. *Scand. J. Gastroenterol.* 41, 372-372.

Arkan, M. C., Hevener, A. L., Greten, F. R., Maeda, S., Li, Z. W, Long, J. M., Wynshaw-Boris, A., Poli, G., Olefsky, J., and Karin, M. (2005). IKK-beta links inflammation to obesity-induced insulin resistance. *Nat. Med.* 11(2), 191-198.

Baird, T., Parsons, M., Barber, P., Butcher, K., Desmond, P., Tress, B., Colman, P., Jerums, G., Chambers, B., and Davis, S. (2002). The influence of diabetes mellitus and hyperglycaemia on stroke incidence and outcome. *J. Clin. Neuroscience* 9, 618-626.

Barcelo-Coblijn, G. (2003). Dynamics of long polyunsaturated fatty acids in rat brain. *Acta Biologica Szegediensis.* 47, 1-55.

Basso, L. and Havel, R. (1970). Hepatic metabolism of free fatty acids in normal and diabetic dogs. *J. Clin. Invest.* 49, 537-547.

Blaxter, K. (1989). Energy metabolism in animals and man, 336 pp. Cambridge University Press, Cambridge.

Bligh, E. and Dyer, W. (1959). A rapid method of total lipid extraction and purification. *Can. J. Biochem. Biophys.* 37, 911-917.

Boure, J. M., Dumont, O., Piciotti, M., Clément, M., Chaudière, J., Bonneil, M., Nalborn,e G., Lafont, H., Pascal, G., Durand, G. (1991). Essentiality of omega-3 fatty acids for brain structure and function. *World Rev. Nutr. Diet* 66, 103-117.

Bradbury, M. (2006). Lipid metabolism and liver inflammation. 1 Hepatic fatty acid uptake: possible role in steatosis. *Am. J. Physiol. Gastrointest. Liver Physiol.* 290, 194-198.

Browning, J. and Horton, J. (2004). Review: Molecular mediators of hepatic steatosis and liver injury. *J. Clin. Invest* 114, 147-152.

Bryhn, M. (2003). Effects of omega-3 fatty acids on mental health. *AGROfood industry high-tech. Pronova Biocare A.S.* 420, 1327-1332.

Chang, G.-Q., Gaysinskaya, V., Karatayev, O., Leibowitz, S. F. (2008). Maternal High-Fat Diet and Fetal Programming: Increased Proliferation of Hypothalamic Peptide-Producing Neurons That Increase Risk for Overeating and Obesity. *The Journal of Neuroscience* 28, 12107-12119.

Cobbold, J. F. L., Anstee, Q. M., Goldins, R. D., Williams, H. R. T., Matthews, H. C., North, B. V., Absalom, N., Thomas, H. C., Thursz, M. R., Cox, R. D., Taylor-Robinson, S. D., and Cox, I. J. (2009). Phenotyping murine models of non-alcoholic fatty liver disease through metabolic profiling of intact liver tissue. *Clinical Science* 116, 403-413.

Corbin, I., Pickup, S., Furth, E., and Delikantny (2004). *In vivo* measurement of hepatic triglyceride composition in murine non-alcoholic steatosis. *Proc. Intl. Soc. Reson. Med.* 11, 896.

Cortez-Pinto, H. and Machado, M. (2008). Impact of body weight, diet and lifestyle on nonalcoholic fatty liver disease. *Expert. Rev. Gastroenterol. Hepatol.* 2, 217-231.

Dallman, M., la Fleur, S., Pecoraro, N., Gomez, F., Houshyar, H., and Akana, S. (2004). Minireview: Glucocorticoids-food intake, abdominal obesity, and wealthy nations in *Endocrinology* 145, 2633-2638.

Day, C. P. (2002). Pathogenesis of steatohepatitis. *Clin. Gastroeneterol.* 16, 663-678.

Den Boer, M., Voshol, P., Kuipers, F., Havekes, L., and Romijn, J. (2004). Hepatic steatosis: a mediator of the Metabolic Syndrome. Lessons from animal models. *Arterioscler. Thromb. Vasc. Biol.* 24, 644-649.

Fernandez-Checa, J. C. and Kaplowitz, N. (2005). Hepatic mitochondrial glutathione: transport and role in disease and toxicity. *Appl. Pharmacol.* 204, 263-273.

Ford, E., Giles, W. and Dietz, W. (2002). Prevalence of the metabolic syndrome among US adults. Findings from the third national health and nutrition examination survey. *JAMA* 287, 356-359.

Garbow, J., Lin, X., Sakata, N., Chen, Z., Koh, D., and Schonfeld, G. (2001). *In vivo* MRS measurements of liver lipid levels in mice. *J. Lipid. Res.* 45, 1364-1371.

Gauthier, M., Couturier, K., Latour, J., and Lavoie, J. (2003). Concurrent exercise prevents High-Fat-Diet-induced macrovesicular hepatic steatosis. *J. Appl. Physiol.* 94, 2127-2134

Hashimoto, T., Cook, W., Qi, C., Yeldandi, A., Reddy, J., and Rao, M. (2000). Defect in peroxisome proliferator-activated receptor alpha-inducible fatty acid oxidation determines the severity of hepatic steatosis in response to starvation. *J. Biol. Chem.* 275, 28918-28928.

Havekes, L., de Wit, E. and Princen, H. (1987) Cellular free cholesterol in Hep G2 cells is only partially available for down-regulation of low-density-lipoprotein receptor activity. *Biochem. J.* 247, 739-746.

Hsu, F. F., Turk, J. (2005). Electrospray, electrospray ionization with low-energy collisionally activated dissociation Tandem Mass Spectrometry of Complex Lipids: Structural Characterization and mechanisms of fragmentation. In: *Modern methods for lipid analysis by Liquid Chromatography/Mass Spectrometry and related Techniques*, W.C. Byrdwell, Editor, AOCS Press.

Hulbert, A. J., Turner, N., Storlien, L. H., Else, P. L. (2005). Dietary fats and membrane function: implications for metabolism and disease. *Biol. Rev.* 80, 155-169.

Jackson, J. E. (1991). A User's Guide to Principal Components. New York: Wiley; 1991.

Kitano, H. (2002). Systems Biology: A brief Overview. *Science* 295, 1662-1664.

Lakka, H., Laaksonen, D., Lakka, T., Niskanen, L., Kumpusalo, E., Tuomilehto, J., and Salonen, J. (2002). The metabolic syndrome and total and cardiovascular disease mortality in middle-aged men. *JAMA* 288, 2709-2716.

Lowry, O., Rosebrough, N., Farr, A., and Randall, R. (1951). Protein measurement with the Folin phenol reagent. *J. Biol. Chem.* 193, 265-275.

Marchesin, G., Marzocchi, R., Agostini, F., and Bugianese, E. (2005). Nonalcoholic fatty liver disease and the metabolic syndrome. *Curr. Opin. Lipidol.* 16, 899-905.

Marra, F. (2008). Nuclear factor-κB inhibition and non-alcoholic steatohepatitis: inflammation as a target for therapy. *Gut* 57, 570-572.

Mehta, S. R., Thomas, E. L., Bell, J. D., Johnston, D. G., and Taylor-Robinson, S. D. (2008). Non-invasive means of measuring hepatic fat content. *World J. Gastroenterol.* 14, 3476-3483.

Pessayre, D., Berson, A., Fromenty, B., and Mansouri, A. (2001). Mitochondria in steatohepatitis. *Semin. Liver Dis.* 21, 57-69.

Picardi, A., D'Avola, D., Gentilucci, U., Galati, G., Fiori, E., Spataro, S., and Afeltra, A. (2006). Diabetes in chronic liver disease: from old concepts to new evidence. *Diabetes Metab. Res. Rev.* 22 274-283.

Piccinino, F., Sagnelli, E., Pasquale, G., and Giusti, G. (1986). Complications following percutaneous liver biopsy: A multicentre restrospective study on 68,276 biopsies. *J. Hepatol.* 2, 165-173.

Post, S., de Wit, E., Princen, H., and Cafestol, X. (1997). The cholesterol-raising factor in boiled coffee, suppresses bile acid synthesis by down regulation of cholesterol alpha-hydroxylase and sterol 27-hydroxylase in rat hepatocytes. *Arterioscler. Thromb. Vasc. Biol.* 17, 3064-3070.

Ratziu, V., Charlotte, F., Heurtier, A., Gombert, S., Giral, P., Bruckert, E., Grimaldi, A., Capron, F., and Poynard, T. (2005). Sampling variability of liver biopsy in nonalcoholic fatty liver disease. *Gastroenterology* 128, 1898-1906.

Rigazio, S., Lehto, H.-R., Tuunanen, H., Någren, K., Kankaanpaa, M., Simi, C., Borra, R., Naum, A. G., Parkkola, R., Knuuti, J., Nuutila, P., and Iozzo, P. (2008). The lowering of hepatic fatty acid uptake improves liver function and insulin sensitivity without affecting hepatic fat content in humans. *Am. J. Physiol. Endocrinol. Metab.* 295, E413-E419.

Saadeh, S., Younossi, Z. M., Remer, E. M., Gramlich, T., Ong, J. P., Hurley, M., Mullen, K. D., Cooper, J. N., and Sheridan, M. J. (2002). The utility of radiological imaging in nonalcoholic fatty liver disease. *Gastroenterology* 123, 745-750.

Salway, J. G. (2006). Medical Biochemistry at a glance; Blackwell Publishing LTD, ISBN-13:978-4051-1322-9, 144 pp.

Sanyal, A. J., Campbell-Sargent, C., Mirshahi, F., Rizzo, W. B., Contos, M. J., Sterling, R. K., Luketic, V. A., Shiffman, M. L., and Clore, J. N. (2001). Nonalcoholic steatohepatitis: association of insulin resistance and mitochondrial abnormalities. *Gastroenterol.* 120, 1183-1192.

Siegelman, E. and Rosen, M. (2001). Imaging of Hepatic Steatosis. *Semin. Liv. Dis* 21, 71-80.

Sinclair, A. J., Begg, D., Mathai, M., Weisinger, R. S. (2007). Review Article: Omega-3 fatty acids in the brain: review of studies in depression. *Asia Pac. J. Clin. Nutr.* 16 (Suppl. 1), 391-397.

Söderberg, M., Edlund, M. C., Kristensson, K., Dallne,r G. (1991). Fatty acids compo-sition of brain phospholipids in aging and Alzheimer 's disease. *Lipids* 26, 421-425.

Stubbs, C. D. and Smith, A. D. (1984). The modification of mammalian membrane poly-unsaturated fatty acid composition in relation to membrane fluidity and function. *Biochem. Biophys. Acta* 779, 89-137.

Sullivan, P. G., Dubé, C., Dorenbos, K., Steward, O., and Baram, T. Z. (2003). Mitochondrial uncoupling Protein-2 protects the Immature Brain from Excitotoxic Neuronal Death. *Ann. Neurol.* 53, 711-717.

Thomas, E. L., Hamilton, G., Patel, N., O'Dwyer, R., Doré, C. J., Goldin, R. D., Bell, J. D., and Taylor-Robinson, S. D. (2005). Hepatic triglyceride content and its relation to body adiposity: a magnetic resonance imaging and proton magnetic resonance spectroscopy study. *Gut* 54, 122-127.

Tilg, H. and Hotamisligil, G. S. (2006). Nonalcoholic Fatty Liver Disease: Cytokine-Adipokine interplay and regulation of Insulin Resistance. *Gastroenterology* 131, 934-945.

Van der Greef, J., Davidov, E., Verheij, E. R., Vogels, J., van der Heijden, R., Adourian, A. S., Oresic, M., Marple, E. W., Naylor, S. (2003). *The role of metabolomics in Systems Biology*. In: R. G. G. G. Harrigan (Ed), Metabolic Profiling: Its Role in Biomarker Discovery and Gene Function Analysis. Vol. 170. Kluwer Academic Publisher, Boston/Dordrecht/ London.

Van der Greef, J., van der Heijden, R., Verheij, E. R. (2004). *The Role of Mass Spectrometry in Systems Biology*: Data Processing and Identification Strategies in Metabolomics. In: G. B. A. E. Ashcroft, J. J. Monaghan (Ed), *Advances in Mass Spectrometry*, pp. 145-165. Vol. 16. Elsevier Science, Amsterdam.

Van Ginneken, V., Verhey, E., Poelmann, R., Ramakers, R., Willems-van Dijk, K., Ham, L., Voshol, P., Havekes, L., van Eck, M., van der Greef, J. (2007). Metabolomics (liver and blood profiling) in a mouse model in response to starvation: A study of hepatic steatosis. *Biochimica et Biophysica Acta* 1771, 1263-1270.

Wang, M. H., Palmeri, M. L., Guy, C. D., Yang, L., Hedlund, L. W., Diehl, A. M., and Nightingale, K. R. (2009). *In vivo* quantification of liver stiffness in a rat model of hepatic fibrosis with acoustic radiation force. *Ultrasound in Med. and Biol.* 35, 1709-1721.

Yamaguchi, K., Yang, L., McCall, S., Huang, J., Yu, X. X., Pandey, S. K., Bhanot, S., Monia, B. P., Li, Y.-X., and Diehl, A. M. (2007). Inhibiting Triglyceride synthesis improves Hepatic Steatosis but exacerbates Liver damage and Fibrosis in Onese Mice with Nonalcolholic Steatohepatitis. *Hepatology* 45, 1366-1374.

Index

B

C

D

E

F

G

H

I

J

K

L

M

N

O

P

Q

R

S

T

U

V

W

Y

Z